A THOUSAND SHALL FALL

Thou shalt not be afraid for the terror by night; nor for the arrow that flieth by day;

Nor for the pestilence that walketh in darkness; nor for the destruction that wasteth at noonday.

A thousand shall fall at thy side, and ten thousand at thy right hand; but it shall not come nigh thee.

PSALM 91:5-7

A Thousand Shall Fall

by

HANS HABE

New York

HARCOURT, BRACE AND COMPANY

TRANSLATED BY
Norbert Guterman

PRINTED IN THE UNITED STATES OF AMERICA
BY QUINN & BODEN COMPANY, INC., RAHWAY, N. J.

CONTENTS

AUTHOR'S NOTE

Nothing has been added to or left out of this book. The names of the characters, the scenes of action, the numbers of the regiments are authentic. I have used fictitious names and disguised circumstances only when the mention of real names would endanger the lives of the persons concerned.

HANS HABE

Part One

BATTLE AND RETREAT

CHAPTER ONE: THE FLIGHT FORWARD

At last the war began.

It was a bright May morning in 1940. Captain Mirambeau of the Twelfth Army Corps had sent me on a scouting expedition that took me into the enemy lines. The day before I had left Pfaffenhoffen in Alsace, commissioned to visit a number of French observation posts and investigate certain errors that had arisen in their relaying of information. A few days previous, I had completed a course given by Captain Mirambeau for scouts of all regiments belonging to the Twelfth Army Corps. Among these was my regiment, the Twenty-first Foreign Volunteers, formed at the beginning of the war and now awaiting action in near-by Mommenheim.

The things I saw at the front-line observation posts were no surprise to me. Captain Mirambeau, who enjoyed our whole-hearted admiration, had prepared us for the worst. I shall always remember this unusual man, for neither before nor since have I met an officer of his caliber. In all the time we spent in Alsace, we never fathomed his secret, probably for the simple reason that no one knew who he really was. He wore no decorations, though he was known as one of the great heroes *de l'autre guerre*. A simple Indian head on his right pocket, emblem of the *Deuxième Bureau*—the French military intelligence—replaced all red, green, or yellow ribbons. His military knowledge indicated that soldiering was his profession, but a young artilleryman who came from the same town as Mirambeau claimed that in civil life the captain was a professor of mathematics at the Sorbonne, and this seemed not improbable in view of his astonishing virtuosity in geometry and higher mathematics. Some of the captain's students went so far as to maintain that his real name was not Mirambeau, and that he had assumed this name in order to hide his real identity, since in the last few years he had performed such services for the French espionage that the Germans had put a price on his head.

Before I left, he said to me: "Don't let anything surprise you, sergeant. You are going to see some strange things." There was bitterness in his voice. "You will find observation posts with steam heat, but no possible view of the enemy. And in every last one of them, you'll find champagne." He stood up and came toward me. There was tension in his whole wiry frame, his lips were pale, he had the narrow head of Savonarola. "If you see any cases of champagne, shoot into them. On my orders. I want observers, not drunks." He paced silently up and down the bare *Cinéma de l'Agneau* which had served as our classroom. "If war should break out today or tomorrow—" he said finally, with a gesture signifying at once warning and resignation.

We had been at war for nine months.

But the real war, whose nature Captain Mirambeau knew and we could only guess, the war that lurked hidden in the forest of Ardennes, in the fields of Belgium, behind the charming little houses of Luxembourg—this war had not yet begun.

Even on that morning, as I crossed the fields to report in Pfaffenhoffen—Mirambeau referred to the place as *Cinqueff* because of the five *F*'s, and I was just thinking about the name—even on that sunny spring day the official communiqué read: *"Rien à Signaler."*

4

The Flight Forward

And then suddenly the war materialized.

I had arranged to meet the observers of two other regiments, who had been sent out to inspect other sectors of the front. Before returning to our posts, we wanted to compare notes. At eleven in the morning we met at the cross-roads in Pfaffenhoffen. I was the last to arrive, and before I could utter a word, the two others assailed me with the news: "The Germans have marched into Holland and Belgium. Tomorrow morning we have to go back to our regiments."

An hour later the first bombers flew over the peaceful city of the five *F*'s.

This is the real thing, we thought. Months of waiting had worn down our nerves. No one had any idea when the war would end, for no one knew when it would begin. In the casemates of the Maginot Line, at the Belgian border, along the sea coast—everywhere the war had turned into a game of tin soldiers. Those who had expected a great experience found only the constraints of barracks life. Millions of soldiers had been metamorphosed into millions of recruits, leading an intolerable life, far removed from the great experience of their fathers. Perhaps the old spirit of camaraderie would have awakened if the fight, the hell fire, had started at once. But their only activity was sweeping the streets of the Alsatian villages, parading, presenting arms, cleaning boots. A great contest began: who could avoid the most work? Petty jealousies, petty vanities, distrust of one's comrade who had withstood the test as poorly as oneself—that was May, 1940.

And all of a sudden it looked as if the war had started. Four of us who were observers in the same regiment planned to return to our headquarters in Mommenheim on Monday. Little Garai and I decided to go fishing Sunday afternoon. Garai was a Hungarian, who for many years had been a newspaper photographer in Paris. He was a dark-haired, sickly youth with thick glasses, and there was certainly nothing warlike about him. But he had volunteered at the outbreak of the war, and in the few tense moments thus far experienced he had shown unusual coolness.

"I'm glad it's started at last," he said as we cast our lines. "Now it will all be over in eight weeks."

"You think so?"

"I'm sure of it."

He spoke with utter calm, admitting of no doubt as to the outcome of the war.

We sat silent. It was the first hot Sunday. The sun glowed in the summery sky. All at once the fields had turned a deep green. A soft breeze stirred the long grass. The water smelled as it smells only in summer—damp and a little rotten. The village lay behind us, peaceful and still.

Suddenly Garai looked up.

"Planes!" he said, and instead of throwing himself prone he sprang to his feet.

Three enemy machines flew low over Pfaffenhoffen, nearly grazing the church steeple. Proud to show off what I had learned in school, I cried out, "Messerschmitt!"

I had recognized the German pursuit planes by the jagged cut of their wings. But now they were past us. At first they sped away, but suddenly they turned back and circled over our meadow. At the same time the machine guns began to pop.

"They're shooting at us," said Garai calmly. Still holding his fishing pole, he stood erect and looked upward.

On the opposite shore of the brook someone said "*Merde!*" But it was only because a big fish had got away from him.

Even under fire, we didn't fully realize what was happening. We had been too accustomed to look on everything as a joke. Suddenly a woman's scream startled us from our calm.

A baby carriage had been upset in the middle of the meadow. We saw it as a white spot amid the green. A woman, also in white, bent over the baby carriage and screamed.

The planes spun circles over the city. The siren in the church tower began to howl, five minutes too late, drowning out the woman's cries. The sun was shining; it was still Sunday over the fields.

Garai and I ran across the meadow. The mother covered the dead child with her body. A machine-gun bullet had bored through the top of the baby carriage and struck the child in the head. The first victim of the war to meet our eyes was a baby.

When we returned to the village, the people were just crawling out of their houses. Terrified faces stared at the cloudless blue sky. At the station three workmen had been hit as they were bending down to crawl under a car. They were dead. The siren had stopped blowing. On the chimney of Moritz's Brewery a stork was playing with its little ones.

Returning to Mommenheim, we learned that the colonel had declared a state of alarm. You couldn't go out in the street without a steel helmet; you couldn't leave town; you couldn't remove your shoes or clothes at night. If you left your lodging, you had to cling to the walls; if there were several of you, you had to walk in single file, never abreast. The Sunday church service had been prohibited.

That made the war look like a purely disciplinary measure, directed against us personally. In general, the French command confused discipline with unpleasantness, and this was not the least reason why the war had to be lost. Cause and effect were hopelessly confused. Since discipline was something unpleasant, it followed that if a soldier's life was made unpleasant enough, he would automatically learn discipline.

7

As soon as the war broke out, we were to all intents and purposes condemned to house arrest. This, our captain claimed, would make enemy aviators think that Mommenheim was deserted. But that didn't prevent him from calling us to assembly twice a day in the courtyard of company headquarters. Two hundred of us stood at attention, crowded into the narrow space between the captain's house and the adjacent inn, an ideal target for German planes. The German spies employed in the inn—Alsatians for the most part—leaned out of the window and listened comfortably to every word spoken by our officers.

In Mommenheim, I and the eight regimental observers under me were lodged in a charming peasant house on the main street. My hosts were fine people, whose tongues spoke German but whose hearts spoke French. I had some opportunity to become acquainted with the Alsatians. When we were quartered in the house, only the old peasant, over seventy years of age, his daughter-in-law, and her children lived there; the husband had been in the Maginot Line for four months. I soon became good friends with the old man, chiefly by admiring his marksmanship. We were soldiers from all four corners of the earth, but I must own that old Grüter was more warlike than any of us. All day long he hunted pigeons. The high command had issued an order that the pigeons in Alsace-Lorraine be exterminated, because they hindered the military carrier pigeons in the performance of their duty. This measure seemed to me neither logical nor humane, nor even zoological; why not kill the women who waved (and sometimes even cooed) at us from the sidewalks as we marched off to the front? Besides, I never heard of a single carrier pigeon being used in the whole war. But no matter: the pigeons had to be exterminated, and that made old Grüter one man who was getting his fun out of the war—his third.

I can still see him, a statue of human stupidity, standing in the middle of the courtyard, aiming at a pair of cooing doves. His rifle dated from 1870, and went off only every tenth time he pulled the trigger. But when it did, he accompanied the report with an enthusiastic "Poof," and a bleeding pigeon tumbled and fluttered down the steep roof.

The day we got back from Pfaffenhoffen his son came home for twenty-four hours. He was a red-bearded giant with blue eyes, a corporal in a regiment of fortress artillery, a man in his forties. First he went to look at the cows, then he embraced his wife, and then he sat down at the table for a political argument with his father. The window was open and we were chopping wood in the courtyard, so we happened to overhear the argument, which offered a picture of all Alsace. The father, who had grown up under the German régime and had gone through the World War as a German soldier, was an ardent French patriot, and not just because of the pigeons. The son, brought up in France, enjoying the blessings of France and now clad in the uniform of the republic, desired a German victory. In his mind he was already preparing a camp for the German army of occupation. A bad servant of either master—"a German under the French, a Frenchman under the Germans, *nulle part de mise*," as Chamisso said of himself—such was the typical Alsatian as I knew him. And this time, moreover, he was the gravedigger of the French Republic.

As soon as it started, we knew that we had only a few days, perhaps hours, left in Alsace, and that we should soon be sent to the Belgian front. This gave us one more reason for shunning discipline. The very first night we crept out of the house one by one, and repaired to an inn that seemed safe from patrols. But we had not bargained for the sight that met our eyes. That morning the German artillery had started to bombard Haguenau. For eight months the inhabitants had been basking in the tranquillity of the Maginot Line; now they all fled at once. Up to that moment the thought of leaving their homes had never occurred to them. The authorities had apparently overlooked the minor detail that the German artillery could easily fire thirty-five or forty kilometers, even over fortifications. The idea of evacuating the population had never entered their heads until this morning.

The inn was packed. Whole families were crowded together at the tables. They seemed woefully helpless—the men in their incongruous Sunday best trying so hard to appear strong, the women in their flower-bedecked black hats, the country girls in their red silk blouses. Most families had brought along a dog; the little dogs sat in the women's laps, the big ones strained at their leashes despite all efforts to pacify them. The waitresses tripped over the leashes, and the whole inn had the air of a dog-pound. At length we found a table, at which only a father, a mother, and daughter were sitting. The mother was clasping a food basket in which she had carefully packed hard-boiled eggs, a roast chicken, and red wine, all neatly wrapped in napkins: the poor woman was totally unaware how out of place such peaceful zeal would soon be. The daughter, a little plump girl in a straw hat, tried to smile at us, but her smile turned slowly into a grimace, and she began to cry. Her tears fell on the packages that she held clasped like a baby in her arms. Most of the refugees had brought along all sorts of touchingly useless belongings, and had left the important things at home. From time to time the father at my table stood up to go into the courtyard, and I soon learned that he was looking after his pig, the family's most precious possession. The pig was parked in the courtyard of the inn, with seven or eight of his kind brought by other peasants; the local butcher was expected soon, to choose among them. At some of the tables business deals were in progress. I have rarely seen anything more moving than these women of Haguenau, holding out bundles of asparagus to the local vegetable dealers. I could visualize them at the last moment before taking flight, casting a parting glance at their garden and then quickly cutting a handful of asparagus. Now they released the little bundle of asparagus in exchange for a few coins, and lost the last contact with their beloved patch of earth.

We sat at the table, and we didn't know what to say. The other soldiers, at other tables, were likewise silent. Like us, they had not yet experienced their baptism of fire. Like us, they had not yet learned the meaning of war. The peasant at our table came back and consulted with his wife on the price offered by the butcher. They quarreled. The daughter wept, the dogs howled, and the beautiful Alsatian beer grew warm.

Suddenly the dogs pointed their ears and listened. We too listened. And then we heard, growing clearer and clearer, the sound of approaching airplane motors. It was the typical sound of German engines. Anyone who has been in the field will never mistake it. Whereas the Allied planes have a long-drawn-out, metallic tone, the German motors have a deep, growling sound, almost like a cough: French planes sound like a whistling locomotive, German planes like a barking dog.

The landlord ran to the switch and turned out the light. At the same moment the aerial machine guns began to spit fire. There was a stir around the tables. No one spoke, no one screamed; even the dogs were quiet. We could see silhouettes rise and fall. "Don't stay by the window!" a man whispered to his wife, as though he feared the aviators might hear him. The man at our table stood up and started for the door. His daughter held him back. The machine guns rattled. The planes seemed to be flying in circles over our heads.

Then all grew still. The Messerschmitts had gone away. The landlord turned on the light. And what I saw then made me blush for the first time in this war—though not for the last. From under half a dozen tables, steel helmets emerged. Even before that, the peasants had given us strange looks— these steel helmets in the inn, so strangely in contrast to the flower gardens on the women's hats. But before, that look had been hesitant, shy, a look of questioning surprise, as if to ask: Can it be true that you are protected, while no one cares about us? But now there was something hostile and despair- ing in that look, as though the last hope were collapsing. When one of the soldiers crawled out from under the table, his helmet had slipped down over one ear. He tried to smile, as if to say that his crawling under the table had been only a joke—but his smile was a failure, and he had to put it back in its case, like a piece of rejected merchandise. Beside him sat a peasant woman with her child in her arms. She hadn't stirred.

The landlord stood in the doorway and motioned to the man who sat at my table. For two minutes they stood whis- pering. Then the man came back. He seemed to have aged. He did not argue with his wife. All he said was: "I've sold the pig."

And in answer to her inquiring glance: "He's dead. The Germans shot him."

Next morning we left Mommenheim, heading for the Bel- gian front. But no one thought we would be sent straight into the front lines. All of us, common soldiers, commissioned and non-commissioned officers, were certain that we should first spend a few days in a quieter sector. This opinion was not based merely on a childish optimism hopeful of "gaining" a few days' time. We had good reason to believe that the Twenty-first Volunteers would not be subjected at once to the most violent enemy fire.

Our regiment had been organized in the second month of the war, and our training had not begun until the middle of November, 1939. More recent volunteers, totally untrained, had been incorporated in our regiment, so that by May, 1940, many of our number had enjoyed as little as six or seven weeks of training.

What training we did have had been gathered in a terrain that was unfit for any military exercise whatsoever. Barcarès, on the Mediterranean near Perpignan, had originally been a bathing beach. After the Spanish civil war, wooden barracks had been built there for Loyalist refugees. The only stone house in the locality was the friendly Hôtel du Lido, which had formerly housed excursionists from Perpignan but had been transformed into an officers' casino. The beach was hardly an ideal drill ground. At every step you sank up to your ankles in sand; it was impossible to set up a single machine gun or dig a single trench. The regiment's only maneuver took place in the camp at Larzac, and this consisted only of a few long walks and two "offensives" which were rather a failure, as the high command had somehow forgotten to provide planes, tanks, or even machine guns and cartridges in reasonable quantity. At least half of our four thousand recruits had barely had time to learn their specialty; more than fifteen hundred had never handled a machine gun.

But this was not the only reason. Our equipment was something to weep over. Just before marching we had received an infinitesimal number of the new Mousquetons, the modern French rifles which were about as good as the German ones. Not more than five per cent of the regiment—in my company of two hundred men no more than seven or eight motor-cyclists—had these guns; the rest of us ordinary mortals had rifles of vintages ranging from 1891. I myself had an impressively long and thin Remington, weighing all of twenty pounds. The lock on this rifle No. 1751 was so worn that the cartridges kept falling out. Yet it was an effective weapon compared with some of the others in the regiment, which were so hopelessly and irrevocably rusted that loading seemed out of the question. These twenty-pounders made me think of the watches little girls get for Christmas, with the minutes and hours attractively painted on their dials but no works inside. The leather slings for the rifles were totally absent. The entire regiment used the cloth straps intended to hold on our gas-masks. Needless to say, these straps, so indispensable for the gas-masks, were never replaced. We killed two birds with one stone. The rough cloth chafed our shoulders, making the rifles intolerably heavy; at the same time the gas-masks were rendered unserviceable. (The gas-masks, moreover, were of inferior quality. They were not adequately sealed around the eyes, but at the last moment, as though to compensate for this deficiency, we were given a new sack weighing at least three pounds, ostensibly to protect us against a new German gas. During the whole campaign, I dragged this monstrosity around with me, only to discover, when taken prisoner, that the Germans had never heard of any new gas, and themselves had stuck to their small, handy, but well-sealed masks.)

It would take too long to go into all the details of our equipment. Instead of army motorcycles, we were given faulty ones rejected by dealers. We never had the prescribed number of machine guns. Cars and trucks were delivered without any repair tools. As for uniforms, we had interminably long coats which made marching difficult and were un-

bearably hot in summer. Instead of knapsacks we had waxed
cloths in which we wrapped our belongings as best we could.
Groaning under the unnecessary weight, we looked like
tramps or street beggars.

The day we left Mommenheim, "reserve stocks" were distributed. Every soldier received eleven pieces of biscuit, one
can of sardines, and one of cold storage meat, known as
singe (monkey) in the military jargon. We noted at once
that the tins had been covered with a thick layer of paint—
dark blue or dark brown. A soldier has his curiosity. As soon
as we were safely aboard the train, we took out our knives
and began to scrape the paint off our monkey-meat. And all
of us discovered almost simultaneously that our iron ration
had been manufactured between 1916 and 1920. There had
been time enough for the smallest baboon to grow into the
biggest gorilla. That was how France embarked on a war.

On our way to the front, we halted in the woods of St.
Mihiel and the general inspected us for the first time.

"*Mon général*," said our colonel, "of my twenty-three
hundred men, eight hundred have no rifles. Are we going to
fight a war without arms?"

Our march to the front was like a flight forwards.

By the time we got under way, the Germans were already
in France. Holland had fallen, the Germans were deep in
Belgium and at the gates of Sedan. Our officers, to be sure,
spoke of a counter-offensive, but no one believed them. What
they said and how they said it all sounded very unconvinc-
ing. In Alsace there were rumors that thirteen generals had
been court-martialed and shot. Who had spread the rumors
no one could find out. They sprang up overnight and you
heard them from all sides. There was always a certain plausi-
bility about them. (They were not true at the time, though

they foreshadowed what was to come.) The newspapers came late and said nothing. A counter-offensive? We shook our heads.

From Mommenheim our regiment proceeded to the station of Hochfelden, eleven kilometers distant, and there we were loaded into cattle cars. It took us a whole day to cover the eleven kilometers, as the high command feared to move large masses of troops along the highways. We marched off by companies: two hundred men at a time, in single columns at either side of the road, with a three to five yard interval between men. The villages we passed hadn't begun to be evacuated, and again I felt a burning shame in the presence of the civilian population. The people looked after us without comprehension as we slunk along the walls: we were dressed like tramps, our helmets were too large or too small, our shoes were in tatters—*l'armée du Négus,* as we called ourselves.

Altogether, we rode and marched for five full days. Every time we saw a plane we played dead for half an hour. We crept through the towns at night like thieves. I am convinced that if we had made more use of trains and trucks, instead of playing Indian on narrow trails; if we had reached the front in twenty-four hours instead of wandering all over creation for five days to "mislead the enemy"—we might have lost twenty men en route, but we would have been a regiment on our arrival and not a band of demoralized, tired tramps. One slogan was borne in upon us, over and over again: "The enemy is stronger!" By day and by night, we were never allowed to forget it. That thought devoured our souls and gnawed at our hearts, until an army was turned into a defeated mob.

At one o'clock one morning we landed in St. Mihiel. The town was bathed in clear metallic moonlight. Cautiously we slipped out of the cattle cars. Every move had to be made quietly, inconspicuously, as though the enemy were on our heels.

"Habe, your helmet is shiny!" said my company commander, Captain Billerot.

Automatically I reached for my helmet.

"Smear some dirt on it," he whispered.

It took more than an hour for the regiment to assemble on the platform. Never have I seen a more ghostlike assemblage. We all looked like corpses in the moonlight. I thought of the German ballad about Napoleon reviewing his dead troops. We were dead soldiers, all right. But where was Napoleon?

Slowly the procession began to move. In single columns we crossed the city of St. Mihiel, so glorious in the memory of the last war. The closed shutters were like the hollow eye-sockets of a blind man. The moonlight clad the houses in flowing white robes. Our footfalls echoed eerily. Aside from the barking of an occasional dog, there was dead silence in the dead city.

We had barely left St. Mihiel when we heard the well-known sound of motors. Did the Germans know we were advancing, or was the St. Mihiel station under constant observation? In any case, the air was suddenly full of the screaming German bombers. At the same time a clanking arose from the road: our tractors had just been unloaded and were racing along with an unearthly clatter trying to catch up with our column. The icy moonlight painted our faces white. In the air the menacing roar of unseen planes, down below the tractors, dragging their chains like a castle ghost.

But then a command rang out: *"Planquez-vous! Planquez-vous!"* The eternal order to hide.

The French Adjutant Lesfauries, two of my scouts, the Swiss Kellenberger and the Russian Imoudsky, a red-headed

Hungarian named Dési, and myself, turned into a narrow side path. After a few uncertain steps, amid stones and mud, we came to a rocky cavern that looked like an adequate refuge. But as we came closer, an angry voice cried, *"Qui est là?"*

We stopped as though nailed to the spot.

The voice repeated with insistence, "Who is there?" It sounded half like a concierge, half like Cerberus. But before we could answer, a human form, apparently belonging to the voice, crawled from under the cliff. He had on a bedraggled cap of the sort worn by railroad workers. His appearance was more like that of a concierge. Aside from the cap, the caveman had only his pants on, with the suspenders dragging behind him.

"Why do you keep bothering me?" he asked.

I offered him a cigarette, and that seemed to mollify him a little. I ventured the question, "What are you doing here, monsieur?"

"I live here," said the apparition indifferently. "This is an air raid shelter from the other war. It's good and solid—not the kind of junk that you fellows put up. My wife and I lived down there in the gatekeeper's house. I was the gatekeeper."

He stretched out his arm, and we looked in the direction indicated. Before us lay a broad meadow bathed in a strange twilight. The sky was turning gray in the east. In the white field there was nothing whatever to be seen. "The house is all gone," said the old man. His hair was wild and unkempt, his face covered with gray beard stubble. "Our house was blown away. So we moved into the shelter." He came a step closer and drew aside a curtain which he had hung over the opening. In the cave a candle was burning. A woman and two children were sleeping in an improvised bed.

The man tugged at his cigarette. The whirring of the airplane motor hadn't died down for an instant. But in the heavens there was nothing to be seen.

"Do you want to come in?" the old man asked suddenly. And when we declined: "There's no sense in it anyway. Every night some soldiers wake me up. But the bombers haven't been dropping any bombs for days now. They don't have to."

He spat.

"There's no one left in St. Mihiel. I'm all alone."

We exchanged glances. Our legs ached and we were dying of sleepiness.

"Have you any news?" asked Adjutant Lesfauries. He was a publisher from Paris, and he asked everyone he met for news. You could tell that he missed his six editions of *Paris-Soir*. Even from the lips of a caveman he hoped to hear news. Strange to report, the caveman had plenty of news.

"The Germans are in Reims. The Germans are everywhere. We are surrounded. On all sides."

He leaned against the cliff. The white light flowed over his face, and all our faces seemed covered with hoar-frost. The frogs croaked in the swamp.

"Where are you bound for?" asked the man from the underworld, absently straightening his suspenders. "Have you another cigarette?"

"We are on our way to the front," replied the adjutant.

The old man said nothing for a moment. He had the look of an evil old ape.

"Where?" he asked slowly. I thought I heard mockery in his voice.

"To the front," the sergeant repeated.

And then the old man began to laugh. He laughed a loud full-throated laugh, awful to hear amid the buzzing silence.

"To the front," said the old man, imitating the adjutant's voice. He laughed so loud that his wife in the cave must have heard him. But that didn't seem to bother him. "To the front? There isn't any more front!"

He doubled up with delight. The croaking frogs seemed to be laughing with him.

We turned away. Then there was a great silence. The planes had stopped whirring, the tractors were silent. When we turned around, the old man had vanished, as though he had really been nothing but an apparition. But the feeble candlelight still sifted through the hole in the cliff. And there was still a note of laughter in the morning air.

That morning we slept hidden behind the graves of the American soldiers who had stormed St. Mihiel.

We went on, zigzagging through northern France, on our way to the counter-offensive, as they said.

It is impossible for me to recall the names of all the towns we passed. But after St. Mihiel we were always on foot—no more trains and no more trucks. We marched thirty-five, forty, forty-five kilometers in a night, and in the end we had advanced no more than fifteen kilometers.

More and more soldiers fell by the wayside. Among us we had men of over forty; after several marches of thirty, forty, or fifty kilometers they fell down and could go no further. Where our trucks were, and what they were carrying, remained a mystery. They had vanished. Most likely they were taking another route. The soldiers began to throw away their equipment. Seventy pounds was too much to carry; we tossed our excess baggage overboard. On the fourth or fifth day, scarcely any of us had his blanket left: the ditches by the roadside were full of brown military blankets.

One rainy afternoon we stopped to rest in the soldiers'

cemetery of Verdun. For two days it had been raining steadily, it was cold and windy, and all signs of spring had vanished. A few of us sat on the pink tombstones of the French;
others, across the way, by the black wooden crosses of the
Germans. Meat tins were opened and thrown away, egg
shells were strewn on the graves of our fathers. Our colonel
ran up and down searching the sky for planes.

The commander of my company, Captain Billerot, had
been a lieutenant in the World War. He was a dour-looking
capricious fellow, with ill-humor written all over him, a professional soldier who at fifty had risen no higher than a captain. He had been appointed to our company only a few
weeks before, and he knew only a few of us by name. Before
him Lieutenant Saint-Brice had commanded our company.
He had been a notary in Angers and was an officer of un-
common intelligence—a real man, of whom I shall have more
to say later. He had been the idol of the company, inspiring
a natural respect; we would have followed him through hell
fire. I do not know whether that is why he was relieved of
his command at the last moment and replaced by Captain
Billerot, who for many years had been a sort of foreman in
an armaments factory, and had no desire whatever for an
active command. The command had probably been entrusted
to Billerot because of his "experience" in the military trade.
In general, the high command seemed convinced that soldiering was nothing but a routine that had to be learned. They
expected us to "repeat" the last war, with the same methods,
the same weapons, the same personnel, and even the same
miracles.

Actually Captain Billerot seemed rejuvenated as soon as we
entered the Verdun territory. In his 1914 helmet, he always
marched in advance of his troop. Whenever the opportunity
offered, he recounted his experiences in the great war. "Write

that down," he advised me, with the special smile peculiar to those incurable bores who are forever giving us poor novelists hand-outs. ("Really, you know, if I only got around to it, I could write the most wonderful novel about my life.")

Captain Billerot had only disagreeable experiences to relate. Over and over again he told me how he had twice lost seventy-five per cent of his company, how he had once escaped from no-man's-land with two machine guns on his back, how his orderly had had a house cave in on him while he was delousing himself. The rare occasions on which I saw him really cheerful were when he was talking about the appalling loss of life at Verdun. Captain Billerot, with the fleshless, paper-thin nose, was not a bad man. But his face had gradually turned into a steel helmet, and his soul had become as wooden as a rifle butt. He was too simple a man to realize that the memory of his harrowing losses gave him pleasure only because of his own miraculous escape from death.

Now, in the cemetery of Verdun, overcome by the fairest of his memories, he felt called upon to make a speech. It was six o'clock in the evening, and the rain was still pouring down. He assembled us amid the graves.

"Volunteers!" he addressed us. "We are advancing into the front lines. I know this region like the palm of my hand; you can trust me. It was here that I fought during the last war. Not far from this spot I lost seventy-five per cent of my company. The shells were sizzling and whistling from all directions. (He gave an imitation of the sizzling and whistling, and lingered for a time on the picture. The rain poured down our necks.) As soon as we reach the lines, each of you must say to himself: from now on my life isn't worth a sou. Anyone who escaped from here, even in the last war, could call himself lucky. (There followed a few particulars about the clashes in which Captain Billerot had lost seventy-five per cent of his company.) And so, today I must have a serious word with you. (We listened eagerly. All of us still awaited a revelation from the mouth of the old warrior.) Volunteers! Whatever happens, the material with which you have been entrusted must be brought back. Anyone returning without his rifle will hear from me. If a comrade falls beside you, you must not concern yourself with him. It is your duty to save his weapons. I myself . . . (here followed the story of the machine guns he had saved). Say to yourselves that from now on your life is worth nothing. Go forward! I count on you, as you can count on me!"

The speech was over. The captain drew his raincoat tighter and walked away like a man who has performed his work well.

Among the graves of Verdun stood two hundred men whose life had ceased to be worth a sou.

CHAPTER TWO: BAPTISM OF FIRE

THE DEAD MAN—LE MORTHOMME—THAT WAS THE NAME OF the last village before the front—a tiny hamlet a few kilometers north of Grandpré. We reached le Morthomme in the morning; the sun had just crept out, and spring lay over the fields. The grass gave forth a smell of warmth, the fruit trees had white and pink blossoms, and if you looked aloft you saw circles, spirals, and little blue lines dancing about like merry butterflies. The fruit trees were colorless and odorless as in a moving picture. Between ourselves and nature lay a veil which we feared to penetrate. To breathe the spring was to think of what we had left behind us. Of all the springs we had lived through: the Prater in Vienna; a garden behind the houses of Dornbach; the Danube at Budapest; the green park at Presinge; the first hot night in Nice. But all we could do was shut our eyes and forget those springs. For our lives were no longer worth a sou. Through le Morthomme marched the dead men of the future.

Little Mayer marched ahead of me. I don't know what has become of him but I shall never forget little Mayer. His full name was Samuel Mayer, but as he was a Rumanian we nicknamed him Mayerescu. At first I wondered what idiot of a regimental doctor had declared Mayer to be "fit" when he volunteered. Later I learned that two or three recruiting stations had pronounced him unfit, but that he had kept on trying until he found a doctor, blind or senile no doubt, who was willing to declare Samuel Mayer-Mayerescu fit to carry arms. And one day Mayerescu turned up in Barcarès. His glasses were sliding off; on his narrow ash-blond head he wore a hat twice too big for him; his right shoulder was considerably higher than his left; in his hand he held a shabby and cumbersome suitcase. He was twenty years old and had just graduated from the *lycée*. His near-sighted eyes were always ringed with red from too much reading, and his pants fluttered around his spindly legs. Whatever he picked up, he dropped; at target practice he missed not only the bull's-eye, but the entire target. His steel helmet, which he wore with a certain pride, often admiring himself in a little white pocket mirror, sat on his head like a melon. His gun seemed to drag him down to earth. Back in the hinterland all of us, more or less cruelly, had made fun of Mayer. Now he marched before me with his badly tied bundle on his back, still carrying a gigantic cook-pot that a sadistic corporal had tied to his pack. His shoes were big enough for him to wade in and pained him terribly. Sheer enthusiasm kept him going. He fell and he picked himself up; he fainted and revived himself; he shook like a leaf, yet endured. Such was Samuel Mayer-Mayerescu from Bucharest, Volunteer Number One.

Little Mayer suddenly turned round: "What is that?"

We had just passed the first houses of the village. And all at once I saw four or five Negroes running down the silent street. Seldom have I seen such unconcealed terror in a human face. The Negroes had neither rifles nor any other article of equipment. They ran and screamed, over and over: "No go! No go! Oh, no go, oh, terrible. German cut your throat. Oh, no go!"

They accompanied their cries of terror with gestures of which only Negroes are capable. They raised their arms to heaven and moved their long thin fingers back and forth across their necks, as though cutting their own throats.

They ran as though they expected to run to the end of the world. And no one thought of stopping them.

While we were eating dinner in le Morthomme the first enemy planes appeared on the horizon. Only Kellenberger, a Swiss—in civil life stage-manager of the Tabarin night club in Paris—jumped up to get his binoculars. The former chorus-master was noted for his curiosity, and this time the curiosity was stronger even than his appetite. The rest of us lay on the meadow until we were called.

I had tied on my bundle and was writing a last letter when Colonel de Buissy arrived. He was a corpulent man of nearly sixty, and he had served for thirty years in the Foreign Legion. During the first World War he had fought with the Legion in Europe and distinguished himself in many encounters, but most of his life had been spent in guerilla warfare in Africa. A square-built giant with broad shoulders and broad hips, he was a typical French colonial officer: less subtle and less sensitive than the English, often perhaps more brutal, but essentially more sincere and more direct. Now he was somewhat surprised at a war so different from African campaigning. His broad kindly face seemed weary and gray.

"Are the scouts ready?"

I smiled mechanically, out of habit. For months they had taught us to smile when the colonel spoke to us. *Servir avec le sourire*—that was Colonel Paul de Buissy's favorite saying.

But this time the smile didn't seem to impress him.

"No more jokes," he said. "We'll soon be under fire."

I ventured a question: "Where are the lines?"

He shrugged his shoulders: "I don't know. Wherever we

find the enemy." He turned and left us. It was not until later that I learned the meaning of his answer.

Our company was supposed to march at nine that night, but it was eleven before we started. For two hours I stood by the side of the road, leaning on my rifle, while the others passed us by. Our company had been appointed to cover the regiment's rear. It was five past eleven when the instructions came to our captain: "Marching orders for the Company. Get to the Ferme St. Denis by four-thirty at the latest."

We had scarcely left Le Morthomme when we were drawn into the general movement of troops marching northwards for the last time. The night was dark. The narrow highway to Briquenay was jammed with men, cars, horses, cannons, automobiles. Fresh forces and supplies were advancing, exhausted men and casualties were being withdrawn from the front. A constant movement of men, animals, and equipment —over a road not wider than two or three yards, somewhere between Le Morthomme and Châtillon.

We marched in single file, desperately trying to keep contact with one another. Horse-drawn artillery blocked the road. Cursing drivers kept lashing at their horses; horses bucked and refused to move forward. A modern Czech tank, recognizable by its streamlining, had been driven into the ditch. It was burning, but no one paid any attention. In the light of the flames bursting from the tank we saw two army doctors removing a wounded man from an ambulance to carry him on foot. Some crazed horses had kicked the radiator of the ambulance and put the motor out of commission. The wounded man roared with pain and the two physicians tried to lift the stretcher above their heads. The flames from the burning tank licked at the wounded man's face.

Orders were to march at intervals of three to five yards,

27

but after the first few steps the very idea seemed absurd. How could our advance remain concealed from the enemy, with the roads so jammed you couldn't have dropped a pin? We kept contact with one another as well as we could. We slipped between cars, under the sweating bellies of horses. The drivers didn't give a damn what happened to the infantrymen; they recklessly drove their horses forward. Again and again we were pushed into the ditch, again and again we fell down and scrambled up in breathless haste for fear of losing our comrades. A horse collapsed and could not rise again; a tank passed over him. The heavy caterpillar treads cut into his living flesh. Stray cows from a herd at the roadside ran out on the highway. Bellowing with pain, they ran amidst the tanks, trucks, and cannon. A few horses, their bellies torn open by bombs, lay across the road. For the first time I encountered the sweet smell—a mixture of sugar, ether, and decay—that reveals the presence of a dead horse anywhere in the vicinity. Everybody was looking for everybody else: officers looked for their men, soldiers for their superiors, drivers for their cars. And no one knew where he was going. To the question, "Where are we going?" the answer was always the same, "We don't know. Forward."

All this was accompanied by a Witches' Sabbath of sounds from lumbering tanks, screeching artillery cars, yelling drivers, and neighing horses. But all these brutal noises were nothing in comparison with the delicate tinkling of the ambulance bells. French ambulance cars have no sirens or horns, but a thin little silver bell which is pulled like the house bell of an old mansion. Here, amid the wildest, rawest noises, the *tinkle-tinkle* of the ambulances sounded like an announcement of death. The ambulance drivers rang their death bells with desperate violence as they tried to make way for their cars. The air was filled with sharp metallic silver tones that cut you to the quick. There were dozens of ambulances filled with injured men returning to le Morthomme. Dozens of empty ones were moving in our own direction. They seemed to hurry so as to be ready when the living and unwounded now marching forward would be dead and wounded. We marched and marched, with bent backs. The death bell was our marching song.

At four-thirty we were supposed to occupy our posts at the Ferme St. Denis. We had left le Morthomme shortly before midnight. At two in the morning we had covered scarcely one third of the way.

Little Mayer marched in front of me. Our sergeant took a literal view of justice. Each man, regardless of his own weight, had to carry the same amount. He had loaded Mayer with kitchen pots and soup buckets. These gastronomical weapons, the only modern ones in the French army, were made of gleaming aluminum; they might have been the pride of Prunier's or Drouot's kitchen. Here, in the livid moonlight, they were a gleaming beacon for enemy aircraft. Redheaded Dési, the Hungarian electrical engineer, trotted behind me. He had been entrusted with a bicycle, and he cursed as he pushed it. The front tire was punctured and the little leather tool kit on the handle-bars was empty.

Little by little the roads became less crowded. At the sides, in the ditch, soldiers were lying or sitting: a uniform black mass in the semi-darkness. Now and then a voice rang out.

"What regiment?" we asked as we passed.

"Third Company?"

Most of the time there was no answer. The men in the ditch were asleep—many had marched for thirty or forty kilometers. They had fallen asleep as they marched, and had dropped when the short whistle gave the signal for *"Repos!"*

Near Boult-aux-Bois we crossed the great Reims-Stenay

29

highway. Here Captain Billerot lost his way for the first
time. After five kilometers he finally found the right road.
Before us spread the large plain extending from the Aisne to
the Meuse, broken occasionally by a clump of forest. A great
silence set in. You will remember, my comrades, this choking
silence that had nothing in common with the peaceful silence
of the fields, nor with the final tranquillity of your native
graveyard. The silence we had known before was the absence
of sound: this new silence was the inability to hear any sound.
We all felt that the noise was lurking in wait for us, surrounding us. The silence burst out, now at one place, now at
another, with the suddenness of a cry. We jerked our heads
up as though startled by a sound; but only the silence had
spoken. Far ahead of us, on the horizon, but to the right and
left of us as well, where the plain and the sky merged, we
could see the flames of cannon fire. There was lightning at
regular intervals; lightning that came not from the sky but
from the earth. It seemed to rise from below the horizon—an
artillery barrage from Hell against Heaven. We were too far
away to hear the cannon, and there was something spectral
in this silence—a silence in which noises could be seen but not
heard.

"It's like the movies," said the voice of Bruno, the Russian
film operator beside me.

"Hm."

"Sure. When the sound track is broken. When you see
people open their mouths and have no idea what they're saying."

"Are you tired?"

"Not any more."

"What do you mean?"

"I am too tired to be tired."

We walked side by side. The silence surrounded us. Now

that the company had regathered on the deserted road, we felt alone and forsaken. There was lightning on all sides. We felt distinctly that we were not moving toward the enemy, but marching into a carefully prepared trap. Yet no one stopped. When our captain ordered us to rest, we did not sit down. We feared that we would not be able to stand up again. We remained standing and we fell asleep leaning on our rifles.

"Is it you, Garai?"

The bespectacled Hungarian photographer was at my side.

"Yes."

"Holding out all right?"

"I've got three blisters on my feet."

"How many?"

"Three."

"I've got four."

We spoke of blisters, kilometers, loads. No one spoke of home. All behaved as if we were performing an old accustomed trade. We were glad to have "technical difficulties" to think about. We were glad of the blisters on our feet.

A dog howled in the stillness.

"It's Noemi," said Garai. "You know, the Pole. Lieutenant Jirou-Najou's orderly. Up to now everybody envied him. He got all the gravy. He had a fine time."

"And now?"

"Now he holds the lieutenant's wolf-hound. His hands are all sore. The dog keeps tugging at the leash. It must be the stench of corpses. A mutt like that is worse than a gun. A gun can't smell corpses."

"Where's the lieutenant?"

"He's following us in a car."

The road lost itself in a wood. We breathed easy, thinking that here we were sheltered. But soon the trees became sparse, and when we left the wood we saw that we were on a raised highway. At the first crossing soldiers reappeared. They seemed to be sentries posted to observe the plain lying below us. Our captain approached one of the soldiers.

"What regiment?"

"I can't say, *mon capitaine*."

Our captain gave a short laugh.

"Afraid of parachutists? All right. What are you doing here?"

"Scouting duty."

"Where's the enemy?"

The sentry hesitated for a moment. He looked down into the plain. Then he said briefly, "Everywhere, *mon capitaine*."

I approached the scout. He was a man of at least forty. He had a big mustache and had surely been in the World War. He looked like a hero of the Marne who had stepped out of the frontispiece in a textbook.

The horizon was bathed in pink light.

"Dawn," I said.

"No," said the man of the Marne, without looking at me. "That's a village burning."

Our captain ventured another question.

"Does this road lead to Belleville?"

"I can't say, *mon capitaine*."

"I am supposed to relieve the Forty-eighth Infantry. Fresh troops."

For the first time the man with the mustache showed a little animation.

He turned around. Behind him, leaning on their guns, the "fresh" troops were asleep standing up.

"The Forty-eighth Infantry is no longer there, *mon capitaine*."

"What do you mean?"

Again the soldier turned to stone.

"Because it ran away."

"Impossible!"

The man of the Marne pointed silently at the sides of the road. Knapsacks, waterproof cloth, sleeping bags, blankets, cans of food lay scattered in the ditch.

"What's that?" asked the captain.

The man cleared his throat.

"Souvenirs!"

In the word "souvenir" there was contempt for those who had left no memory behind them but the sleeping bags and unopened cans they had thrown away. And there was sadness at the thought of a France that was no longer.

The captain changed the subject.

"Do you know how far we are from the Ferme St. Denis?"

"I don't know."

The captain shrugged his shoulders. The sleeping company began to move. The village burned. The lieutenant's dog howled. The man of the Marne disappeared in the semi-darkness. Dési cursed his broken bicycle. All we knew was that the Ferme St. Denis was nowhere, and that the enemy was everywhere.

In Belleville we made a short halt at a cross-roads. All the inhabitants had left the place. It was a gray village with a cemetery in the middle and a wide main street. A few steps led up to the church. The place must have been a rather depressing mixture of a village and small town. The houses seemed to have more than one story and somehow less than two.

There was scarcely anything to remind you of life: Belleville was the first wrecked town that we saw, the first of hundreds. The shambles of Belleville impressed us even though we were so dulled by fatigue that we had thought ourselves capable of no human emotion. What struck us was not the destruction and devastation, not the utter wreckage, but the *half* destruction, the *half* demolition, the things that had remained undamaged in the midst of the destruction. Human beings are so constituted that they feel death only in life, that in viewing what is lost they weep only for what has remained.

The whole façade of one house had collapsed. It would probably have gone unnoticed, if not for a baby's crib hanging down into the road from the first floor—a touching white crib with a high railing and pink pillows. It made me think of the doll's houses I had as a child, with three solid walls and a fourth that you could take down when you wanted to look inside. A heavy shell had struck another house in such a way as to destroy the kitchen completely—the range hung down the wall like a rotting intestine. But the adjoining bedroom, with its beds, washbasins, and a Madonna, was entirely undamaged. All of us have seen pictures of bombed cities, in newspapers, illustrated magazines, and newsreels. But these pictures contain only detached fragments; they give no idea of the truth for they show only the bare destruction instead of the living contrast. Here, in Belleville—"the pretty little town"—the contrast was particularly striking. The artillery, all apparently aiming at the same target, had razed one side of the street and entirely spared the other—a sight which we later encountered almost everywhere. The bakery shop with its peaceful front seemed to look with astonishment at the barber shop across the street—where the barber chair had been blown upside down. A grocery store belonging to a certain Madame Tissier seemed startled at the sight of the mill that had strewn its white wealth all over the street.

I had just fallen asleep on the steps of the church at Belleville when I was awakened by a shrill whistle: the first shell

landed about twenty yards from me, right in the middle of a
house gate. A few minutes later we were in the wildest tur-
moil. The enemy was invisible: this was the worst of our
first baptism of fire. I felt that I could have seized the shell
in my hand as it buzzed by, yet nothing was visible but its
effect. At that time we had not yet learned to hear the cannon's report. It was not till we heard the metallic buzz over
our heads that we flung ourselves on the ground. A house
began to burn. A corporal yelled. The Spanish volunteers,
the only ones who had seen this kind of thing before, looked
for a shelter. And yet I don't think anyone was afraid. The
soldier's life is organized with such satanic skill that he does
not reach the zones of greatest danger till he is too tired to
perceive his peril. We were too tired.

We had barely strength to look at one another. We were
all white as chalk. Grobla, a Polish Jew, lost his glasses at the
first shot. They fell to the road and broke to splinters. He
crawled on his belly with laughable zeal, desperately seeking
the scattered fragments, as though he could glue them together. Suddenly I remembered how I had met him a few
days before Christmas in a store at Perpignan: he was buying
a doll for his daughter and a toy train for his son. And now
he was crawling on his belly looking for pieces of broken
glass. Adjutant Lesfauries, the Paris publisher, lay in the
graveyard, his face buried in a freshly dug grave. His steel
helmet had slipped down on his neck, and he held both hands
over his ears. Kellenberger, the Swiss night-club manager,
kept piling hay on his head with feverish haste, like a child
playing ostrich. Only the Spaniards were calm and self-con-
trolled. From their cellars they yelled something incomprehensible to little Mayer, who stood there helplessly looking
around, still bearing his soup buckets and cook-pots on his
narrow back. He was the only one among us who had for-

gotten to throw himself on the ground. He looked around desperately for help and then began to hop back and forth across the intersection, which was the Germans' apparent target.

Apart from the yelling Spaniards, no one thought of helping him. Then and there, in this first hour of our baptism of fire, I was overwhelmed by a deep anxiety that was never to leave me: a feeling of distrust, of being forsaken. As far as you could look, there was not an officer in sight. The Headquarters Company of the Twenty-first Foreign Volunteers underwent its baptism of fire without parents or foster parents. At that moment, consciously or not, we lost our confidence in our leaders, the confidence that is the most elementary requirement for any army that wants to win.

Captain Billerot had disappeared. We sought him like helpless children. At that moment his gold stripes, "signs of a rich experience," his medals, marks of heroism in a previous war, could have wrought miracles. At that moment the company commander still had everything he needed: our trust and our loyalty. But he had vanished into thin air. Another officer of our regiment appeared as if from nowhere. This was Captain Berley. He had lost his way, entered Belleville with his C.R.E. (*Compagnie Régimentaire d'Engins*), the mortar and anti-tank gun company. In Belleville, he tried to reassemble his company, reduced to one half of its effectives. Captain Berley was a kindly gentleman from Calvados; he always had his pockets full of excellent liqueur candies from his native town. In civilian life he was a tax collector, and perhaps for this reason he never left the side of his lieutenant, Dr. Pecqueraud, who in "life"—*dans la vie*, as the Frenchmen say, thus clearly separating war from life—was a notary. Now the tax collector and the notary stood on the highway of Belleville looking for their company. They too would have liked to find Captain Billerot, hoping he would give them some advice.

At four in the morning, the artillery barrage diminished. A brilliant spring day was dawning. A wounded Spaniard lay outside the cellar in which he had taken refuge. He had just crawled out when he was hit by a shell splinter. Adjutant Daroussat, an old soldier, leader of our sappers, went for a little walk and came back smiling. He reported that the road we were to take in order to reach our positions had been shot to bits. It lay in full sight of the enemy. By daylight no man could pass it alive. But for another half hour it would be relatively safe. Every minute was precious, he said.

But our captain was not to be found.

I tried to dress the wound of a Greek beside me who had been grazed by a shell splinter. He moaned and vomited. I asked Captain Berley whether he knew how to get in touch with an ambulance. No, he didn't know; nor did he know how to find out. But he said I could stop an ambulance if any passed by. Besides, I should mind my own business; was I in the medical corps or the observation corps? I saluted and started to go back to my Greek. The captain felt he had been too harsh with me, and offered me a liqueur candy from Calvados.

"*Il ne faut pas chercher à comprendre*," he declared. This was his favorite saying.

The sun was shining with fresh morning vigor and we were all assembled when Captain Billerot finally made his appearance. Where he had been during the bombardment remained his secret. He gave the company the marching order. Adjutant Daroussat called his attention to the dangers.

"We'll go down the road one by one," said the commander.

Then he approached Captain Berley, who told him that he had lost his way.

"I am glad I found you, Captain Billerot. I don't know where the Ferme St. Denis is situated. And I have no map."

Captain Billerot went closer to Captain Berley. The two company commanders, responsible for the lives of four hundred men, discovered, two kilometers from the front, that neither of them had a map.

In violation of the order to take the road from Belleville to Châtillon-sur-Bar only at night or at daybreak, both companies marched out in clear daylight. For months the military principle of never criticizing our superiors' decisions had been drilled into us. We followed our officers and I must confess that I was pleased with Captain Billerot's obvious courage in deciding to reach the Ferme St. Denis at any cost, even if a trifle belatedly. I knew that our colonel and his staff had taken a different road to St. Denis, but I also knew that his entire regiment would be paralyzed until his headquarters company and the anti-tank company had taken up their prescribed positions.

However, our forced march to the Ferme St. Denis was to prove futile, and not alone because our commanders had no idea of its location. What hindered our advance was a weapon which our old warriors had not taken into account and which they had not experienced in the World War: the *Luftwaffe*. No sooner had we stepped on the sloping road than we heard the hum of airplanes. This humming was particularly loud, the sound of the motors was particularly deep and groaning, and the two machines that appeared over our heads were of a particular cut: short, rather plump, with semi-oval noses. Their bodies gleamed in the sun and they flew low, at a height of about five hundred yards—what they call *basse altitude*. The captain asked me if I could identify the aircraft.

I and the other observers—the Hungarian Garai, the Rumanian Dr. Barati, the Russians Imoudsky and Ouchakoff, and the Swiss Kellenberger—established that they were beyond doubt German planes, but of a model completely unknown to us. We had never heard of anything like it.

At this point I must speak of this plane, which pursued us for weeks and caused the death of thousands of French soldiers—the dread ghost that haunted every front-line soldier. It played an essential role in the German victory over the French. Later, when our own D.C.A.—*Défense Contre-Aérienne*—shot down one of these planes, we found out that it was a modified form of the Arrado monoplane, a German training machine. This plane was heavily armored; in non-technical parlance it could be called a flying tank. Its chief difference from a tank was that it was not built for any aggressive purpose: it carried only one machine gun and no bombs. It was completely unsuited for an air battle—its maximum speed was from 120 to 140 kilometers per hour. But all these drawbacks were compensated for by its invulnerability: machine gun bullets fired by pursuit planes could seldom damage the little Arrado; as to the shots fired by the D.C.A., it is better not to mention them. Only in the rarest cases, when the pilot himself was hit or when a shell pierced the gas tank, could this flying Achilles be shot down. The Arrado was an observation craft—the best that has ever been invented. Its almost absolute invulnerability enabled it to fly lower than any other plane—German observation planes often accompanied us from milestone to milestone at an altitude of less than three hundred yards. Not a single troop movement escaped these planes. Particularly devastating was their effect on artillery. Hovering about with no fear of punishment, they always appeared during an artillery duel and radioed the exact location of our batteries. Most of the time, their very appearance was sufficient to silence the French guns. If they continued firing, however, their positions were betrayed faster than they could change place with the help of horses—tractors were a rarity in the French army. The observation planes also caused immense damage in the rear by informing the Germans of the approach of reinforcements, particularly of the armored units indispensable for the preparation of an attack.

It is impossible to describe the psychological effect of this weapon, which can be justly appraised only by the two million Frenchmen who are in German captivity and who fought the war in the front lines. The French nicknamed the German armored plane "Coco": even in the hottest moments the French never run short of humorous names. Much more revealing, however, was the Arrado's semi-official designation: in the divisional reports it was called the *Mouchard*—"stool-pigeon" or "informer." During the entire war hardly a single French troop movement was carried out unbeknownst to the Germans; no battery could fire undiscovered. The German army made a virtue of the noble German saying that "the greatest scoundrel of all is the informer." Everywhere the flying squealer sowed the seeds of terror and insecurity. The troops advancing to the front felt betrayed even before leaving camp: the *Mouchard* could penetrate deep into the country without fear of resistance. Wherever the flying conspirator appeared, confusion arose: an anguished feeling that you were betrayed and unable to hide. Wherever he appeared, the impression of crushing German superiority, of something superhuman, an impression already fostered by our superiors, was intensified. It was as though we could not venture a move without detection by Hitler's eye. The invulnerable monster hovered above us like fate.

Closely shadowed by two *Mouchards* we went down the

quiet road to Châtillon—one by one, in full sunlight. The German planes flew lower and lower. We distinctly saw the heads of the pilots. We felt their eyes upon us. Each man had the sensation that he, and only he, was pursued by the gleaming aircraft. No French pursuit plane appeared in the sky. The D.C.A. was silent. The war showed its true face—it was not a war, but a hunt. We ran with lowered heads, our guns in our hands. The informers seemed to lean out of their planes, and to grin. But that of course was only our imagination.

A short distance before Châtillon there was a wood to the right of the road. Captain Billerot, still in advance of the column, ran into the woods, signaling us to follow him. In a few minutes the two companies were among the trees. No one understood what happened. On the highway, advancing in single file, we were relatively safe, for it could not be supposed that the German batteries would open fire on a miserable company when all they could do was kill a few soldiers. It was not even certain that the *Mouchards* had deemed it important to announce our presence to the German division. But Captain Billerot, who, in the World War, had never come into contact with stool-pigeons of the air, lost his head. He declared that to continue our advance was unthinkable: his responsibility, he said, was too great, and we had to make ourselves "forgotten." How well we succeeded in this endeavor became clear a few minutes later. The four hundred men with their officers had scarcely been assembled in the woods when hell broke loose. Now that the objective was no longer soldiers spread out on a highway, but four hundred men in a small wood, the Germans spared no "expense." We lay pressed together like sardines in a can, because the wood was small and God had obviously made it for a solitary pair of lovers and not for two companies of infantry. We buried

41

our heads in the damp ground. The soil had the familiar taste of wood, of spring. For the first time I felt many things that later I was to feel every day. I was suddenly close to the smallest and lowest creatures, the insects and worms, everything that crawled and writhed humbly and flatly on the ground. The worms went on moving while the shells exploded, and did not seem worried over all these human noises; the bees buzzed in ridiculous, comforting competition, and sometimes, between two bursts, a bird sang. As we dug into the ground with our ten fingers, it sometimes seemed that we were already in our graves, half alive and half dead: and most curiously, the whistling shells meant life and the buzzing bees and singing birds meant death. We often had the feeling that we would have to jump up and run out of the woods, to free ourselves from the hostile trees which hid the heavens and protected us—protected us from Heaven?

Nadai, the tall radio engineer, lay beside me. This calm, silent man had been transformed since we reached the front. With his head stuck into the ground, he calculated aloud that we had ten more minutes to live, at the most. He took, so to speak, a technical view of death. He proved to me that the Germans were beginning to get our range. And indeed, the shells were exploding closer and closer. The first ones had fallen on the highway, the next near the edge of the wood. Now the first trees were beginning to fall. Fragments rained all around us.

"They're cutting down on the range," said Nadai, white as chalk. "Five more minutes at the most."

Ouchakoff, the architect, lay at my feet and said, "Those are seventy-sevens."

How could he have known that? There were some men at the front who knew everything: the caliber of the guns, the make of the rifles, the rapidity of the machine-gun fire. But perhaps they didn't really know a thing. When Ouchakoff was very scared, he consoled himself with scientific explanations.

Berkovitz, the bald little mechanic from Paris, yelled something to me, but I could not hear him in the infernal noise. His bald skull shone among the trees. He had put his steel helmet on a certain spot below his belly. At last I heard him.

"It's more important to me than my head," cried Berkovitz. The captain yelled at him but he pretended not to hear. He pressed his steel helmet to his belly.

The shells burst a few meters from us. A few trees were burning. The shell splinters were falling hard by. One piece fell so close I could reach it with my hand.

"Shouldn't we get out of here before we are all dead?" Nadai asked the captain.

The two company commanders, the active captain and the tax collector from Calvados, did not budge. Only the young notary comforted us: "Let's act as if we were already dead. Then maybe they'll stop."

The *Mouchard* cruised over our heads. Between shots we could make out the heavy, gurgling noise of the motors. From time to time the *Mouchard* looked down to see if we were really dead, or only pretending.

We spent twenty-one hours in that wood. Afterward we buried seven men who pretended they were dead.

Once and for all. . . .

For twenty-one hours Captain Billerot was cut off from the colonel's headquarters. Then he decided to send out three men in search of the Ferme St. Denis. Adjutant Lesfauries, Sergeant Kervran, and I volunteered. We all had our bellies full of that wood. Sergeant-Major Gerber joined us at the last moment.

After four hours we found the Ferme and our colonel, but we had lost Gerber on our way. The colonel told us he had taken up position with his three battalions without knowing the whereabouts of the regiment we were supposed to relieve. This regiment, the Forty-eighth Infantry, had vanished, he said. A battalion of anti-tank guns that happened to be near-by had rushed to his assistance and for the moment was holding back the Germans. Captain Duvivier had gone off to find the divisional commander—his exact whereabouts were not known. Infuriated that the two companies had not yet arrived, Colonel de Buissy asked me if I could show him the exact location of the woods in which Captains Billerot and Berley were entrenched. I could not, because the colonel owned only a Michelin automobile map: the only military map in the regiment had been taken by Captain Duvivier.

The colonel was also worried about Gerber's disappearance. It was unlikely that he had been killed or wounded, for the Germans had stopped shooting hours before. Gerber was an Alsatian who spoke German better than French. He claimed to be a theological student, but his rosy-red Alsatian cheeks, his sly little blue eyes, and his broad hips indicated that he was no "despiser of good food." In Alsace, we explained the sergeant-major's frequent disappearances by his predilection for the fair sex, and Gerber hinted that we were not far from the truth. But after we approached the Belgian frontier and every womanly being, indeed every civilian, had been left far behind us, Gerber kept disappearing as frequently as before. Every evening we lost sight of him; every evening he had to be looked for. Now, again, the earth had suddenly swallowed him.

The colonel asked me whether I would undertake to find my way back to the wood and guide both companies to the Ferme. I set out. Considering that the Germans seemed to be asleep and that the *Mouchard* had gone home, I decided to avoid the woods and follow the main road straight through Châtillon. This road offered an amazing spectacle. Everywhere I saw guns, knapsacks, cans of food, cartridge cases in the ditch. Equipment worth hundreds of thousands of francs was strewn along the road: no one thought of picking it up. All these things had become too heavy for the infantrymen. On the other side of the lines, I later learned, soldiers were brought to points only two kilometers from the front in trucks and buses, but the French infantrymen had to walk hundreds of kilometers on foot to reach the lines. And while the German infantry soldier entered his trench without an overcoat, carrying only his gun, a canteen, and a bag of food —both tied to his belt—the French soldier looked more like Santa Claus than a warrior. Whether he liked it or not, he had to drag his seventy pounds of equipment. Here, too, discipline and punishment were fatally confused. The authorities tried to complete the defective training of the French soldier, who had been allowed to take things easy during the eighteen months of his regular service, by "hardening" him at the front. The Germans' method was the exact opposite: hardships during the training period, and every possible comfort at the great historical moment.

A short distance beyond Châtillon I met a soldier sitting on his knapsack and devouring a can of meat.

"What regiment?" I asked him.

"Forty-eighth Infantry."

"Where's your regiment?"

"Don't know."

He quietly went on eating.

"Where are you going now?"

He looked sullenly ahead. He was a square-built, dark-haired fellow. His dark eyes had so dull a look that I thought: he wouldn't notice if a bullet hit him.

"Don't know," he said at last. "I'm looking for my regiment."

I asked him whether they had been ordered to retreat.

"How do I know?" said the soldier. He rubbed his knee, adding: "All of a sudden someone began to yell: '*Sauve qui peut!*'—and then we ran for it."

"Were the Germans there?"

He reflected awhile.

"No, we didn't see any."

He rose, looking at me with distrust.

"Let's go!"

He took his canteen and made ready to follow me.

"What about your gun?" I asked.

He cast a glance on his gun lying in the ditch—a farewell glance.

"Much too heavy," he said. "And rusty. Can't get it open. There're plenty of guns all over the place."

He thrust his hands into his trouser pockets and limped along by my side. But there was nothing unusual in his limp. All of us limped.

For a long while we said nothing. Then the man sighed.

"What will become of us?" he asked, speaking to himself more than to me.

I shrugged my shoulders.

"I'd like to know why we had to start this damn war," he soliloquized. "Maybe for the sake of the Polish gentlemen? Why in hell did we have to bother about them?"

"But we didn't start it," I objected.

"But we declared war. There was no need for it."

"Hitler wanted to enslave all mankind."

"*L'humanité . . . je l'emmerde.*" He spat. "For the last

46

two weeks I haven't had a bite of warm food." He rummaged in his pockets and produced a broken cigarette. "Hitler didn't attack us. We should have made peace with him a long time ago."

As I remained silent, his distrust seemed to increase.

"What's *your* regiment?"

I showed him the green facings on my lapels.

"Twenty-first Foreign Volunteers."

"Volunteer?"

"Yes."

"Why did you join? Did you want to become a French citizen?"

"No. I wanted to fight the Nazis."

"The Nazis? Why? What did they do to you?" He shook his head. "Volunteer! Stupid bastard! When you weren't even a citizen!"

We came to a house where two shell-stricken Negroes sat smoking. They belonged to the Twenty-fourth Colonials. They joined us. They, too, were "looking for" their regiment. One of them was a corporal and understood French. He asked me whether it would soon be "over." He, too, thought Germany hadn't done anything to him. I tried to explain that France was in danger. He didn't seem to understand.

"Hitler no come Senegal," he kept repeating. He smiled, showing his teeth, and spoke at quick intervals to his comrade. "Hitler no come Senegal. I no come Germany. I and Hitler no enemy."

A stray German shell exploded a few yards ahead of us. We threw ourselves on the ground. The Senegal Negro—the one who did not speak French—shouted, "*Sauve qui peut!*" It sounded like "shof ki po." He probably did not understand the meaning of his cry. He had heard it at a moment of great

47

peril, and from that time on he repeated it whenever he thought himself in danger.

Our batteries replied. It was plain that we were close to the artillery positions concealed in the woods around Châtillon. The hard report of the seventy-fives struck our ears with terrific force.

"We'll get it soon," said my French companion.

He lay where he was and obviously spoke from experience, for scarcely had he finished his sentence when the familiar metallic whistle cut through the air. The German observers on the other side of the Canal des Ardennes had obviously discovered us. I regretted having chosen the road.

The Frenchman lay in the ditch beside me, the two Negroes about five steps from us. The sound of bursting shrapnel grew clearer and clearer, closer and closer. I lay on an abandoned knapsack. At every explosion the Senegalese yelled: "Shof ki po! Shof ki po!"

Soon it began to sound like an oriental prayer.

The Germans shortened their range. Now the shrapnel burst on the field to the right of us. Suddenly I heard an inhuman cry. It was one of the Negroes. The other, the Black Corporal, threw himself sobbing and lamenting over his comrade. I crawled as close to them as I could. The Negro's whole back had been torn open by a shrapnel splinter.

He was the first dying man I saw at the front. His eyes were wide open, his mouth was foaming. His tongue, a thick, black tongue, moved between his lips. And like a last wish or the name of someone he loved, he mumbled the words: "Shof ki po! Shof ki po!"

Run for your lives! This was the slogan of the French army.

Run for your lives. Shof ki po.

48

CHAPTER THREE: SPIES ALOFT

For three long weeks the twenty-first foreign volunteers held the front entrusted to it, between le Chesne and les
Petites Armoises. Having hastily gathered his troops, Colonel
de Buissy ordered the Third Battalion to throw the Germans
back of the Canal des Ardennes. In the first onslaught Captain Count Ravel's company succeeded in forcing the enemy,
five times superior in number, to retire two kilometers; he
took the southern half of le Chesne and blew up the bridge
on the canal. Our division, the Thirty-fifth, held a sector
about thirty kilometers south of Sedan, where the Germans
first broke through and destroyed the army of General Corap.
After the break-through, the German armored columns drove
west and north to fight the battle of Flanders; but the German infantry continued to attack our front in an effort to
widen the gap in the French forces and get behind the Maginot Line. From Attigny to Sy the Thirty-fifth Division held
the Germans in check for three weeks, and while to the north
and west and later the south the Germans advanced a hundred
kilometers daily, the "wedge" we had driven into the victorious German army of Sedan held out until the final French
collapse.

To do justice to this epic of the Thirty-fifth Division, I
must give an idea of the circumstances under which we had
to fight.

From the first day, our bitterest enemy was hunger. Fearing that the smoke of the *roulants*—the field kitchens—would be noticed by the Germans, the officer responsible for our commissary stationed the kitchens in the village of Boult-aux-Bois, more than twelve kilometers behind our lines. Twice a day our light cars—we had finally received a few—went to Boult-aux-Bois. The food they brought back was ice-cold, because the road from our positions to the kitchen was under fire and the cars had to stop frequently. After about a week the connection became impossible by daylight, and food arrived only once every twenty-four hours—at midnight. And even then, it was sometimes impossible for the drivers to leave Boult-aux-Bois. And as our reserves of sardines, biscuits, and "monkey meat" were soon exhausted, we often had nothing at all to eat for stretches of forty-eight hours.

During the first days there was complete disorganization, and we were left entirely to our own resources. I established an observation post one kilometer east from the Ferme St. Denis, and we lived by "hunting." Our grand master of the hunt was Gomez, the first volunteer in the French army.

Gomez was a pale, puny little fellow, a Spanish Loyalist who had fled across the border at Le Perthus. He had been dragged through one concentration camp after another, and at the outbreak of the war had volunteered in the French army. The concentration camp where he happened to be at that time was near Barcarès—the town where our regiment was formed—and Gomez was the first to enlist. Until the German offensive, the swarthy little man was practically unnoticed. He was regarded as timid, weakly, and effeminate; everybody made fun of him because he bowed like a dancer when he saluted. Now Gomez suddenly revealed the most unexpected talents. It came to light that in civil life he had been a butcher. Driven by hunger, Gomez bared his arms revealing athletic muscles. The owners of the Ferme St. Denis had left a few pigs. After two days of hesitation, Gomez finally assaulted the innocent animals with his trench knife. The poor beasts squealed and grunted. Bleeding from their wounds, they tore themselves loose and ran into the yard; little Gomez ran after them with his dripping knife. Our colonel was present. He averted his eyes, but did not interfere. Hunger was too strong for squeamishness.

Evacuated in the greatest haste, the population had abandoned nearly all their cattle. In the fields, cows ran around by the hundreds. Unmilked, their udders grew heavy and hung down to the ground. They ran bellowing across the meadows; they grew wild and intractable. Often a cow or a steer jumped into the trench where I had installed my observation post, breaking beams, upsetting instruments, tramping on papers. Many times a cow lay down right in front of my telescope and gazed at me with sad reproachful eyes. Many died or were killed by gunfire. No slaughter was ever more absurd. We were forbidden to shoot them; and as for those which were accidentally killed by gunfire, it is difficult to butcher a cow and cook beef in front-line trenches. During the whole war—that is, from May 10th on—we starved, while we watched the sleekest cattle die before our eyes. There was no sign of any commissary service, and no one to drive the cattle behind the lines and slaughter them. In Paris meat was rationed, the army was starving—and our whole region stank with rotting carcasses.

The enemy made a clever use of these carcasses.

My observation post was concealed at the edge of a wood and, in the beginning at least, it did its job: from this post we could see everything without being seen. From the edge of the raised Forêt de la Maison Rouge I could survey the hollow occupied by our own battalions and the hill lying oppo-

site which was regarded as no-man's-land. We supposed that
the German positions were on the other side of the hill. On
the gently rising slopes of no-man's-land were scattered several carcasses of cows. One morning I saw an unusually big
cow on the declivity. Directing my telescope at the hill, I
noticed that four or five such super-dimensional cows had
been placed at various spots. They were obviously dead and
swollen and their legs were stretched out in the air. We
marked the exact positions of the animals on our sketches.
A few hours later we re-directed our glasses at the suspicious
carcasses. We noticed with amazement that the dead cows
had moved nearer! They were still dead, monstrously swollen, their legs stretched in the air—but they had moved several yards down the hill, toward the positions of our first battalion in the hollow. I telephoned my immediate superior,
Lieutenant Saint-Brice. After some hesitation—he could not
understand why we were making so much fuss about these
"suspicious" cows—he transmitted my report to divisional
headquarters. The batteries stationed behind us were ordered
to open fire on the animals. The experiment succeeded beyond all expectations. The first shells had scarcely landed
when German soldiers began to slip out of the cows' carcasses
and run like mad. Many were hit before they could shed their
skin. Optical instruments and guns tumbled out of the cows'
bellies. The regiment opposing us—at that time it was an infantry regiment from Düsseldorf—had used this Trojan Cow
method to smuggle a few observers into the immediate
proximity of our positions.

This and similar incidents meant that the Germans were
preparing an offensive. For two nights, in my observation
post, I heard the noise of tanks: the surest sign of imminent
action. We passed most of our nights listening to the silence,
clinging to the darkness, trying convulsively to wrest its

secrets from the great nothingness. Even harder than our battle with the silence was our struggle against false sounds and noises. Alone with the night, I often felt impelled to claw the wall of darkness with my ten fingers. It was a long time before I learned to distinguish one sound from another, a noise from its echo, the prolonged rolling of an exploded shell from the screech of approaching tank treads. In these nights I often recalled how Captain Mirambeau had taught us over and over again to concentrate all our attention on the noise made by the *chars d'assaut;* no attack was possible, he explained, before the enemy had brought his tanks up to his lines. And twice now I had made out a sinister clanking of tank treads on the other side of the hill.

Colonel de Buissy decided to have mines laid between our positions and those of the enemy. Imbach, an Alsatian lieutenant, was commissioned to collect a group of men for this dangerous task. The group was to be led by an old Legionnaire, Lieutenant Castaner, who during his twenty-year stay in Africa had learned and adopted the Legion's customs. He was a swarthy tightly knit man with a short black mustache, shining black eyes, short legs, a considerable paunch, a bullish neck, and red hands. He never took a walk without his riding crop, and under the pretext of good-fellowship, he hit his soldiers so hard across the back that they bore the traces of his friendliness for days. He always traveled with a suitcase full of pornographic books, had the *Vie Parisienne* sent him in the trenches, and chose as his orderly Fodor, a Hungarian painter, who knew nothing about polishing boots, but made up for this deficiency by drawing naked men and women at the lieutenant's orders. As his non-commissioned aide the lieutenant was given Adjutant Ferdinand Daroussat, a magnificent old soldier who had fought in the World War, and who, in his quiet little house in the Ardennes had never dreamed that he would ever be called on to fight again. His small property was situated less than forty kilometers from our positions, but it had fallen into German hands long ago. Most probably his house had been burned, his wife and his daughter had fled along some highway. His eldest son was on another sector of the front: for six weeks the two soldiers had no news from one another.

I had just been relieved and was lying near my shelter with Torczynsky. He was a little Polish-Jewish tailor from Galicia. During the training period he had won no laurels: he looked rather clumsy when presenting arms or marching in a parade, he always forgot to salute the flag, and always shot beside the target. But once he got to the front he was transformed. He never wearied of marching and carried the knapsack of many a tall, strong comrade. He was often laden like a mule, for many abused his good nature. At dusk, when he came back from digging trenches and shelters in the front line, he would sit down and sew our torn trousers, patching the holes on our knees and seats with old puttees. Whenever he went to the near-by stream to wash his *gamelle*—an impossibly large pot with a lid attached by a chain—he took five or six of his comrades' pots and washed them all. Now he lay by my side telling me his life story. He told me of his native village in Poland, and of his trip to Paris. He had eleven sisters and brothers: not one of the brood knew what had become of the others. In Poland, the authorities had confiscated his house and refused him a passport, though his father had distinguished himself in the Polish struggles for independence. Little Torczynsky had been seventeen at the time, and had dreamed of France, the land of liberty. He had left home. But between Poland and France there is Germany. He managed to get across the German border, and was arrested. Finally released, he walked at night and hid during the day.

He worked, made a living, and was deported. In Brussels he sold his watch and sent half the proceeds to his father. He smuggled himself like a piece of goods. He was eighteen, had never committed a real crime, and knew the prisons of Germany, Holland and Belgium. He helped a refugee woman to deliver a child in a barn. He fought for his right to live, and learned to despise the superfluous. Eight months before the war, when he finally reached Paris, he was nineteen years old. He began to make a living, fell in love with Paris, and sent for his mother to join him. His only identification was an expulsion order from France. On the first day of the war he enlisted.

The volunteer mine layers gathered on a small path in the woods, a few yards from my shelter. There were thirty-five of them—among them Hegedues, a Hungarian tailor; Spitzer, a Rumanian Jew; Ramos, a Spanish refugee; and Da Souza, a Portuguese miner. Most of the men were Galicians from Polish ghettos. None of them knew how to present arms or carry a flag. But all of them, all these Isaac Purlichs and Moses Kleinmanns, volunteered whenever there was a dangerous task to be done. We heard Castaner shouting and slashing the bushes with his crop. Old Daroussat made jokes and gave practical advice. Lieutenant Imbach came by my shelter. He halted, looked at us, and called through the bushes: "Castaner! Can you use another man?"

"Yes!"

Torczynsky stood up. He knew at once that that meant him. Imbach wore a steel helmet that had been worn by his father in the World War. It was a German steel helmet.

"So it'll be Torczynsky. You join them. *Ça vous fera une belle promenade.* A nice walk for you. . . ."

I accompanied the little tailor to the road. The thirty-six men walked by. To those I knew I said *"Merde!"* and shook hands with them. They all had a tense and distant look. None of them showed any sign of fear. But there was something remote in every face: they had the look of men gazing into another world. Only old Daroussat with his furrowed face—fashioned of good old leather—whistled as he passed. To him, death was an old acquaintance.

Torczynsky was the last to go by. He was not pale and he carried the shovels of two of his comrades on his narrow shoulders. I said *"Merde!"* and we shook hands. It was getting dark.

That night the Germans made their first push toward Tannay. They surprised our mine-laying group. Five men who tried to place their mines under withering machine-gun fire failed to return.

Among them was Samuel Torczynsky.

My company was installed in the forest of Noirval. It was a thick forest, typical of the Ardennes region, bleak and cold, with its tall pines forming a roof over our heads. From it we could see the friendly green meadows sloping down to the battered village of Noirval, but we were strictly forbidden to venture out, for then we should have been in full sight of the Germans. They were like an inaccessible childhood paradise, these meadows with their high, unmowed, sun-soaked grass, in the yellow light of a dying afternoon. A gentle May wind played with the grass like a princess with her deerhounds, reminding us of all our past: the grass was like a woman with fluttering hair walking along the dunes, somewhere in Brittany. It was just as well that the meadows and the sun were kept away from us soldiers. Not a ray of the sun penetrated our forest. Sometimes a butterfly flew by mistake into the damp semi-obscurity, but never stayed for long. Only the cuckoo's barking cry was heard now and again—a cold, military bird.

They said we were going to spend some time in the forest of Noirval. So far no one spoke of retreating: we seriously discussed where we would be sent on furlough after forty days in the front lines. For the moment everybody's chief concern was to dig himself a "bombproof" shelter. This was easier than we had expected, for we found old dug-outs from the first war. Incredible as it may seem, this forest had not been cleaned out in twenty years. It had merely been waiting from one war to the other. To be sure, the World War shelters were no longer quite satisfactory. They were not deep enough. They were nothing but square holes that you could lie down in and be relatively safe from shell splinters. What we really needed were little cellars covered by huge logs and tree trunks with earth piled on top. But we could deepen the existing dug-outs; so they came in handy—just as our own shelters would come in handy to our sons; humanity progresses by crawling deeper and deeper underground. In the meantime our mining activities brought real treasures to light. Kellenberger, while digging a hole by my side, hit something hard, and pulled out a German steel helmet, a World War helmet with a golden point and a golden double eagle. Each of us in turn tried on the helmet of the man who had clearly been killed here: he must have had a particularly small cranium, for his helmet scarcely covered the tops of our heads. I suddenly thought of my father who had fought in the World War on the German side: I think he was somewhere in the Ardennes with the Austro-Hungarian Fourth Imperial Artillery Regiment. As I was thinking, the helmet passed from hand to hand. I dug out a curved sword—another World War relic. Adjutant Daroussat maintained that it belonged to a French cavalryman. Imoudsky, the Russian designer, found a rusty pistol. Thus equipped with old-fashioned instruments of death, we looked like a group of small-town actors content with any props they can find. Later, while looking for round logs, we found saddles and leather bags, stirrups and bridles of our own era. Thus we discovered that shortly before us a cavalry squadron had been stationed here and had run away, abandoning their mounts and equipment.

Each one of us ultimately dug an "individual" shelter in which he could stretch out. I envied little Garai and red-headed Dési, who needed only narrow childish holes. They had been sitting in theirs for some time, reading three-weeks-old newspapers, while I had to go on digging my own hole—more than six feet long. It was over two yards deep and had an exit with stairs. At night we were forbidden to sleep outside our shelters, and it was scarcely advisable, for at three-thirty nearly every morning the German planes came over and showered us with bombs. Even in our shelters we would wake up, but not for long: after all, we couldn't dig ourselves any deeper. Far more unpleasant than the bombs were the worms and bugs. All night long they crawled over your face. There were night-crawlers that loved to twist themselves through your puttees into your trousers, and little black insects that crawled against your forehead. Worse than bombs was the smell of rot and clay that clung to your clothes, the damp earth glued to your uniform. I thought of Edgar Allan Poe's corpse who woke up in his grave.

From time to time hunger drove me to Noirval or Châtillon. There were French batteries in both towns, and their personnel was still able to procure a certain amount of food. Moreover, the artillerymen lived in houses, and had facilities for cooking. They warmed water so you could wash and shave, and almost feel like a human being. On these strictly forbidden visits I was accompanied by a scout of the First Battalion, Désiré Weiss, who gladly risked his life for a bowl of hot soup. The artillerymen treated us royally. After days of starvation, we gobbled down every luxury they offered us and invariably grew sick at our stomachs. Our friends serving the Fifth Battery of the Twenty-eighth Artillery Regiment were quartered in a house ruined by shell fire, and they even had a bed. This house apparently belonged to the owner of the Châtillon general store; adjoining his residence was the shop, in which only the iron shutter was still intact. Only one wall was missing in the dining room, and that gave it the appearance of a stage-set. It was full of family portraits. On the bureau stood the framed pictures of two young soldiers, and if you didn't look carefully they both seemed to be the same young man. But despite the family resemblance, a closer study revealed the difference: the two were father and son in two different wars. And now the father was no doubt a fugitive on some highway, while his son still addressed his letters to this house, long since abandoned by his parents.

For two days—since the last air-raid—we had received no provisions. Nahmias, our driver, was a good fellow but no hero: three times he had failed to reach Boult-aux-Bois, where our kitchen was. The road was swept by German artillery at regular intervals, and Nahmias said it was full of holes. I was so hungry I volunteered to go to Boult-aux-Bois myself, and Weiss wanted to go with me. Our chief desire was to fill ourselves with soup at the field kitchen; the rest would somehow take care of itself. We reported to the captain and he let us have the little Peugeot, our only usable light car. That night I had no observation duty: Imoudsky and Kellenberger were at the post. Weiss and I set out at eleven at night.

The night was still. The sky was wide and full of stars. We were elated to be out of the hostile, skyless forest. I thought of all those who were looking at the same sky in other places, far from here. It was so comforting to have the same sky over us. We were incapable of more complicated feelings.

I put my steel helmet beside me on the seat. Somewhere a shot rang out. For a minute a machine gun rattled. But all that was far, far away.

"Have you any idea how far away that firing was?" I asked Weiss.

"Two kilometers at least," he said.

It does you good to hear an exact figure. Two kilometers is pretty far. I saw that I was beginning to drive faster: perhaps I wanted to put an even greater distance between myself and the firing.

"I've heard that the Ninth Company had heavy casualties this morning," said Weiss suddenly.

"Did you know anybody in the Ninth?"

"Yes, quite a few."

"Do you know what happened to them?"

"No."

Again we were silent. Were we thinking of the dead? Scarcely. Of the danger? Very little. What were we thinking of? Probably nothing.

"Maybe there is more comradeship here at the front, after all," said Weiss.

"You think so?"

"Yes. We depend on one another."

"Do you call that comradeship?"

"Maybe. What do you call comradeship?"

I could not answer at once. Finally I said, "At any rate I haven't seen any of the comradeship described in books. I don't know if the books are lying, or if things have changed since the last war. Today the dangers are greater, and the moments of relaxation rarer. I think that ties of comradeship grow during the moments of relaxation. At times of danger everybody wants to save his own skin."

"Yes," said Weiss, "people help one another because they need one another. Just as in school. The war is like school. Neither has much in common with life. School friendships never last."

Thus we philosophized in the night. The road began to rise toward Belleville. I tried to drive as noiselessly as possible. It was as though we were not listening to the silence, but the silence to us. Now and then a sigh arose from the fields. There was nothing human in that sigh: it was as if the earth were moaning—but guardedly, for fear of the bombs that tear its body. We were driving in a vacuum. The silence was not silent, but airless. I had a feeling that I should have to smash the glass bell beneath which we were breathing, or rather trying to breathe. Or perhaps we were lost on the moon, and had ceased to breathe.

"Will there be any hot soup?" I asked.

"And hot meat?" said Weiss dreamily.

"The gentlemen in the kitchen must have eaten everything themselves," I said maliciously. "And why not, if we don't come and get it?"

My stomach was growling.

We passed through Belleville, the town where we had received our baptism of fire. A dead town. I was driving without lights, and there seemed to be no end to the place. Since the day when we rested in front of the church, the whole place had been transformed into a single ruin. Only the church was still undamaged.

I stopped at the edge of Boult-aux-Bois to inquire about our kitchen. A few artillerymen were sleeping at the roadside. I awakened them. They had been there only since the day before and knew nothing. Now it was pitch dark. I went back to the car and told Weiss to wait for me. I groped in the darkness, stumbling over men sleeping at the edge of the wood. I stepped on a soldier's hand and he cried out. I stopped. I found a sentry guarding a cellar with ammunition in it. A field kitchen? He hadn't heard of any. The moment I left him, he fell asleep. I groped my way back to the car. I admonished Weiss to be patient. But I myself lost all patience. Behind the fourth house to the right, Nahmias had said. I rushed into the darkness of the village. I felt my fury mounting. The darkness took on shapes and the shapes danced before my eyes. I was no longer hungry, but I had a feeling which, if possible, is even more primitive than hunger: it was the animal viciousness of a man who cannot, absolutely cannot, get the woman he loves and desperately desires. Only a sexual disappointment could be as wild, as unbridled as my disappointment when I felt myself cheated out of my soup. I lost all interest in the soldiers I was stepping on. Perhaps I even tried to trample them. A sleeping man cried out; I snarled at him. I was dully aware that I would be ashamed of myself once my hunger was satisfied. But I felt that it would never again be satisfied.

My rampage ended in the arms of a young officer who lay awake beside his cannon. I could not see him but he had the pleasant voice of a young girl.

"The Twenty-first Infantry kitchen? Moved out yesterday, *mon pauvre ami.*"

"Where to?" I asked, white with fury.

"I don't know."

"And why?"

"I don't know. It was probably too hot for the gentlemen here." He uttered a dry laugh. "We had bad weather here yesterday."

I tried to get an explanation. After all a kitchen couldn't

have left without reason, without instructions, without orders, abandoning hundreds of men to starvation. Where was
the officer responsible for this?

The lieutenant had no answer.

"I hear they retired to le Morthomme," he said. "If you
want to try there . . ."

No, I had no wish to drive any further. I looked for my
car. Weiss had fallen asleep from hunger. Without a word
we started on the road back. After Belleville we drove
through a rain of shells. The Germans had probably heard
the sound of our motor. Perhaps they thought we were carrying ammunition. And actually we weren't carrying so much
as a pot of cold soup.

All around us the catastrophe was approaching. The Battle
of France began. On June 5th, the German offensive was unleashed—from the English Channel to the Maginot Line. The
march on Paris started. In the capital, Reynaud's Cabinet was
nearing the end of its tether.

Of all that, we had only the vaguest idea at the front. We
had radio sets made in 1920. We couldn't use them for send-
ing out information because the Germans listened in, and
they weren't much good for reception either. We heard only
fragments of the communiqués, and by the time the disjointed
phrases reached the lines, they were completely distorted. One
day was almost like the next. At three-thirty nearly every
morning, German planes came over to bomb our positions.
At six, an artillery duel began, in which we were, if anything,
superior. Our seventy-fives, the pride of the French army in
two wars, were indeed superior to the German seventy-
sevens. Our ammunition also seemed superior. Up to the beginning of June we fired three to four times as many shots
as the Germans. Out of a hundred shells fired by us there was

hardly a single dud, while the German shells often failed to explode. One day my observation post recorded all the duds: every eighth shell failed to explode. With a soldier's natural optimism (born of our instinct for self-preservation) we assumed that the cause of the duds was sabotage: the shells, we surmised, had been made in the Skoda works in Czechoslovakia. I don't know whether the explanation was true, but the facts were. Though defenseless against German air attacks—for weeks not a single French plane had appeared, and our anti-aircraft defense could not be taken seriously—we retained superiority in artillery to the very end. And the Thirty-fifth Division always succeeded in throwing back the German infantry, which regularly attacked, nearly every dawn and dusk. What the great German motorized units could do to us once we were betrayed—well, that still lay in the future. For the time being we lived in the soldier's vital element: ignorance.

From six in the evening to six in the morning of June 8th, I was on duty in the first line, in my observation post. From three-thirty to five-thirty it was impossible to stick my head out of my shelter. The artillerymen who had taken position near by with their small anti-tank guns, counted the shells that fell on our sector. Within two hours, on an area one kilometer square, six hundred and fifty shells fell. It was clear that God alone protected us.

I had established my post at the edge of the forest. To observe the Germans unseen, I had chosen a point about fifty yards inside the woods, but in the immediate proximity of the Chesne-Châtillon highway. In this way I could survey my sector by looking across the road, but I was concealed from the enemy. That morning of June 8th, at five-thirty, when I crawled out of my shelter, there was nothing between me and the German positions. Fifty yards of woods, my cover from the enemy, had been razed by German shell fire.

Throughout the next hour I reported the presence of enemy tanks. There was no let-up in the sound of their rattling treads. Dozens of German bombing planes landed behind the Canal des Ardennes. The complete openness with which the Germans were preparing their offensive gave everything a dreamlike character. Not a French plane appeared on the horizon. Our artillery, too, seemed less active. One of the boys in the anti-tank company, a six-foot Breton, a magnificent specimen of that country where the peasants are sailors and the sailors are peasants, came to my shelter—his nest had just been destroyed by a bomb. He told me that several batteries covering our rear had withdrawn. We lay side by side, flat on our bellies. He told me of his peasant property, of a quarrel with his brothers over inheritance. He said he intended to rebuild a burned barn after his return. His words cheered me.

About six in the morning my telephone, which had been silent for four or five hours, rang. As our wires were not underground, they broke whenever there was artillery fire. Our linesmen had to repair the wires under the most furious bombardments. Vincent Vallace, Spaniard, Isaac Purlich, stateless, Jacques Tini from San Marino, Eugen Gleichman from Budapest, Bernard, the Swiss, always volunteered for this job. And today they had re-established the connection between the colonel's headquarters and my post.

I heard the deep, manly, and yet melodious voice of Saint-Brice, my former company commander and present liaison officer: "3a?"

"Yes."

"This is 10b."

"I'm listening."

The lieutenant's voice sounded broken, like a harp with a broken string.

"3a! You are instructed to destroy all your papers and your notebook."

"Yes, *mon lieutenant* . . . Anything else?"

"No. Nothing else." The businesslike tone changed. Again it was Saint-Brice's good, warm, reliable voice. "Have you anything to eat?"

"I've found two cans of food."

"When you're relieved, bring me something. I haven't eaten for two days."

"I will."

I looked at the artilleryman. Then I turned to the second observer. He was a young Rumanian doctor from Montpellier, who was highly regarded as a heart specialist. But no foreigner was allowed to be promoted in the army medical service, and so he had preferred to serve as a plain soldier. Now he was assigned to my post.

"We have been instructed to destroy our papers."

I must have been very pale when I said this. Dr. Barati's small, yellowish, freckled countenance turned green. The freckles stood out like green confetti on his prematurely ravaged face.

"What do you make of it?"

I quoted the words I had learned by rote: "In case of assault by the enemy, observers must destroy their documents and equipment. In no case may observers retire without an express order."

Barati asked: "Have we been instructed to retire?"

"No."

I looked through the telescope that protruded from the ground. Across from us, on the hillside, I could clearly see the outlines of German tanks. But they did not seem to be moving. They were like prehistoric beasts. And there was still the noise of more tanks coming up.

"Shall we light a fire?" I asked.

My friend from Brittany protested. He said we would be spotted at once. We took spades and shovels and began to dig a deep hole. The artilleryman helped us. When the hole was deep enough, we threw into it the report book and the code book, after having torn each page separately. Barati asked whether we had also to destroy our instruments. I said I had no orders. This seemed to pacify him. He was going to cover the hole, but I stopped him.

"Do you know, Barati, what will happen to us if we fall into German hands?"

"Yes. We'd both be executed. You on account of your books. I for being a physician who has taken up arms. And a foreigner, too."

"It's better to die than be captured."

"It's better to die than be captured."

Barati tore at the chain attaching his identification tag to his wrist.

"Should we bury the chains too?"

"Yes."

The tall Breton watched us without understanding, as though we were creatures from another planet. He placed his heavy, hard peasant hand on my shoulder.

"You don't mean that?" he asked.

I looked at him. Even now his narrow face with the bad Breton teeth and long bony nose showed no emotion. The machine guns began to rattle in the hollow. Now there would be fighting at close quarters.

"Have you no relatives?" asked the Breton.

"Yes. My wife. My parents," I answered.

He turned to Barati. "And you?"

"My parents. And my fiancée."

He shook his head.

"All right," he said after a while, somewhat heavily. "What if you are killed? Don't you want your relatives to know what has become of you?"

The three of us huddled together in the small shelter, a yard underground: the famous heart specialist, the peasant from Brittany, and myself. Dr. Barati and I looked at one another. We left the chains on our wrists. Each of us seized his spade and hastily shoveled the clay over our papers.

"I'm going to bring you something, my boys," said the Breton. He smiled as much as he could, and the dancing wrinkles around his eyes showed that he was satisfied.

We tried to keep him back, but he crawled out on all fours from our shelter. Shells were bursting all over the place. Five minutes later he was back, unharmed. He had several hand grenades around his belt. He gave us the small, graceful, yellow things as if he had brought an apronful of pears, fresh from the tree.

The time was six-twenty. And all of a sudden a vast, deafening silence settled over the country. It was as if a godlike conductor had, by one motion of his baton, brought a whole orchestra to silence. Not a breath stirred. On the other side, everything seemed petrified. The morning was dewy and springlike. Nature arose from her bath. Only if you deliberately tried could you still smell powder and fire. Such great, sudden silences of nature occur only on the battlefield.

The husky Breton walked upright to his destroyed shelter. Thus began June 8th of the year 1940.

In the late afternoon I went down to Noirval. I was unable to resist temptation, though it had been expressly forbidden. I ran through the forest and cautiously crossed the open field. I reached the ruined village without mishap.

The church lay in the middle of the town and was almost untouched. I had come secretly to Noirval two or three times before, and easily found my way. A few of the church windows had been blown in by concussion. Some of the gargoyles had crumbled, and loose stone lay across the entrance. I kicked it aside and went in.

I was alone. I went on tiptoe. I laid my steel helmet on the first bench and knelt down. On the main altar was a painting of Christ clothed in blue, with outstretched arms. To the left stood a statue of the Maid of Orleans, with the tricolor wrapped around the pedestal.

A great silence lay over the chapel. The war seemed far away. I looked up to the altar. Behind the curiously unreal blue figure of Christ stood a simple crucifix. And as I looked up to the crucified Christ, I felt for the first time the profound symbol of the cross. The Lord's arms nailed to the cross—arms outstretched in compassion. In His deepest suffering He was ready to receive the sorrows of mankind. In no other posture could they have killed Him: the Pharisees, the unchained mass in love with Barabbas, the mediocre and the short-sighted, those who carped at the miracle, the narrow of mind and spirit—in no other position could they have killed Him, only with open arms, clasping the world in His bleeding, tortured hands. He could not have died on the road, sinking down beneath the weight of the cross He was bearing, or like a defeated warrior beneath the sword strokes. Even in death He retained the power to choose, and so He died upright, with eyes turned heavenward, His arms outspread: Suffer the little children to come unto me!

A few shells burst in the distance. From the infirmary

behind the church a cry arose. An ambulance drove past with tinkling bells.

I spoke the thirteenth psalm of David:

"How long wilt Thou forget me, O Lord? for ever? How long wilt Thou hide Thy face from me? How long shall I take counsel in my soul, having sorrow in my heart daily? How long shall mine enemy be exalted over me? Consider and hear me, O Lord my God: lighten mine eyes lest I sleep the sleep of death. Lest mine enemy say: I have prevailed against him; and those that trouble me rejoice when I am moved. But I have trusted in Thy mercy; my heart shall rejoice in Thy salvation. I will sing unto the Lord, because He hath dealt bountifully with me."

Above the altar the Lord's face seemed to smile, giving forth an indescribable radiance. It was as though the Lord in His blue garment had descended from His pedestal and stretched forth His arms to help me. To receive me. Involuntarily I stood up, as though two arms had raised me. And all at once I sensed the arrogance of man, the superfluity of all earthly things. Life and death: what power had they? Life and death were in His hand. Christ of Noirval, cloaked in blue, was moving across the fields.

Through the broken windowpanes the light of a dying afternoon poured in. Here there was none of the mystical half-darkness of the Roman churches. The chapel was bright. The image of our Lord was bathed in gold. Does man really need war in order to find Him, I asked myself. And I knew that there was no other way except the way of suffering. And the words of the psalm seemed to me almost a sacrilege: "How long wilt Thou forget me, O Lord?" Never had He forgotten me. In suffering less than in joy. I stepped closer to the altar. I was like the man possessed of an unclean spirit, who dwelt in the tombs, and whom no man could bind, not even with chains. And when the Lord asked me, "What is thy name?" I replied: "My name is Legion; for we are many."

For a moment I felt that I was not alone. I took my steel helmet from the bench and turned around. In the last pew Colonel de Buissy was kneeling.

I passed him on tiptoe. But he caught up with me as I was mounting the narrow path to our wood. Both of us walked with a crouch, to be as inconspicuous as possible. The colonel was a giant with a great red neck and powerful shoulders. It was strange to see him stooped over.

"Have you got a pass?" he asked in an attempt at a joke. "*Non, mon colonel.*"

He said nothing. He was unarmed. He carried a big heavy stick on which he leaned. Sometimes he stopped to catch his breath. I looked at him. Night was slowly falling. For the first time this iron warrior seemed an old man. He had thirty years in the Foreign Legion behind him, and had been seven times wounded in the World War. When he took a step, the earth groaned. Two thousand men feared him. And for two thousand men he was France, that they loved. Now he leaned on his staff as though it were a crutch. His short white hair seemed to have grown whiter.

He stopped and looked at me.

"Do you remember the show we put on in Perpignan?" he asked.

"Yes," I said. Of course I remembered. We had produced a revue that I had written.

"What silly things we do!" he said. And added: "My family is in the North. In Lille. God knows what has become of them . . ."

"They must have been evacuated, *mon colonel.*"

7I

"Evacuated?" He uttered a dry laugh. "For the third time in three generations," he muttered, as though to himself. "Remember the parade in Rivesaltes? And when we left St. Laurent de la Salanque? All the women in tears."

"I remember."

He coughed. "It's not our fault. The regiment fought bravely. Didn't it?"

He needed support.

"Yes," I said. "Yes, *mon colonel.*"

"You fought bravely," he repeated. "I'm proud of you. We're not to blame. You're not to blame. Even though the general—"

He was silent. He struck the bushes with his heavy wooden cane. We passed by the seventy-fives that stood by the roadside, hidden in the thicket. They had just begun to fire. We stood barely two yards away, and we could feel the hard wind as a shell passed. The colonel seemed to hear nothing.

"The general," he said, still speaking as though to himself, "the general says: Each foreigner less in France is one less mouth to feed."

The blood rose to my head. The colonel spoke softly as though the enemy might overhear him.

"We didn't want it. But we fought."

It was as though he were entrusting me with a secret.

Before we went into the wood, he turned back again. The church lay in smoke and fog.

"May God forgive them," he said.

I didn't know what he meant.

That night a patrol belonging to our Tenth Company brought in two prisoners. Three members of the patrol had crept up to the German lines and surprised a German ad-

vance post, including a lieutenant and five men. The lieutenant was killed. Three men fled, and two were taken prisoner.
One was wounded and the doctor said he was too sick to
talk. I was sent for to question the one who was unharmed,
before we handed him over to the division. According to
regulations, the prisoner should have been sent on within an
hour, but we had no means of transport. That meant he
would have to spend several days with us.

The hearing took place beside the colonel's shelter. A few
tables, a typewriter, two or three chairs stood protected
by dense trees. The colonel lay down on the table. His old
rheumatism troubled him, and Nicola, the fat genial officers'
cook, massaged his back. It was almost dark. A few officers
paced nervously back and forth. They were expecting to
hear from divisional headquarters. It wasn't orders they were
waiting for, but news from Paris. The division had a radio.
The colonel groaned beneath Nicola's experienced hands.
From time to time an exploding shell illumined the scene.
The German soldier stood between two trees, facing the
table. I could see his face only when a shell struck, or when
our own artillery was firing. An expressionless face with unframed spectacles. The man probably had blond eyebrows,
but I couldn't see them. I could only see that his face was
hard and barren. Lieutenant Saint-Brice questioned the
prisoner, and I translated.

"Your name?"

"Franz Xavier Mertl."

"Your rank?"

No answer. I repeated the question.

Finally he said: "You can see for yourself."

I translated the answer. Captain Guy, standing behind us,
grumbled something in irritation. But at length he told me
to look.

I stepped up to the man. In the darkness I had to feel his arm. I was like a blind beggar on the road. I could literally feel the prisoner's grin. I felt around and finally found the attached wedge.

"*Gefreiter*," I said. "That corresponds to our corporal."

"What regiment do you belong to, Corporal Mertl?" Saint-Brice asked.

No answer. I repeated the question. I felt his shoulders. The man didn't stir. He stood at attention the whole while, as though turned to stone. In the darkness it was very hard to find anything, but I knew there must be something sewn on his shoulders. At length I found it. I tried to read it as a blind man reads Braille.

"It's a P, *mon lieutenant*. The man belongs to a Panzer division."

"Ask him what number!"

"What number?" I asked.

"Not talking."

The answer was short and simple, the first clear answer. But nothing could destroy Saint-Brice's calm. He was still exceedingly friendly. He asked new questions. I translated them. The corporal said nothing or replied, "Not talking."

Suddenly Saint-Brice asked: "Have you had anything to eat yet?"

"No."

"Do you want something to eat?"

"No. I'm full."

"Something to drink?"

"No."

"Oh, a fakir?" Saint-Brice joked. He tried general conversation. "What do you fellows think of our seventy-fives?"

"First class," the man replied.

"And how about your seventy-sevens?"

"Better."

"Do you know what regiment you're facing?"

"Twenty-first Foreign Volunteers," was the prompt reply.

"How many batteries have you in position?"

No answer. The conversation halted. Now it was quite dark. We could hear the colonel's groaning and the table creaking beneath his weight.

"So you're planning an offensive for tomorrow?" asked Saint-Brice, undiscouraged.

"*Heil Hitler!*" the man replied. This I didn't have to translate. Saint-Brice asked me if I had translated the question properly. He didn't understand.

"When do you mean to attack?" Saint-Brice asked.

"*Heil Hitler!*" the man replied.

I don't know if he gave the Hitler salute. But he may have. In any case the leaves stirred above his head.

Saint-Brice told me softly to strike up a conversation in German. Maybe the fellow would thaw.

"You seem to be from the South," I began. "You're a Bavarian, aren't you? I know Munich very well. Studied in Heidelberg too. Is it as gay as it used to be in Munich?" No answer. I went on. "The Hofbraukeller? How'd you like to go home? When did you have your last furlough?"

Not a sound out of him. It was like speaking to a black wall. Suddenly I had the oppressive feeling that I was alone.

"Corporal Mertl!"

Nothing. I turned to Saint-Brice, just in order to hear a human sound. Saint-Brice said something but I couldn't hear what it was, for just then a shell landed, scarcely thirty yards away from us. No sooner had the first echo died away than I heard a roar behind me.

"*Heil Hitler!*"

The man with the bare face stood there and roared. He was greeting the shell.

Now several officers were standing around us. Commandant Le Guillard, whose son had been killed the day before, nervously stroked his mustache. The colonel had stood up and was smoothing out his uniform.

I was friendly with Saint-Brice, so I ventured a suggestion.

"May I question the man, *mon lieutenant?*"

"If you like. But don't touch him."

"Of course not, *mon lieutenant.*"

I let a minute go by. All waited. The man made no move.

"Come over here," I said.

He stood like a ramrod.

I began to shout. "Come here."

He stepped up to me. We stood face to face, barely six inches apart. The others were dumb with amazement at what now took place. I roared. And the man answered. Suddenly he began to speak. He was no longer silent, and he didn't say, "*Heil Hitler!*" I did not curse or insult him. Actually I did nothing. I repeated the questions to Saint-Brice. But I shouted. I shouted so loud that the woods were full of my voice.

The hearing took twenty minutes. By that time Corporal Franz Xavier Mertl from Ulm had told us just about everything we wanted to know.

I accompanied Saint-Brice back to his shelter. We felt our way through the wood, through the thicket, tearing our uniforms, scratching our hands.

Saint-Brice sighed and waved his hand through the air.

"*Un drôle de peuple—les Allemands,*" he said.

I spent thirty-six hours at the regiment's headquarters, three kilometers behind my observation post. Then I went

forward with Dr. Barati to relieve Kellenberger and Imoudsky. Our two comrades could scarcely communicate with
the rear, for the telephone connection was almost continu-
ously broken. I decided to take a young Portuguese with
me—a good fellow by the name of Firminio Malagrida. If
necessary he could carry messages for us. Before we started
off, Barati went to get our ration for the next twenty-four
hours. Aside from the cheese which we had brought with us
from Alsace, there was not much. But they gave Barati a
double portion of *gniol*.

We knew that this was a bad sign. Since we had been in
the first lines, we had received a daily portion of *gniol*. I
had always thought it a myth that they gave soldiers alcohol
before an attack. I never believed that it was easier to murder
your fellow man after taking a drink. And indeed, it did
not seem to me that we were any more bloodthirsty after
downing our half-pint of *gniol*, a drink consisting of almost
pure grain alcohol. We were no more bloodthirsty, but we
were more optimistic.

This time there was a double ration of *gniol*. The liquid
poison was poured out of a gigantic basket bottle into our
bidons—our two-quart canteens. And then we started out.
I went in advance. Barati and Malagrida followed at intervals
of three steps.

It was six in the evening when we reached the observation
post. We had been marching nearly two hours, for the path
was impassable and we had to work our way through the
thicket. Kellenberger and Imoudsky were glad to be relieved.
They were black all over with earth and powder. Our artillery, which had previously been firing five shots to one of
the enemy's, was almost totally silent.

Kellenberger was furious. An hour before, the Germans
had appeared on the opposite mountain slope to pick up

their wounded. They bore a big white flag with a red cross. In their hand they carried gray chests, ostensibly containing bandage. Kellenberger saw it all clearly through his telescope. But no sooner had they carried away their wounded than they opened the chests and brought out telephone sets. From one of the chests, on which a great Red Cross was painted, they took a machine gun which they set in place. Kellenberger telephoned for artillery fire, but up to now nothing had happened. The Germans had long since vanished. Of course the machine gun was so buried as to be invisible. But Imoudsky showed me through his telescope the place where it had been. He had noted its location. Relieved, the two of them crawled out of the shelter. We could see them for some time, for at every second step they had to throw themselves on the ground. Shells were bursting left and right.

I took over the post at the telescope. From this moment on there was one shock after another. The Germans crawled out of their dug-outs. All at once I saw that on the part of the hill sloping down to us they had apparently built shelters during the preceding nights. Heads grew out of the soil like mushrooms. Many of the soldiers didn't even have their steel helmets on. Their highly polished gas-mask containers glittered in the evening sun. Barati telephoned to Saint-Brice, asking for artillery fire. Nothing happened. Meanwhile German officers appeared on the mountain ridge. They wore gray flat caps—not a one of them had a helmet on. The air was clear and I could observe every move they made. I could almost see their individual faces. The officers behaved as if there were no enemy facing them. They spread out maps and pointed across to our positions with gloved fingers. Some had field-glasses and looked across at us. It is a strange feeling when an artificial eye meets an artificial eye. We focused one another in our glasses. Never can two enemy eyes look so hostile as two telescopes. The hardness of glass strikes against the hardness of glass. Behind it something crouches, ready to leap. A man perhaps.

I myself took up the telephone. It was some minutes before I was connected with Saint-Brice, but the Germans hadn't stirred. Barati at the telescope reported that orderlies appeared from time to time, announcing something to the officers. All this with utter nonchalance. The orderlies saluted as if they were back in the barracks at peacetime. I gave the location of the officers within a yard.

"We have the whole German general staff in a heap, *mon lieutenant*," I cried desperately into the phone.

"I know it, my boy," Saint-Brice answered.

He hung up, and nothing happened.

Again I took up my post at the telescope. I described aloud everything I saw, and made Barati phone every two minutes. From time to time a shell fell to the right of me, on the road.

Was I really bent upon killing? I don't know. Rage rose up in me and obscured everything. No, it would be a lie to say that I remembered these men were on the enemy side, that they belonged to a nation which had marched forth to subjugate the world. Soldiers of murder, enslavement, injustice. Unworthy to live, since they were unworthy of freedom. No. You don't think thoughts like that, when you glare from glass-eye to glass-eye. But neither do you think that those fellows over there are human. Fathers, husbands, loved ones. You have forgotten why you volunteered in the struggle of humanity. And you've forgotten humanity. Nothing remains but the fellow over there who will kill you if you don't kill him.

A rage rose up in me. Why didn't they shoot?

The tall Breton manning the anti-tank guns came over to say good-by. For two days, he said, they had been out of ammunition. For two days he had done nothing but write letters while his dug-out was being shot to pieces. Well, he could write letters somewhere else. He asked us if we were staying on. I said we had no order to withdraw. He shook his head and gave us his hand. He didn't say a word but he seemed sad. There was nothing we could do; his visit was like a condolence call. We were dead men and survivors all in one.

The night fell slowly over the countryside. The church tower of Chesne-Populeux sank slowly beneath the gray fog. For a moment I thought of past summer evenings. At Beau-vallon-sur-Mer, at Budapest, at a meeting in Marseilles. A lost summer is a lost year, I said to Barati. He said nothing. He looked tensely at a spot, barely twenty yards ahead of us, where we knew the observation post of the Eleventh Infantry Regiment to be. The Eleventh Infantry belonged to our division and covered our right flank. It was a military error to have our observation posts so close to one another, overlooking the same sector. But the terrain was unfavorable and they could be arranged in no other way. I was well acquainted with the observers of the Eleventh, for we had attended Captain Mirambeau's inspiring lectures in Pfaffen-hoffen together. Barati now stared across at their dug-out. A moment later I too saw the observers crawl out of their shelters and hurry off with their implements on their backs.

I called to them.

"Hello, Pierro!"

Pierro approached to within five yards of us. Now we could hear every word.

"What are you doing, Pierro? Are you being relieved?"

"No, we've been called back to headquarters. The regiment is moving back."

"And what about us?"

"I don't know," said Pierro. "We have been instructed to take everything with us."

We waved to each other.

"*A bientôt.*"

"*A bientôt.*"

Barati, Malagrida and I exchanged glances. They too? said our glances. Are we alone? But that wasn't possible. If one regiment in a division is withdrawn, the others have to be withdrawn too in order to even out the line. What is going on? we asked one another. But no one spoke.

Night fell. The sound of tanks became more and more distinct. The armored units must have been assembled right behind the village of le Chesne. I called Saint-Brice again. A tired voice answered.

"Armored units?"

"Yes, lieutenant."

"I'll pass it along to the division."

That was all. We waited. And again nothing happened.

Suddenly Barati said: "I think there's no more artillery behind us."

I looked at him like a madman. No artillery behind us? Only an infantryman knows what that means. It means the end. It means more than the end. It means total emptiness.

"Absurd!" I said. But I doubt if my voice sounded very convincing.

My eyes bored into the darkness. I awaited rocket signals from our post in the front line. Three red rockets meant an enemy tank attack. From time to time I heard the sound of caterpillar treads in the darkness, and then in the darkness I saw red stars on the horizon. It was a hot night, and the stars in the sky were close to us. But there were other stars beside the stars of heaven. Stars that came out of the depths. These were the light signals of the Germans behind the hill. Red, yellow, green stars sprang up from the earth. If not for the uninterrupted sound of the rolling iron monsters, the whole thing would have seemed like fireworks in summer. The terrace of a house on a mountain slope; somewhere below, a village celebrating; a crackling display of color. But here every color meant death. And I waited for the three red stars.

Ordinarily we took turns in sleeping. You get too tired if you stay awake all night, and you begin to see ghosts. We watched in two-hour shifts. But tonight sleep was impossible. Barati and I stared into the darkness. Only Malagrida, the slender Portuguese miner, with the long chin and deep black eyes, the smiling, obliging, comradely Malagrida had dozed off. He was lying on the step leading down into our shelter. When a German rocket illumined his face, we could see that he was smiling. Perhaps he was dreaming of the fireworks in the park at Bussaco.

It was half-past nine. Something stirred on the road that led past the wood where we were watching. I heard steps and whispering human voices. Were they Frenchmen? A moment later I recognized the voice of Lieutenant Gaie of the Second Company. I called to him.

"Where are you going, *mon lieutenant?*"

Big fat Gaie, who in Perpignan always wore white gaiters, a powerful cheery young man, replied in a weak falsetto: "We're moving back."

"The Second Company?"

"No, the whole First Battalion."

While he was still speaking, the three red stars went up. No, this was no vision. The two of us saw them at once.

Did they come from our trenches or from the German side? No, they doubtless came from the valley where our First and Second Battalions were still stationed.

I lifted the receiver and turned the crank. But instead of a human voice, only silence met my ears. Never can human silence be as fearful as this mechanized stillness. An impenetrable, malignant, unmusical silence filled the receiver. I turned the crank like mad, but all I could hear was my own ringing, like a scornful echo.

From the path I still heard the tramping of passing troops. Minutes went by. I recognized voices. I called to a comrade. He belonged to the Seventh Company. Yes, he said, the Second Battalion, which had been holding the southern half of le Chesne, was moving back. Why, no one knew. The Germans had not attacked. There had been no fighting. Perhaps we were being relieved, said one, but no one took this idea seriously. Their boots dragged over the stony ground. You couldn't hear any individual step, just a continuous shuffling. And three men knew that when the last step had died away they would be all alone.

I had to make a decision. The telephone was out of order. No instructions could get through to us. But on the other hand, we couldn't leave our post without orders. Barati went over to the shuffling troops and spoke to an officer. Then he crawled back to me.

"That's the Third Battalion," he said. "There is no one left."

Both my companions looked at me. I was in command of these two men, the Rumanian physician from Montpellier and the Portuguese miner from Bussaco. There is no lesser commander in an army than a commander of two men. But what difference does it make whether you are responsible for two men or for two thousand? Is a man justified in speaking for others? Responsible? Yes, a man must be responsible, but to whom? Has he any duty except to Him who never asks—and who gives no man rights over another?

I stared into two faces. Two pairs of eyes gleamed in the night.

I knew what these two men wanted. I knew what I myself wanted. To get away from there. There is no heroism in such senselessness. But I could not act as I wished. I could not help being untrue to these two men who trusted me.

I scribbled a few lines on a piece of paper: "Since interruption of the telephone service, the observers of the Eleventh Infantry and of the Anti-tank Battalion have withdrawn. At 9:40 P.M. our three battalions retreated. Please send instructions."

That was all I could do at the moment. I gave Malagrida the note. "Take it to the colonel or to Lieutenant Saint-Brice. Come back as quickly as you can with the answer. It is now ten o'clock. You can be back by midnight."

Malagrida took his rifle, which was almost as long as himself. He had a perilous trip ahead of him, but he was glad to be moving. We shook his hand in silence. He was our only hope.

The minutes dragged indescribably. The German artillery fire grew in violence. From our own guns there was no answer. All life seemed to have gone out of the forest. We remained in our shelter. It was no longer possible to send information to headquarters. We scarcely spoke. We packed our instruments. If Malagrida came with orders to withdraw . . .

All steps had died away. We were afraid to speak. From time to time we listened to the night. Our nerves were stretched to the breaking point. For the fourth time I packed and unpacked my binoculars. I had to do something.

The Germans now seemed to be aiming at the path through the woods, the path by which Malagrida had gone and by which he would have to come back. Everywhere trees were burning. We tried to comfort one another by reckoning that Malagrida couldn't be expected before half-past twelve. I drank the last drop of *gniol* out of my bottle.

It was just after midnight when I heard steps. I climbed cautiously out of my shelter. Then I heard voices. Two men were speaking. They were speaking German. Barati was about to climb out after me. I seized him by the wrist. We held our breath.

"Das ist wohl der Weg nach Châtillon!" said one of the men in unmistakable Prussian. By that time there must have been three or four of them. They spoke in a loud voice and stood erect.

I thought: What if Malagrida comes back now! I felt for my gun. It was still the good old Remington No. 1751, and I knew that it couldn't be fired.

There there was silence. The Germans had gone away. But still we said nothing. I pulled out my pocketknife and tried to wipe the rust off the blade. Barati began tearing up letters.

The phosphorescent dial of my watch said one o'clock.

"Malagrida won't come back any more," said Barati.

I had the same thought.

Malagrida must have been killed on the way. In recent weeks five observers had been killed on that trail.

Or Malagrida had just deserted us. Yes, the two of us thought that. I owe it to you, Firminio Malagrida from Bussaco, to write it down. We didn't trust you. . . . Why do men in dire extremity not trust each other?

But you did not betray us, good little Malagrida. At one-forty you came softly out of the burning wood. Like a vision. "And the angel of the Lord appeared unto him in a flame of fire out of the midst of a bush: and he looked, and behold, the bush burned with fire and the bush was not consumed."

Malagrida crept down to us. I motioned him to speak softly. But how else could he have spoken? He could scarcely breathe. He bore his gun like an infinite burden. He hurled it into the ditch. We were afraid to ask him anything.

And then he said: "They're gone!"

"Who?" both of us asked at once.

"All of them!" said Malagrida, and drank eagerly from Barati's canteen.

I didn't understand.

"Have you spoken with the colonel?"

"There isn't any more colonel."

"Were you in the woods where our company is encamped?"

"The woods are empty."

He said it almost with indifference. He lay there and panted. I looked out. We were alone.

"They've forgotten us," said Barati.

I began to understand. And at the same time I saw that the written law as we had learned it had lost all validity. For the first time the bonds of discipline were loosened.

"We're going," I said.

The two others quickly followed me. On the wet clay floor of the ditch which had sheltered us for four weeks lay our miserable possessions. A sleeping bag, a change of shoes, a cook-stove, blankets and sweaters. Of course it was impossible to take all that with us in addition to the instruments, which weighed over two hundred and fifty pounds. After a quick consultation we decided to leave all our belongings behind and to save the "eyes of the regiment." There was nothing heroic about our decision. We were just doing our duty. We were three soldiers unable to lose confidence in the army in a single night.

And I still doubted Malagrida's story. Perhaps he had got lost and gone into the wrong forest. I was sure that we should find the colonel and his whole staff in the forest at Noirval. We started out. My conscience was not clear. I had left my post without orders. I feared our encounter with the colonel more than the shells that were falling all around us.

We reached the wood where headquarters had been situated. It was nearly three in the morning. In the east, over Châtillon with its ruined houses, the dawn was graying. At the edge of the wood a mighty tree trunk lay across the path. Here a sentry had stood day and night. I called to him. No answer. We climbed over the tree trunk. The dugout of the staff lay to the right of us. Here the colonel, the chief-of-staff, and several other officers had their shelters. I cried out: *"Mon colonel!"* No answer. I cried out: *"Mon commandant!"* No answer. *"Mon capitaine!"* No answer.

I went to the colonel's shelter. I jumped down and sank into something soft. I bent over and felt: it was a featherbed. And this was the sole reminder of human life.

I climbed out. I upset a chair and took fright at the sound. It didn't occur to me that the enemy might hear me, and I began to scream: *"Mon lieutenant! Mon lieutenant!"* But the wood gave no answer. Only here and there the crackling of a branch.

I ran to my own shelter that I had dug for the hours when I should not be on observation duty. The other observers had their shelters beside it. I cried out their names. They too gave no answer. In my own dug-out I bumped into something pointed. It was the soldier's helmet from the World War.

Barati and Malagrida had thrown themselves on the ground. I sat down beside them. Now what are we going to do? all three of us asked at once. We felt a good, strong warmth rising up in us, flowing from one of us to the other. We were three children who had been left alone. Three comrades. Comrades can never be more than three.

The treetops turned violet in the first light of the new day. It was June 11th. There was nothing before us and nothing behind us. The treetops were as far away as the heavens. And everything about us took on gigantic proportions.

Three men waited in the wood. They were alone in the face of sixty thousand men, six German divisions.

CHAPTER FOUR: EVEN CRIMINALS

TELL LIES

WE WALKED FORTY-EIGHT KILOMETERS, VIRTUALLY WITHOUT rest. And then we found our regiment.

Before starting out we held a short council of war. We decided that only the road to the southwest, to Vouziers and Séchault, was open, and that the regiment must have retreated in that direction.

We had scarcely left Noirval when we saw that the villages around us were burning. Before that we had lived in the comforting blindness of our forest. Ahead of us, to right and left, the sky was red. Burning villages have a color of their own. It was neither red nor pink, but a strange skin-color stretched across the dark horizon. In the east the sun went up and its rays mingled with the fiery corona. You couldn't tell exactly which was the east. Suns were going up on all sides.

We marched as fast as we could through the burning villages. Here and there a house, a wall stood meaninglessly. The walls of the houses were black and there was a strange crackling in the air. There was nothing grandiose about the crumbling walls. They burned with the crackling sound of burning paper. Some walls were quite untouched, and only the roof and the interior of the house were burning. I thought of the paper houses of my childhood, when we covered the windows with red wax paper and lighted candles inside. At Christmas time the Bethlehem players came and showed us the manger in which the Lord was born. The houses by the roadside were like the houses in the Christmas stories. They inspired no horror, because there was nothing real about them. From time to time a wall fell. But it did not fall with a crash, it merely crumbled like bread in a man's hand. The smell of corpses mingled with the smell of fire, till it was impossible to distinguish between them. We ran through the villages. For in the villages it was hot.

I do not know what drove us onward and why we thought that all would be saved if only we could find the regiment. We expected each day to provide something new that would give us courage to bear one day more.

Abandoned arms and equipment marked the trail of the retreat. Aside from that, we encountered only corpses, and from them we could glean no information. Malagrida was possessed by the idea that the dead men by the roadside were not dead. Four or five times he turned a dead man around and shook him in an attempt to wake him up. I said nothing until I saw the little Portuguese trying to move a half-charred corpse to speech. Then I was afraid he had gone out of his mind. At last we persuaded him to abandon his vain efforts. From then on he uttered not a word.

Aside from a few cats, the only living creature we met was an old woman. When we first caught sight of her, we thought her an hallucination. It was in one of the villages between Vouziers and Séchault. She sat in front of her burning house on a bench that the flames had miraculously spared. She was very old—but perhaps she had aged only in the last few days. Her dirty grayish-black hair hung down in strands over her furrowed face. The face itself was calm. She sat on the bench and stared straight ahead of her. The flames nearly licked her back.

We came up to her and tried to talk to her. She stared at us and gave no answer. Only when we asked her if she was hungry did her features show a little animation. Then she raised her eyes. They were burned out like the houses across the street.

"Are you hungry?" she asked finally, in slow disjointed syllables.

"No. But are you hungry?" we repeated.

"Yes," she answered. "I'll bring you something."

At this she arose from her bench, painfully propping up her back in her hands. And before we could touch her, she went rapidly, erectly into the burning house. The flames devoured her like a witch burning at the stake. We stood there, grasping at the void.

As we marched, we began to understand what had happened. While our regiment had held up the Germans, nearly all the regiments behind us had been withdrawn. Between us and the hinterland lay a gap many kilometers wide. And the Germans had set fire to the countryside before us and behind us. Whichever way we turned the heavens were aglow. We could only lower our heads and march. Without thinking, without looking up, like children playing ostrich. From time to time we had to hurl ourselves in the ditch. German planes were bombing the district. Perhaps they thought there were still troops about, perhaps they were bent on sheer destruction. In any case there seemed to be no plan in their raids. Twice the dive-bombing *Stukas* hurtled from the sky. Their effect was crushing. The sound alone, like a vertical thunderbolt, nearly destroys your consciousness. Never did I see any French planes attempting to combat the *Stukas*. Henri de Montherlant, in *Mors et Vita*, cries out in amazement when for the first time in two years of war he sees French planes. *"Il y avait donc des avions autres que les boches!"* Unfortu-

nately we had no two years to wait. Never did we feel the
unequal nature of the struggle more poignantly than on this
June morning when the *Stukas* sowed death in dead soil.
They bombed villages that were already burning, tore open
earth already gaping with bomb craters, and killed men for
the second, third, or fourth time. They fell from heaven like
avenging angels with flaming swords: but on the road over
which the French army of the east had retreated, there remained only three weary volunteers with sore and tired feet.
It would have been ludicrous to die at such an enormous
expense.

Near the Bois de Cernay we found the rear guard of our
regiment, consisting of a few stragglers who lacked the
strength to go on. There was no longer a single auto to
carry them. They had walked forty-five kilometers. They
were undernourished and sick. They lay at the edge of the
road and didn't even ask us where we came from. In reply
to our questions, they shrugged their shoulders and said they
"were waiting for the Germans." One of them was Hajos,
the composer, a highly gifted young fellow. In February we
had been on furlough in Paris together. Hajos took me to
the *Folies Bergère*, where, up to the outbreak of the war, he
had put on his own revues. Now he lay on the highway,
with his face to the ground. He said he couldn't bear to look.
There was no use asking him what he couldn't look at. He
held his hands over his ears and pressed his nose flat into the
dusty gray road. At length I persuaded him to come with us.

All at once the instruments on our backs grew fearfully
heavy. Now that we knew the regiment was near, we became fully aware of our fatigue. Only now did we realize
that during the whole flight we had felt no weariness and had
scarcely minded the weight on our backs. The straps must
have gradually rubbed the skin off our shoulders; and now,

all of a sudden, our shoulders began to hurt like wounds. We had marched as though in a dream, in an infinite vacuum, at the center of a non-existent world, spurred on by non-existent terrors, yet without fatigue, which is a thing of this world and has no place in the world of dreams. And now a few kilometers before our goal we felt the soreness in our feet, our shoulders, our minds.

It was dusk when we reached the Bois de Cernay. The first man we found was Adjutant Lesfauries lying in a shell hole beside little Berkovitz. Berkovitz, as usual, had his steel helmet on his belly and Lesfauries called to us: "What's new, boys?"

Apparently he thought we had gone to the corner to buy the *Intran*.

Soon afterward we met the colonel, and he was full of praise. We threw ourselves into a bomb crater and fell asleep. We were too tired even to relieve our shoulders of the unbearable weight. We fell asleep, each of us with his eighty pounds of instruments on his back.

When I woke up, Lieutenant Saint-Brice lay beside me.

I asked him what had happened.

He stared straight ahead of him and said with infinite sadness in his voice: "Nothing. They just forgot about you."

They told us we should be moving on. On foot—thirty, forty, fifty kilometers. . . . Some said they could go no further. Some were already on their feet, eager to get started. But all of us felt the need of a guide, a strong spirit—to tell us what had happened, to support us. We needed something to lean on. The old soldiers perhaps? But even from the old soldiers there was no help. They seemed more speechless, more stunned and confused than ourselves.

We lay in a giant crater, which a *Stuka* had torn into the

forest floor. In these woods it is never spring. The floor is damp and the moss is green and slippery like seaweed. The fallen yellow and brown leaves are from the last autumn or the autumn before last. Autumn dwells in these woods. All through the summer it sleeps here, waiting for its time. The treetops are like the guardians of a palace. They protect the sleeping autumn from the intruding rays of the sun. But from the *Stukas* they offer no protection.

In the ready-made mass grave where we lay, we spoke of all possible things. More strongly than ever the question arose of what would happen if we lost the war. Each one silently asked himself: Then what? But no one dared to think any further. Even Vago, who had always been so full of optimism, was silent. He was a Hungarian architect, a student at the Beaux-Arts, who had designed one of the pavilions at the World's Fair. A little fellow, he had seemed no more than nineteen years old when together we left Paris for Barcarès. Meanwhile he had become a corporal and had grown a beard to enhance his dignity. He had a noble, Christ-like head, and with his beard he reminded me of his uncle, the architect of the new League of Nations building. Even under the most violent enemy fire, Vago had spent at least an hour a day tending his beard. He had a little comb and a pocket mirror, and with oriental patience he would stroke his soft, burnished blond hair. Never had I seen him spend a free minute in any other way. Now he lay apathetically beside me. He seemed unequal to the hardships. With deep, sad eyes he gazed at Kellenberger, the Swiss, who, being physically stronger, was making plans for the future.

"Whichever way the war turns out," said Kellenberger, "there will be plenty of night life in Paris."

He was stage-manager at the Tabarin.

Somewhere in the forest a rain of bombs was falling. We

had seen this bomb rain before. These were small bombs, almost harmless. The Germans sprinkled them about by the thousands; and often they were made of nothing but wood. But the sound they made in falling was unbearable. They whistled like a hundred sirens.

Lieutenant Saint-Brice came along the roadside and beckoned to me. I joined him and we sat down in the ditch.

He was pale and unshaven. He had a red-blond beard and his uniform was dirty. But behind the lenses of his spectacles his good, calm eyes were the same.

"Why did we move back?" I asked.

He shrugged his shoulders.

"The colonel is furious," he answered finally. "He didn't want to give up the sector without a fight. But—"

He held his head in his hands.

"I don't understand," he said softly. "They told us that the division to the left of us had given way, so we had to retreat a few kilometers, just to straighten the line. And—"

"And—?"

I could see that he was hesitating.

"And they told the division to the right of us that *we* had given way, so *they* would have to retreat."

"Yes, but—"

I couldn't follow the thought to its end.

"The same thing happened with the division on our right," Saint-Brice concluded. "And so on. All along the front."

"But that's impossible. That would be—"

The sentence remained unfinished.

"Do you think there's still any hope?" I asked.

Saint-Brice looked at me as if to see whether I meant the question seriously.

"Hope?" he said. "Maybe a miracle. What else? How would you expect us to win this war? Did we ever talk of victory? Never. We didn't even know the word *victoire*. Only the word *paix*. For nine months our generals dreamed of making peace before the war got really started. For nine months they sabotaged all possible preparations. We knew it . . . but what could we do?"

"Then you think they wanted to lose the war?"

"No, they didn't want to lose it, because they didn't want to begin it. They wanted peace with Hitler. Can't you understand that? They didn't want to admit that this was a war of two ideas. They—"

"Then they were traitors."

The word had slipped out, and I regretted it at once. But Saint-Brice gazed before him with unchanged calm. In the wood behind us the little bombs whistled.

"Traitors? No! They are honest. They are the only honest men. They at least admit that in this ideological war they are on the other side. Why shouldn't they? These aren't two nations fighting. We are the dishonest ones. We are afraid to say: Yes, we are dying for an idea. This time we were proud that we didn't march off to war singing. But you don't win a war without singing. It's not a question of a few cannon more or less. The important thing is for people to know what they're dying for."

I had no time to answer, for an orderly came to take Saint-Brice to the colonel. I only asked him: "How is the whole sector going to retreat by a single road?"

Saint-Brice pointed to the highway as he left me. He said nothing. As I looked after him, I saw that his back was bent.

On the road the troops streamed backwards, without interruption. The cannons blocked the highway. Far and wide there was no auto, no tractor. Only horses. When an enemy plane appeared, and there were only enemy planes, the drivers, screaming, lashing, cursing, drove their horses into the woods. And the horses didn't want to go. They didn't know the meaning of *Stuka* or Junkers 88; they didn't know that the heavens were spitting fire. The bear in Heine's *Atta Troll* believed that God was a giant polar bear, and these horses thought that God was a giant white horse. They didn't believe that a horse's God could permit such crimes. Only when the soldiers lashed out furiously with their whips did the horses spring aside. They jumped into the woods, wedging wagons and cannon between trees. Or else they leapt into the ditch, upsetting the wagons and cannon, which had to be abandoned. "*Planquez-vous! Planquez-vous!*" rang out from all sides. "Take cover." That was our motto. The men in the woods were afraid that the artillery wagons on the road might betray their presence to the bombers. The men on the road feared that the bombs aimed at the wood might fall on them. "*Planquez-vous! Planquez-vous!*" A thousand voices echoed from the wood, the voices of invisible ghosts.

I crawled back to our mass grave. Adjutant Lesfauries, chief of our telegraphers, was making a speech. He wanted to go home to his wife before Paris fell.

And he could not understand why France hadn't asked for an armistice long ago.

If there was any news, no one was interested in where it came from. Suddenly it was there, and no one asked for its source. If someone said it came from the colonel or any other officer, that was sufficient. And from time to time there were reports purporting to come from "the division." The division was something big, mysterious. The division was something invisible in the background of the regiment. The division was in contact with the army corps, the army corps was in contact with G.Q.G., *le Grand Quartier Général*. The

G.Q.G. could not be wrong. If a report was said to come from the division, everyone believed it.

Before we started out, a report came that Russia had declared war on Germany. Germany had been forced to shift the greater part of its troops to the east in headlong haste; that meant a breathing spell on the western front. In a few days, a few hours perhaps, the counter-offensive would begin. Details were added to the story. Encouraged by the happy news, the R.A.F. had set fire to the German munitions factories on the Ruhr. English troops had landed again in Dunkerque. The Poles and Rumanians were marching with the Russians.

And so we went on—retreating. But all weariness was set aside. For two hours no German plane had shown itself. That too seemed a good sign. Apparently they had something else to do beside follow us.

Top Sergeant Gerber, the Alsatian seminarist who disappeared every evening, was the center of common interest. He was a radio operator, with an E.R. 11 set, which to be sure had been made in the year 1920 and had been on strike for several days. The good news, however, seemed to have breathed new life into the old box. Gerber reported that he had gotten Paris, and Paris reported that the Russians had crossed the German border.

We had lost all awe of the forty kilometers ahead of us. Adjutant Daroussat marched ahead of me singing. He was a man of over forty, but he was undismayed. He merely thought it was a pity that we would have to march back over the same road in a few days. He thought it would be interesting to see some different country.

We marched by broad daylight. My company marched down the steep road in single file. But even in single file we presented a clear target to enemy planes. This hasty retreat in broad daylight seemed contrary to all good sense, certainly it was out of tune with the news reports. But there must have been strategic grounds for it, we thought.

Everything looked rosy. We seemed to be in for a streak of luck. At night there was even something to eat.

We left the southbound highway and took a side road leading westward in the direction of Reims. All we knew was that the Germans had broken through in the north and had passed Rethel. That we should suddenly change our direction from southwest to westward seemed the best sign that all was not yet lost. Resistance was apparently being organized in the west.

A fine balmy evening descended over the countryside. The woods were bathed in a light violet color. My stomach grumbled. It was heavy from emptiness.

The road climbed rather steeply. We came to a grade crossing near the village of Manre. Here for the first time we encountered our companions of the days to come, the Eighteenth Battalion of *Chasseurs à pied*. These "huntsmen" are also known as *Les Joyeux*. I do not know who gave them this cheery name, for in reality there is nothing very gay in the history of the *Joyeux*. These battalions—there were several—consisted of convicts, set at liberty for the duration of the war, in so far as the soldier's life can be described as liberty. The idea was apparently to prevent "slackers" from evading their duty of patriotic murder or military burglary by committing civilian murder or burglary; it would be just too soft if a criminal could spend the war in a well-heated prison. After the war broke out, common criminals were "granted" postponement of their sentences, while the really desperate cases were formed into battalions of their own and sent to the front. The battalion was the largest unit of *Joyeux*, for it was held that an entire regiment of convicts would do more harm than good. The battalions of *Joyeux* were distributed among different regiments. Their officers were not criminals, but to be assigned to the *Joyeux* was the worst punishment that could be meted out to a French officer. And these officers never spent more than a month or two with the *Joyeux*. During this time they were permitted to have only official relations with the officers of other regiments; and they did not enjoy the privileges of other officers. It goes without saying that the joyous battalions were consistently sent to the least joyful spots. The reward for good behavior was a pardon after the war, provided the joyous soldier was still alive by that time.

At the Manre grade crossing we met the *Joyeux* for the first time. Never was the name of this glorious battalion more justified, or more appreciated. In the dim, forgotten pre-war past, these good soldiers may have slaughtered women and robbed banks—but now they gave us the most precious gifts that one soldier can bestow upon another: food and good news. The *Joyeux* were camped around the abandoned gatekeeper's house, and were in the midst of a real banquet. Weeks before, we had lost our field kitchens, or destroyed them for fear their smoke would give us away to the bombers. But the joyous boys calmly cooked on the gatekeeper's stove, and an idyllic friendly smoke arose from the pretty red chimney. They must have been here for some time, for they had slaughtered several cows. They offered us a menu complete from rare roast beef to hot coffee. Their officer was tinkering with a big brown radio in the living room; he claimed that it had just stopped talking. To which division the *Chasseurs à pied* belonged and what they were doing in this region, it was impossible to ascertain. I doubt if they themselves had any clear idea on the subject. In this sinking world, they had made a home for themselves—who else could have adapted themselves to such conditions?

Our orders had been to keep moving in single file, to keep contact with the advance guard of our regiment; but at the railroad gate there was a hopeless tangle. Totally unconcerned over the rest of the world, we crowded around the kitchen from which the promising odors arose. Never have hosts been friendlier than these released convicts. They shared with us everything they possessed.

I was one of the last to go in. Only two pieces of meat were left, and at least twenty men were waiting. At the stove stood a tall, thin fellow with protruding cheek bones, a toothless mouth, and a shaven skull, covered with the first fuzz of new hair. He looked at me with big hyperthyroid eyes. Then he looked toward the other convicts. There were four or five of them in the kitchen. Their eyes held a brief council of war, then the tall man said: "I'll give you our supper. We'll find something. Poor devils!"

And he handed me a big bleeding chunk of meat.

"*Mon pauvre vieux . . .*"

He had at least fifteen years of prison ahead of him and no reason to feel sorry for me.

The lieutenant poured coffee. I asked him: "Have you any news, *mon lieutenant?*"

"Have I, my boy! The Russians have crossed the Polish border."

"Then it's true?"

"I'll say it's true!"

I stepped out into the road. My shirt was sticking to my back. In the air lay spring, juicy roast beef, the past. The sky was dark violet, the color of a ripe plum. My stomach ached worse than ever.

At about ten that night we came to a forest, and there at

last we were allowed to rest. The colonel and a few officers who had ridden on ahead were waiting for us. The colonel sat on the ground with a map spread out in front of him. He sent for me and pointed out the spot where I should install my observation post next day.

"Then we are not going any further, *mon colonel?*"

"No, we are taking up positions. We shall wait for the Germans here."

He seemed in good spirits. He indulged in a pipe but held his hand over the bowl to hide the glow from possible planes.

"We shall soon know more," he said. "I am expecting the general."

I made my way through the thicket and rejoined my comrades. They had installed themselves for the night as best they could, with their guns beside them. All of us had bleeding feet; we hadn't removed our shoes in days. But that no longer mattered. We spoke of the great miracle.

"What did the colonel say?" they asked me.

"We're taking up positions tomorrow."

"And—what about the news?"

"True, of course," I said. "It's all true."

Scarcely had I spoken when through the leaves we heard the officers welcoming the general. He had come with another officer and his orderly. He spoke in a loud voice.

"Yes," he replied to the colonel's question. "Russia has declared war. Rumania and Turkey have not yet declared war, but they are mobilizing. The German advance has been stopped."

He spoke distinctly and we could hear every word.

"Nearly the whole German Rhineland is in flames. The English have bombed the Ruhr with eight hundred planes. We're giving them some of their own medicine."

Then he bent down toward the colonel. Most likely they spoke of our next day's action.

When the general had gone, the colonel came over to us.

"Well, boys, let's have a glass together! You have earned it."

Nicola, his cook, brought out the great basket-bottle of *gniol,* and poured us each an eighth of a liter. The colonel himself did not drink. He never drank. But he sat down beside us, with his chief staff officer and Lieutenant Saint-Brice.

I clinked glasses with Saint-Brice.

"*A votre santé, mon lieutenant!*"

"*A la vôtre, mon vieux!*"

The fiery liquid flowed down my throat.

"So the Russians after all . . ." I began.

"Yes, the Russians," said Ouchakoff beside me. He was a White Russian, a Czarist refugee, an anti-Semite. But suddenly he had forgotten all that. He was only a Russian. "The Russians have always saved the world," he said. I do not know on what he based this historical wisdom, but we all agreed. There was nothing to which we would not have agreed. A mood of complete well-being had taken possession of us. It was the bliss that comes before death. Inwardly we were bleeding and sore: our nerves lay bare like the bowels of a dead beast. No: all this life at the front, this dangerous life, which the professional liars call virile; this wild, hunted life had not made us harder and stronger. It had made us soft. We were accustomed to sorrow but not to joy. We were unequal to it. In the presence of good fortune we were weak.

I felt the warm tears dripping down my cheeks. Only deep down in my most secret soul, I asked myself: What if it isn't true? But the shadow took no form. I drank and spoke. We drank and spoke, spoke and drank.

Our hearts ran riot, our eyes wept. With blissful smiles we fell asleep.

At that same hour the first motorized units of the German army were entering Paris.

I am absolutely unable to explain how rumors arose those days, what made us accept them as true or reject them as false. War is a great collective tragedy: the collective spirit engenders war and at the same time makes it bearable. The moment an army ceases to be a collectivity, the moment each soldier begins to feel his own individual tragedy, the army is spiritually divided and the war is lost. Our faith or lack of faith began to depend on our individual moods—and how can an army exist when every soldier is dominated by his own moods?

Yet our instincts rarely deceived us. The pace of our retreat was so rapid that we had no time to set up our radios: from that time on our instincts were our radios. Human intuitions are probably no more miraculous than radio waves; only they have not yet been mechanized, and hence are incomprehensible to most people. We found that our mental radio sets functioned faultlessly when we couldn't use the mechanical ones. How else can it be explained that, the moment we awoke the following morning, we knew that the rumors we had accepted as true the night before were false? Nothing had happened during the night. We had cried and laughed and had fallen happily asleep. Not a one of us had doubted. The next morning we awoke in the knowledge that we had been duped. But no one dared to tell his neighbor what the incomprehensible waves had communicated to him. We lay there silent. Now and then one of us tried to resume our conversations of the day before. But the words fell flat, and no one bothered to pick up the fragments of talk. As though overwhelmed by an absurd shame, we avoided looking at one another. We still did not admit that we had been fooled. But we were ashamed of ourselves for having believed. In the end all of us kept silent.

This disappointment—coming "from the air" like our previous enthusiasm—attained its climax at about eight o'clock in the morning when we were ordered to break up camp and start on a forced march to Vienne-la-Ville. This town was about thirty kilometers southeast of the woods where we had spent the night; but I learned that Captain Billerot's orders were to lead us along the twisting railway track which took about forty kilometers to reach the same place. All this meant that we were still retreating—and under the most dangerous conditions, by broad daylight.

Our forced march to Vienne-la-Ville was one of those medieval tortures that no modern army need be exposed to. I could not help smiling as I recalled the words of Captain Mirambeau, our brilliant instructor: "Because of the progress of mechanization, modern war entails a maximum of danger with a minimum of hardship." In our experience, a maximum of hardship had always been accompanied by a maximum of danger.

The special brand of torture that characterized our flight to Vienne-la-Ville consisted of marching on sharp stones for twelve full hours. The highways or the fields seemed too dangerous, the woods impracticable. As the Germans knew there were no more trains running, our commanders thought the safest bet would be to march along the railway track. And so we marched, in single file, for forty kilometers, on the crushed stones between the rails. The soles of our shoes were wet, worn thin and often torn. At every step the stones cut into our flesh.

Of course the German planes spotted us even before we

had reached Autry where the railway began. They did not take the trouble to send for bombers, but contented themselves with dropping to a thousand feet and strafing us with their machine guns. *On était canardé,* as they said in the French military jargon.

As usual there was no reaction from our side. All sign of an anti-aircraft defense had vanished, and we had been forbidden to fire our rifles for fear of "revealing our positions." We hid in the bushes and waited for the Messerschmitts to weary of the hunt. One thing we learned in this war was what it feels like to be a pheasant or a deer.

Luckily it began to rain soon after we reached the railway track. The happy huntsmen seemed to have withdrawn to their hunting lodges. We marched, dripping wet, on the stones, or tried to jump from one wooden tie to the next. But the space between them was too wide. We were too tired to take such long steps. None of us understood why the trains were not running and why we were the only living things, so to speak, moving along the railway track. Not in a single place were the rails damaged or ripped up, nowhere in the vicinity were there bomb craters to be seen.

A violent ringing suddenly struck our ears. We were coming to a station. It gives you a strange feeling to be slowly approaching a station, not in a train but on foot, with nothing awaiting you: no porters, no station-master, no newspapers, no beer, no travelers. And yet there was only one living thing in this station: the bell. It rang shrilly without interruption. The clock over the entrance was still going too, showing the time with embarrassing precision. The civilian population had probably been evacuated only a short time before.

The rain beat down with increasing fury. The sky was black. Many of us were too exhausted to drag ourselves to the station. The instant our captain's whistle blew—it went off with unfailing regularity after every fifty minutes of marching—the men dropped down wherever they happened to be. Their faces were wet with the rain. They lay in the puddles. Their knapsacks were soaked through. Twenty, ten, fifteen steps away was a building where they could have taken shelter. But they could go no further. They lay on the stony ground in front of the house, under the clock. And the bell went on ringing.

With a few others I dragged myself to the building. The doors were open. Now and then the wind swung one of them, and it creaked on its hinges. Piles of documents and letters lay on the station-master's table. A gust of wind raised a few papers in the air and blew them about the room. The walls of the waiting room were plastered with time-tables for "summer 1940." The old brown chairs with their perforated backs had been lined up along the wall. The torn corner of a poster rustled. The woman on the poster—a bathing beauty with a naked back, symbolizing the Côte d'Azur—looked at me out of silly advertising eyes.

When I went into the waiting room, a soldier was sitting on the bench. He was half leaning on the small iron stove in the center of the room. "Who is this man?" I thought. "He looks familiar. But he must be from some other regiment. I don't know him." The strange man looked at me, and a soft smile brightened his face. It was a gray, thin face. His lower eyelids drooped beneath his eyes like heavy bags on the back of a weak man. His face practically disappeared behind them.

I spoke to the man; he answered. Then I recognized him. His name was David Laifer and he belonged to our company. He was a sturdy fellow—a printer by trade—who had worked in the company office. His father had fought in the World War as a Foreign Legionary and won several distinctions. I had spoken with Laifer every day in our training camp at Barcarès. This plump rosy Laifer joined in everything and always made himself useful; every Saturday he went to see relatives in Narbonne and came back laden with pastry. For a time he had had the bunk next to mine. And now I did not even recognize him.

I asked him if he had anything to eat. He pointed at his knapsack lying beside him. I unlaced it and found a can of sardines. I asked whether I could open it. He nodded. We shared the contents. Laifer swallowed four or five sardines on a piece of hard bread that I had with me. He was half-starved, but had lacked the strength to open his knapsack.

The door of the station-master's office kept squeaking. I went out to close it, and found little red-headed Dési in the office. He did not notice me. I looked at him and wondered if he had gone out of his mind. This red-headed Dési, the fine little electrical technician who had never lost courage, who knew no weariness, who at the darkest moments had always been willing to discuss fundamentals, was running up and down in the room as though frantically in search of something. He rummaged in the papers on the station-master's table, tinkered with the telegraph set, tried to force open a clock. His steel helmet sat crooked on his red head, and water ran down his neck.

I spoke to him.

He turned around with a jerk and stood motionless.

"What are you doing?"

"I'm looking for something," he said. There was a curious flicker in his little eyes. His freckled face was quite yellow.

"For what?"

"The bell!"

He continued his search, disarranging more papers, opening drawers.

I gazed at him in silence. He approached me, looked into my face and said: "How can you stand it—that bell? I can't stand it. I've got to stop it. But how?"

He sat down, put his hands on his knees, and stared straight ahead of him. His boyish face was aged and worn.

Henri Laifer came in. He was the proud owner of the only remaining motorcycle in our company. He had come by the road and found us here. In civilian life he was a printer, like his brother David. He told us that nothing had happened on the highway. We could have used it in safety. He asked me where his brother was. He had not seen him for four days.

"You just passed him," I said; "he is in the waiting room."

He looked at me, turned white, wanted to say something, but closed his mouth again without saying it. Then he turned around and went out. I knew that he had not recognized his brother.

All in all twelve minutes had passed. The long-drawn-out whistle blew. We went out on the platform. Those who had been lying in the puddles rose up mechanically.

Behind the building a church tower emerged from the gray mist. I looked up at the sign with the name of the town written on it.

The name was Monplaisir—my pleasure.

The shrill sound of the bell that could not be stopped rang in my ears for another kilometer.

Then there were rails, rails, and more rails. They were the symbol of eternity. Parallel lines meet in infinity, said a voice inside me. It was the voice of Professor Stepan, my geometry teacher at the Franz-Joseph Gymnasium in Vienna. The voice seemed to mock me as it repeated: parallel lines meet in infinity, rails meet in infinity. Rails and parallel lines are the same thing. We marched between parallel lines. We were marching into infinity.

To the right and to the left there were woods. Something was moving in the woods. Somewhere there seemed to be fighting. I heard the sound of tanks. The sound was now on the right, now on the left—the sound of a battle.

"What's going on?" I asked Adjutant Daroussat, who passed me jumping from one wooden tie to another.

The old adjutant shrugged his shoulders. He had good color in his cheeks, as usual. He ran along the marching column and helped wherever he could. In his *bidon* he had brought two quarts of *gniol*, and he gave a swallow to anyone who needed it. As adjutant—an intermediary rank between a non-commissioned and commissioned officer—he usually carried no rifle, only a revolver. Now he carried two rifles belonging to two soldiers who could no longer carry them. Even so, he made good time. It is true that he was not burdened by a steel helmet. This old warrior, who had served first in the navy, then in the Foreign Legion, and finally as an infantryman in the World War, refused to wear a helmet. He refused to give up his white Legionnaire's cap. How he succeeded in keeping the cover of his cap always white remained a mystery. But he wore this white cap day and night, despite the protests of his officers, despite the colonel's threats of punishment; he wore it while laying mines, while on patrol duty . . . and now. He knew that his house in the Ardennes was burning, that his wife and his young children were fleeing along some road, that his son was fighting on another front. But he also knew the meaning of duty. He despised mimicry and loved bravery. He helped the weak and patted death on the shoulder.

Such was Adjutant Daroussat. France had such men—along with the rest.

Now he ran past me.

"I don't know what's happening," he called to me. "But come with me, quick."

I obeyed and ran after him.

Daroussat was moving toward a watchman's hut. Gasping for breath, I caught up with him.

"We've got to be first," he said, laughing. He climbed over the fence, I close behind him. He had not been wrong. In the yard we found a hutch full of rabbits. They were munching in happy ignorance. Daroussat snatched three by the ears and pressed two more into my hands.

"We'll take these," he said. "A man must eat."

With the struggling rabbits in my hands, I cast a glance at the watchman's house. Red pelargoniums, the favorite flowers of my childhood, still stood in the window. I thought of my grandmother, an old peasant woman in Balatonboglár—in the heart of Hungary—who raised them.

We quickly drew water from the well near the house. In the meantime the column had caught up with us. Over a hundred men surrounded the well. They pushed and jostled one another. They were thirsty but they did not want to lose the advancing column. In such a matter there was no more comradeship.

Daroussat looked away.

The next time we rested at the edge of the woods. A small ditch, deep but scarcely a yard wide, separated us from the trees. Wild strawberries grew on the other side. They were red, fresh, enticing. But nobody picked them—nobody jumped over the ditch.

The sounds of battle drew nearer. I marched between the rails, holding my struggling quadruped friends. The captain walked for a few steps at my side.

"These are our tanks," he said. "We are covered on both sides."

An awful cry came from the woods. We all knew that cry: the anguished call of the wounded. We exchanged looks, but said nothing. Outwardly the woods had a peaceful look. The rain dripped from the branches, the earth was steaming and fragrant. Somewhere a man was dying.

We left the woods. The sounds gradually died away. Soon the clanking of caterpillar treads was like receding thunder. Covered on both sides, I repeated to myself. Our tanks . . . And Captain Billerot's voice became confused with Professor Stepan's, of the Franz-Joseph Gymnasium in Vienna. Parallel lines meet in infinity. Parallels, rails, tanks. Tanks too meet in infinity. Our tanks. The tracks ran along, they met in eternity.

The rain had stopped. Night had fallen, and we hadn't noticed it. Imperceptibly the sky darkened by rain clouds had changed into the night sky. Only on the horizon there gleamed a yellow stripe.

To the right and left there lay a plain. It was so broad that it seemed illumined. Not far from us, soldiers lay in the grass. Their horses were grazing in the fields. They were two cavalry squadrons. The men lay there and slept the deep sleep of exhaustion. The horses neighed.

"Our tanks," said Daroussat.

We stood side by side and looked across the country. Mist was rising from the ground like small camp fires. A divine hand spread a veil over a fantastic landscape. The soldiers slept as though lulled to sleep by a fairy's hand. Now and then a silvery light trembled on the backs of the horses. I felt the spring, but it was from another world. It was as though we were on our way to the beyond. In the beyond it was spring right now. In all this enchanted scene there lay the deathlike grace of a Goya.

"Quel beau pays était-ce, la France!" said Daroussat. There was no bitterness in his words. They sounded like an expression of gratitude for something that has been and is no more.

Vienne-la-Ville was the first town in which we encountered civilians. As we marched into the northern end of the town, the inhabitants of Vienne-la-Ville were leaving by its southern end.

Up to this point the semblance at least of an orderly retreat had been maintained, but here everything became chaos. Three highways met outside Vienne-la-Ville. From all three sides the army defeated without a fight streamed toward the fourth highway, leading south. The artillerymen slept on their wagons, the horses halted or continued to trot. There was an undamaged gun behind almost every tractor; only a few dragged empty gun-carriages. Nobody stood at the crossing to direct traffic. The carriages ran into one another, became entangled, or were pushed against the house walls. The procession extended as far as you could see, on all three sides. Hundreds of trucks, thousands of horses, innumerable cannon and machine guns. As if by miracle, the traffic jams were disentangled from time to time and the columns resumed their march. To almost every wagon clung infantrymen. They had no idea who was taking them or where they were going, but they clung to the wagons like clusters of grapes. When the load became too heavy, the horses would stop. Then the driver would wake up, crack his whip over his horses, and when this did no good, over the men. But most of the time this too was of no avail. The infantrymen, exhausted from continuous marching, clung to the wagons with a strength born of ultimate despair. Their hands were cramped, as though surprised by *rigor mortis* as they clung to the wagons. Now and then one of them would fall asleep. Then his clutching fingers would relax, and he would roll down on the pavement. The horses drawing the next wagon would trample him, the wheels would roll over him.

We stopped at Vienne-la-Ville. With my scouts I occupied a small yellow house on the left side of the street, abandoned shortly before.

We ourselves saw a man, a woman, and two children run out of it into the night. I don't know where they were going. I don't even know whether they were fleeing from us or from the Germans. Did they themselves know? At any rate they left their house open. Half of the buildings were in flames. If a door was locked, the soldiers bashed it in. Many fugitives saw their houses plundered. Fire was falling from the skies, disaster came from all sides; what good was a key? The people understood how absurd it was to lock their houses. They left them open.

We found a friendly, middle-class home whose owners must have been quite comfortably off. The first place we went was the kitchen. Imoudsky, who was not only a talented painter but an experienced cook as well, discovered a hot roast in the oven. Apparently the family had been preparing supper when frightened by some rumor, and had precipitately left their home. The roast was burned, of course. But I had my two rabbits; Kellenberger cut the throats of two chickens, Garai peeled potatoes, two other men of genius who had joined us piled up innumerable jars of stewed fruit, Barati started preparing noodles with cheese, and only Ouchakoff preferred to hold a scientific lecture about cooking in general.

Having delivered my rabbits and peeled my share of potatoes, I wandered about the house. It was a rather large house, extremely comfortable. There were two or three vases still full of fresh flowers—large, blooming peonies. I tried to imagine the life of the people who had occupied this house only a few hours before. They must have been a young and happy couple. The woman's apron lay on the bed. I touched it gently. It was a bright blue apron with little flowers. In its pocket I found seventy-five centimes. I put them back, and hung the apron in the closet. I moved as though in a dream. But I felt that I would never hold in my hands anything more touching than this bright blue apron with the seventy-five centimes.

A large wash basin stood in the bedroom. I brought water, undressed, and washed myself. I don't remember how many days I had gone without washing. I washed myself in the dark. But while rummaging about for a towel I found candles. I lighted them and saw a mirror hanging over the wash basin. A worn, unfamiliar face looked out at me. The tallow of the candles seemed to have melted on my face. The flickering light covered my face with lines and wrinkles. The mirror was old and scratched. My face, too, seemed old and scratched.

I looked out the window into the street. The endless flood was passing. Men and wagons, horses and guns. Slowly, very slowly, the columns moved forward. They stopped for a while, then moved on again. There was no end in sight. Behind me, the candles flickered.

Before returning to the kitchen I was curious to find out what was going to happen next day. I went out to find our captain, who was quartered in a near-by house. He was lying on an old sofa and seemed at the end of his strength. I was sorry for him. His responsibility had become too great for him. What man would have been equal to such a task? He spoke softly, without opening his eyes.

"We were planning to make a stand here," he said. "But I have just received orders to evacuate the town. We leave on the dot of midnight."

"That is impossible, *mon capitaine!*"

He did not answer. But when I began to speak, he interrupted me: "I know, I know. Our men are in a state of collapse. The forty kilometers we covered today were too much. But what can I do? Those are my orders. . . ."

He thought for a while. Then he sat up.

"We must get to Ste. Menehould. We've got to defend Ste. Menehould. That is ten kilometers from here."

"Ten kilometers too much, *mon capitaine.*"

He thought again.

"At four in the morning we must take up positions at Ste. Menehould, on the south side. There's only one solution: each man may get there as he chooses. I can't force them to march."

"*Compris, mon capitaine.*"

I stood up, ready to go. He held out his hand.

"Thanks, Habe, for still being here," he said. And as I was opening the door he called after me: "Let's hope you find a car to give you a lift."

At that moment I understood beyond doubt that we had lost the war.

Outside, near the door of a barn, I was accosted by Sergeant Gerber, fresh and rosy as usual. He was alone, as always at that time of night: that was when he would disappear.

He stopped me.

"Heard the news?" he asked.

"No!"

"Last night the Germans entered Paris."

My heart stopped beating. Today, I might pretend that at that moment I thought of everything Paris had meant to me. Of the quais, the Place St. Michel, the peaceful streets around the Dôme des Invalides; of the spring when I looked down from the balcony of a house in the Avenue MacMahon. I might pretend that I thought of Paris, the most enchanting, most mysterious, most immortal of all cities—the Paris of the Tuileries, the Arc de Triomphe, the Bois—that I saw before me its pink, silvery sky and felt its air on the tip of my tongue: the soft, seductive, eternally springlike air of Paris. I might say so, but it would not be the truth. No, I felt nothing and saw nothing: or rather I saw only Sergeant Gerber's neck, and I felt only the desire to strangle him.

I controlled myself with great effort. My rank was lower than his and I could not give him orders. I only seized his arm, pressed hard, and said: "Listen, Gerber. If you mention this to anybody, I'll shoot you like a dog."

I spoke softly, but he understood me. He cried out: "Let me go!"

I pressed still harder. I don't know what gave me the idea, but I suddenly whispered in his ear in German: "I'll shoot you like a dog!"

Then I let him go. He ran across the street toward a burning house. The last I saw of him he was being engulfed by the flames. (In reality, nothing of the sort occurred. Later I learned that when the hour came to march out of Vienne-la-Ville, he had an "epileptic fit." He dropped to the ground and for long minutes writhed in convulsions. He was left behind. A few hours later he was discovered giving signals to German planes under the pretext of lighting his pipe. According to some, he was shot on the spot by an artillery lieutenant. Others maintain that he had fits again and again, at appropriate moments, until the Germans marched into Vienne-la-Ville, when Sergeant Gerber reported to his masters. I never saw him again.)

I returned to my scouts, to break as cautiously as possible the bad news that there was to be no rest and that we had to set out at midnight.

The house was filled with pleasant odors. Imoudsky had put on a white apron and was playing the *Hausfrau*. Kellenberger, with a flower in his hair, was the maid. They discovered that as the dining room had no windows, it was all right to light candles. A fragrant red wine was brought from the cellar and, as Ouchakoff expertly explained, was *chambré* according to its age. Ouchakoff lectured us on the relation between the age of a wine and the necessary degree of warmth, but little Garai, the butler, apologized for not having been able to cool the white wine. Dr. Barati solemnly set the table with china, glasses, and a damask tablecloth. He was the only one among us who had scruples. He took great care not to break a dish.

We had been terribly hungry. The preparations, the smells, the abundance had filled us with delight. But we had forgotten to take our stomachs into account. Each had made a great show of his appetite; now none of us dared admit that he could not eat. We poked our food like children who don't want to eat and try to fool their parents. Imoudsky declared that he had eaten his fill in the kitchen. He wiped his hands on his white apron. I thought with silent satisfaction of the blue apron that I had put in a safe place. The rest of us had no excuse at all. We just pushed the food from one side of the dish to the other. I felt sharp pains in my stomach.

From time to time one of us would rise and go out to see what was going on. The procession was still pouring by. This time it was Garai's turn to go. After a few minutes he came back. Even in the light of candles we saw how pale he was. His knees were shaking. He sat down.

We asked questions. But he kept repeating only one phrase: "The Germans are in Paris!"

I blew up: "Who told you that?"

"Lieutenant Saint-Brice."

Then we all knew it was true.

We rose. No one made any further attempt to take food. We were all choking. Kellenberger tried to curse aloud, as was his custom. But the attempt was a failure.

I reported my conversation with the captain. We decided to go to sleep at once, so as to get at least two or three hours rest.

One by one we left the room. Each separately looked for a place. No one could help the other. It was almost as though a woman had died, whom each of us had loved in his own way. Our grief did not bring us together.

Outside we heard the tramp of the sleeping, defeated army.

In the bedroom, Kellenberger lay down on the marriage bed with his muddy shoes. The rest of us still felt a certain reluctance to commit such sacrilege. Imoudsky and I removed a mattress from one of the beds and laid it on the floor. One of the candles was still sputtering. I found a warm blanket and pulled it over my ears. It had suddenly grown bitter cold.

None of us could sleep. I don't know what I thought about that night. I was feverish. I was so hot that I threw the blanket off me, and then so cold that I threw my coat over me. I lay shivering. I had a vision of heavy German boots marching on the Place de la Concorde. I thought of the woman who was waiting for me. I don't know whether I thought of the Germans who were at our heels. Everything was distorted, yet feverishly alive. I tried to sleep and remain awake at once so as to be ready to leave on time. I thought of my captain whom I had promised to be in Ste. Menehould at four in the morning. I thought of getting sick and dying by the roadside. I thought of falling asleep and waiting to see what would happen to me. At the same time, I was afraid of losing my regiment and remaining alone. And all this was mingled with visions of Paris, visions quivering with a feverish clarity, visions alive and agonizing. I saw myself walking through the arcades of the Rue de Rivoli. On the steps of the Madeleine the man whom they call their Führer stood screaming. I shook myself awake, certain that when this dream was dispelled, it would take the other nightmare with it, the nightmare of my present. But nothing happened. Only the candle flickered.

I tried to pray. I prayed in French, German, Hungarian. I tried all languages. I did not know which one God would understand. No doubt He understood all three of them, for I fell asleep. I had at least ten minutes of complete oblivion. I awoke and was almost rested. It was midnight. I took leave of the boys. I looked for my gun, my canteen, and my knapsack. I had lost my own blanket long ago. I took the blanket I had found in the bedroom, but instead of rolling it up, I threw it over my shoulders and pulled my knapsack over it. In this rather unmilitary garb I went out into the street. An icy gust of wind blew into my face. The stream of fleeing troops was still unbroken.

I stood by the roadside and waited.

CHAPTER FIVE: THE CRIME OF

STE. MENEHOULD

THE NIGHT WAS DARK. I SAW NOTHING. THE ONLY NOISE WAS
the monotonous tramp of horses. Suddenly familiar sounds
struck my ears. Somebody was cursing in Hungarian.

I called to the man. He was driving a gun carriage, or
something that vaguely resembled a gun carriage.

"Will you give me a lift?"

The column had just stalled.

"Jump on quick behind! Once we start moving, I can't
stop the nag!"

I climbed in. The "gun carriage" consisted of two wheels.
A machine gun, on a small plank, was wedged in between
them. The man sat on the barrel. I held on to the plank,
pressing my back to his.

"You won't fall off?"

"Hope not!"

He shifted forward a little.

The column started moving and his horse began to gallop.
Behind us trotted a solitary horse.

"Watch out that our horse doesn't get lost," the man said.

He belonged to our regiment. I gripped the plank convulsively. I had my own gun pressed between my knees. Why
am I taking this thing with me? I wondered, as the steel cut
into my stomach. My canteen strap became entangled in one
of the wheels and threatened to strangle me. My legs hung

between the wheels; at any moment they might have been caught and broken. My knapsack weighed heavily on the man's back.

"What have you got in the knapsack?" he asked.

"Nothing."

"Then throw it away!"

I dropped it. The solitary horse running after us trampled it. I would have done anything this man asked of me. Anything so as not to walk with my bleeding, aching feet.

My companion on the machine-gun barrel had a broad back. A fleshy neck separated his steel helmet from his shoulders. That was all I could see of him. His voice too seemed fat. He must have been a man of a certain age.

"Where are you going?" I asked.

The man did not answer.

"Where are you going?" I repeated.

Again there was no answer. He was asleep.

We passed over a stone. There was a jerk and he started slipping between the wheels. I managed to disentangle one hand and pull him up.

"Are you hurt?" I asked.

"I don't know. I'm numb," said my fellow countryman. "It's the fourth or fifth time I've fallen between the wheels. I'm bleeding all over."

He said it without complaining—only as a statement of fact.

Then he said: "Talk to me. About anything at all. If you don't, I'll fall asleep."

"Where are you going?"

"Don't know. I'm just following the column."

"How long have you been going on like this?"

"Four days."

"Without sleep?"

"Without sleep."

I tried to talk. But I, too, was overwhelmed by a desire to sleep.

"Did you suffer heavy losses?"

Again he didn't answer. I shook him to consciousness. He growled. He acted as though he had been awakened from a long, deep sleep and didn't know where he was. His head was drooping.

"How long can we go on like this?" he asked. "We're entirely surrounded."

"How do you know?"

"I know."

My gun was cutting into my flesh. I had slipped down and was holding on by a hair.

"Where are you from?" I asked.

"Balaton-Aliga."

"You don't say!"

"Why?"

I saw the Balaton before me. The land of my childhood.

"My mother was born only twenty kilometers from your place."

He muttered something.

"Got a family?" he asked suddenly.

I said yes.

"And you?"

"I, too," he answered. "In Paris. I mean: they were in Paris. My wife and my two little daughters. But I don't know what's become of them. The Germans are in Paris."

"Yes. The Germans are in Paris."

The conversation stalled. Convulsively my fingers gripped the machine gun. The steel was cold. My hands were hot. Again and again I slipped down.

"What was your trade?" he asked.

"I was a writer."

He laughed. For several weeks everybody had laughed when I said I was a writer.

"You'll have nice things to write about."

We stopped again. The horse bolted. The last days had made him wild, and my friend had a hard time placating the beast. There was a cannon ahead of us. The horse kept running into the cannon.

"And you?" I asked. "What were you?"

"I had a gay trade."

"Gay?"

"Yes."

He laughed hoarsely. I still couldn't see him. I wondered what he looked like, the man with the gay trade.

"I had a wheel of fortune," he said. "It's a pretty thing, a wheel of fortune."

"And you made your living with it?"

"Sure. I traveled from fair to fair. You could win all kinds of things in my booth. Sparkling wines and chickens and blankets and alarm clocks."

He added abruptly: "My wife worked in a factory."

We were stalled at an intersection. Wagons, horses and soldiers were streaming from the side road. I heard the monotonous curses of the Moroccans as they tried to make a path for themselves on their horses. They swore in Arabic. From time to time you could hear the deep, staccato roar of German planes which accompanied but seemed to ignore us.

"Say something," I said to my companion. I, too, was afraid of falling asleep. I shook him. "Say something!" I repeated.

"Come in, ladies and gentlemen!" he called out. "Now is the time. Now or never. Here is something that you never saw before. Every number wins. Two numbers, two wins.

The Crime of Ste. Menehould

No blanks, ladies and gentlemen! No blanks! Something for your home, ladies and gentlemen. This is for the lady of the house. And this for the little ones. You haven't any, Miss? They'll come, they'll come, don't worry! Here, ladies and gentlemen, the wheel of fortune. . . ."

His voice weakened. Then his head drooped forward. I, too, fell asleep. I don't know how long I slept. Perhaps one minute, perhaps ten. But I dreamed of a soldier spinning a wheel of fortune, of laughing German soldiers walking up the Champs Elysées, carrying away a chicken. I dreamed of a woman in a blue apron jumping through fire and shouting: No blanks, ladies and gentlemen, no blanks!

A violent shock woke me up. The carriage had begun to move. I spoke to the stranger astride the machine gun. I talked just for the sake of talking.

"What kind of a factory does your wife work in?"

"Munitions."

"Is she Hungarian, too?"

"No. Parisian. Got a cigarette?"

"Yes. But we can't light it."

"Why?"

"Don't you hear? The planes."

He laughed, the same hoarse laugh as before. He stretched out his arm and pointed at the horizon in front of us. The town of Ste. Menehould was burning.

"That gives more light than a cigarette."

I handed him one of my broken cigarettes. We lighted up.

"It makes you feel better."

"Yes, it does."

Suddenly he began to talk. Now he spoke hastily as if he were in a hurry to tell me his story before—before—I don't know what . . .

"I met my wife at a fair. We had pitched our tents in St.

125

Maxime. Right by the sea. It was in the summer of 1932. It was a hot summer. A happy summer. When I spoke the waves murmured behind me. They played music. A young girl won a bottle of wine. We drank it together. She became my wife. I had a lot of luck that summer. A rich American gave me a new wheel of fortune. Of glittering silver. With bulbs on it. Bulbs of four different colors. On the whole Riviera nobody did as good business as I. Even the fortune teller envied me. And she made more money than anybody else. Are you asleep?"

"No. I'm listening."

"My elder daughter is now six years old. She dances like a fairy queen. Some day you must see her dance."

I felt that his back was moving, his broad back with the big hips. Maybe he was showing me how his daughter danced.

"And the little one?"

"Haven't seen her yet. She was born after I left. Her name's Marie." And then again abruptly: "Do you believe that we're entirely surrounded?"

"I don't know."

"It's probable," he said in a calm voice. "The planes haven't bombed us in the last two days. We're not worth the expense." He took a deep breath from the smoldering cigarette. "They want us alive."

I could scarcely hang on to the carriage.

"The horse is gone," I said. "It isn't following us any more."

"Too bad."

That was all.

I woke up as I fell off the carriage. My gun fell on my head. The wagon following us stopped accidentally only one step from me. The shoe of the horse almost touched me. I felt something warm running over my face. I put my hand to my forehead. I felt something wet, hot. I was full of mud and blood. But I cried out: You, you! It struck me that I knew everything about him except his name. I ran after the carriage. If I only knew his name!

The man on the gun carriage woke up.

"Jump up!" he called to me. "I can't stop the horse!"

I ran alongside his carriage. I handed him my gun. A hand seized my gun in the darkness. An arm seized me under my arm. I succeeded in getting up.

"Don't sit that way," he said. "Sit astride. Hold on to my belt."

I did as I was told.

"How long do you expect to go on like this?" I asked.

"Forever."

It sounded like a voice from another world. Death and the player. A strange timidity prevented me from asking him his name. Perhaps he had no name.

Now I clung to the back of his belt. Each of us kept the other from falling. His large, massive body kept drooping forward. Thus we passed through a town where only the naked walls of the houses remained. Its name was la Neuville. And the horizon was burning.

The dawn came slowly. The road was so clogged you could have bombed it with pins. Cyclists turned up at my side. Soon civilians appeared, women and children. They slipped between the wagons, under the horses' bellies. The horsemen tried to force a path for themselves. At my side I made out a Spahi, a Moroccan cavalryman. He gave spur to his horse, but the road was like a moving wall.

The horses alone were admirable. Were they impervious to fatigue, or had the fire, water, and thunder made them wild? Did they scent the terrible, ultimate danger? Again and again they pulled the train forward. But they were unmanageable. Above us the German bombers traced loops and circles. But no more bombs fell on the overcrowded road. The sound of the motors was like ironic laughter.

Thus we came to Ste. Menehould.

Here again one side of the street was completely destroyed, while the other side had been spared. The right side looked like the main street of a peaceful small town, on a Sunday. The bakery, the tobacco shop, the butcher shop were closed, the shutters rolled down, the show cases boarded. But there was no sign of destruction. The left side of the street was a complete shambles. Only black posts remained. The place previously occupied by rooms showed only charred walls. A door rattled in its frame. But it led only from one void to another.

The man holding the reins awoke. Suddenly he went on with his story.

"Marceline goes to a dancing school, you know. She has the best teachers. One of them used to be prima ballerina of the Paris opera."

"Hey," I said. "What do you look like?"

He did not answer. Again his head drooped to his chest.

At the end of the town, a little before the bridge at the south end, I noticed Colonel de Buissy with his staff. He stood on an open square, watching the column pass by him and collecting his regiment. With lifeless eyes he watched me riding on the machine gun. Automatically I raised my hand to my steel helmet. And then I heard him roar: "Habe, God damn you. What kind of a rig is that?"

I felt my bleeding, dirty face.

But the colonel went on shouting.

"Get down with your masquerade!"

Only then did I realize what he meant. In Vienne-la-Ville in the darkness, I had thrown a blanket over my shoulders.

I hadn't examined it. The night was cold. And the blanket was warm. Now I looked at it. The bleeding soldier with the steel helmet and the gun wore a bright red blanket with blue flowers.

"Down off that carriage!" shouted the colonel.

"Let me down," I said to the booth owner.

"I can't," he said. "Not until the column stops."

I threw my gun on the pavement. Then I let myself drop from the carriage. I fell on my hands and the impact drew blood from them. The driver of the next wagon pulled his horse aside, cursing angrily. I rose. My friend had disappeared in a cloud of dust.

I looked after him. I knew all about him, but I never saw his face.

Our company gathered in the main square. Oddly enough the square was completely intact. Once again, the actual targets had been missed. While most of the houses in the surrounding streets were aflame, the large buildings on the main square stood undamaged. The bank, the post office, the church had a Sunday look about them; the scene made me think of a Sunday afternoon in a small town, with the young ladies in pink and the young gentlemen in dark blue, promenading on the main square, with billiard games in the café and old women gossiping behind curtains. Of all this only the walls remained—like an empty stage without players or scenery.

I lay down on the pavement and fell asleep at once. We had mastered the art of sleeping as never before; we could sleep walking and standing, on stone or on grass, in silence or beneath a rain of bombs. When I awoke, Kohn Gabriel's round, heavy head was resting on my stomach. Kohn snored so loud that the Germans would have been frightened to hear him.

Kohn Gabriel, registry number 1553, was the most amusing of my companions. He had the round, heavy head common to janitors' children, and a face swollen from too much water and beans and gray from basement air, and he possessed neither a home nor a trade. Many among us had been left homeless; their military documents said: *Nationalité: Indéterminé.* They came from the country of *Indéterminé*, the largest European state, and they defended an undefinable empire. (This was perhaps the reason why the *Indéterminés* were so brave, because they, and they alone, knew what they were fighting for. Not for a country, but for something so large, so vast, so decisive that it cannot be defined.) These *Indéterminés*, as we called them, as if the Undetermined were really a nationality, had once had a native country; they were "deprived of citizenship" because it so pleased the Führer. But Kohn Gabriel had never had a country of his own: he was, so to speak, an individual *Indéterminé*, a peacetime *Indéterminé*, an *Indéterminé* for his own account. No one knew where he was born, who his father was and where his cradle stood—if one may even conceive of this lovely piece of bourgeois furniture as ever having had anything to do with Kohn Gabriel.

Kohn Gabriel had no trade either, at least no trade officially recognized. I remember that this huge bedraggled fellow, on whom everything slumped—his shoulders, his long arms, his damp lips—had preceded me at our last inspection in Barcarès. Asked by the non-commissioned officer to state his trade, Kohn Gabriel answered calmly, "Smuggler!" He regarded this as a legal occupation, and its risks as normal occupational risks. For months, in our training camp near the blue southern sea, we had looked on Kohn as a *déclassé*. We failed to realize that he, the smuggler and *Indéterminé*, was properly speaking a true representative of our era: the era of hunting between borders. We all were later to live between borders, smuggling ourselves across like merchandise: Kohn Gabriel had foreshadowed our era; and the era had become his profession. As long as he could remember, he had lived in Paris. He spoke with the accent of its suburbs, knew the language of the apaches, had by fair means and foul supported a good wife and two children, was a pal of every detective in the capital, and referred to handcuffs tenderly as "monocles." Each time he got out of prison he resumed his trade, as though it had been interrupted by a vacation. He smuggled chiefly from Belgium, tobacco for the most part, but also anything else that came his way. The first time he came back from leave, he brought a whole collection of samples: buttons, cigarettes, belts, lighters, suspenders, can-openers, and everything else that might come in handy. This flaxen-haired, clumsy fellow particularly appealed to me one day when he appeared at the office of our company, asking for a three-day "special leave." Pierre Saint-Brice, who was still in command of our company at the time, asked the reasons for his request. "My younger daughter is sick," said Kohn Gabriel, "and my wife has no money." Saint-Brice shook his clean, boyish head. "You're lying again, Kohn," he said. "How do you expect to get money for your family in three days?" Kohn clicked his heels and stood at attention. "I'll steal, *mon lieutenant!*" he reported. Either Saint-Brice did not believe this evil intention, or else he liked the soldier's frankness: under some pretext or other he obtained the special leave from the colonel. Exactly one hour before the expiration of his leave, Kohn came back, beaming. During his three days in Paris he had "found" means for his family. What was more, he brought a suitcase filled with merchandise. He sold us, at most attractive prices, his *"camelotte"* as he called his stationery, razor blades, flashlight batteries, canned meat, and other luxuries. Thus we all cheerfully became receivers of stolen goods for the sake of Kohn Gabriel's sick little girl.

Now the swollen head stirred on my stomach. Kohn Gabriel rubbed his red eyes with their yellowish white eyelashes.

"I'm dead," he said.

"Where did you leave your motorcycle?"

"In the ditch."

"What's happened to it?"

"A flat tire."

"Well?"

"I had nothing to repair it with. Nothing. Nothing at all!"

He rose slowly. At first he crawled a few steps on all fours, then at last he stood up.

I turned away from him. I myself stood up and limped across the Place d'Austerlitz to the church. Both my hands were still bleeding from my fall. I made no attempt to have them bandaged, because I knew that our only ambulance was busy doing something more important. Besides, there was no water to be found in the whole town. The pipes had burst three or four days previously, during the bombardment. The clots of black blood on my hands were indistinguishable from the dirt and the mud of the street. I carried my hands like some strange objects.

A cool silence reigned in the church. My steps resounded on the stone. The smell of incense softly mingled with the smell of the fires. Some childish feeling impelled me to seek the blue-clad Christ, my Christ of Noirval. Was my faith already deep and firm? Probably not; for I walked about the church and found no peace. My trained ear heard tanks approaching in the distance. I listened in the silence of the four sanctified walls. Even the saints on the walls seemed to be waiting. Saint Francis of Assisi looked at me with astonishment. I don't know whether he was astonished at me or at God, for permitting all this. I sat down on an empty bench and waited. I don't know why, in this breathing spell, in this silence between two battles, I deluded myself into believing that faith, of all things, could be achieved without war and struggle. How did I expect the highest blessing as a gift—when the very lowest had not come as a gift? It took some time before I understood that the tempter had approached our Lord in the desert by no accident. Yes, the desert itself was the temptation. The emptiness around me. The absence of any divine sign. I folded my hands. I prayed: God, let me believe in You! I found nothing strange in praying that I be permitted to believe in Him, whose existence seemed questionable to me. But as I prayed, I knew that He would listen to me. I looked down at my hands. They no longer pained me.

When I left the church, Kohn Gabriel was lying on the steps. I sat beside him and he shared a piece of bread with me. As I took the bread, he noticed my hands.

"You're a sight!" he said.

I did not answer.

Kohn took me by the shoulders.

"Look here, you're going to get blood poisoning. Why don't you wash?"

"There's not a drop of water in the whole place!"

"Did you try the ambulance?"

"They have no time. Besides I don't know where it is."

He stopped eating. He tugged at his tooth, a sign of deep reflection with him. Suddenly he jumped up. He seemed no longer tired. With his long, gangling arms he pulled me up.

And before I knew what he was doing, he had dragged me into the church, taken my hands and dipped them into the marble holy water font. Horrified, I tried to disengage my hands. But he said: "Don't be afraid! I don't know whether God is a Catholic or a Jew. But in any case He is good. And if He is good, He can't be petty."

I no longer tried to wrench myself away. His voice sounded strange—as if another man were speaking out of Kohn Gabriel's mouth. It was no longer the voice of the thief who had sold us trouser buttons. It was as though Kohn Gabriel's voice had been purified by the holy water.

He washed my wounds. His hairy, clumsy hands were as tender as a woman's. The cooling wetness soothed my whole body.

As we went out into the daylight, the good Samaritan murmured: "This business with the holy water—you'll have to fix it with God, yourself. I'll have trouble enough with my own God, for going into a Catholic church. Not to mention that I took my hat off."

By his "hat" he meant his steel helmet. He twisted it between his fingers. Once more he spoke the apache dialect of his suburb.

But I soon stopped listening to him. While we were in the church, the bombardment of Ste. Menehould had begun.

I cannot be the historian of the battle of Ste. Menehould—I was there, but those who are in the midst of a battle can see only a small part of it. I don't even know how many divisions held the town of Ste. Menehould; perhaps there was no more than one, the Thirty-fifth, to which we belonged. But today I can clearly see the plan underlying the battle of Ste. Menehould and how the battle came about—in so far as the savage slaughter of Ste. Menehould can be graced by the name of "battle." What distinguishes a battle from a slaughter is the human element. In a battle, both sides are human, while slaughter is, in the true sense of the word, animal; in a slaughter men unleash their animal instincts on defenseless animals. Ste. Menehould was far more like a slaughter than a battle.

The strategic plan underlying it was apparent even to the humblest private. French units, defeated without a fight, had converged on Ste. Menehould from five great highways coming from the north, the northeast, and the northwest. From Vouziers across Ville-sur-Tourbe, from the Luxembourg border across Vienne-la-Ville, from the Argonne Forest across Lachalade, and in part even from Verdun—not to mention innumerable by-roads—the troops streamed into Ste. Menehould, in order to take the southeasterly road—the only one open to our retreat. I am unable to judge whether the plan was to have us carry on the fight with our backs against the Maginot Line, or to have us cross the Swiss border, extending from Basel to the Jura. Most probably there was no plan at all at that time—unless it was the treacherous plan of "promenading" us through the countryside until the military situation should make an armistice inevitable, or until the psychological moment when every soldier had only one desire—to lay down his arms unconditionally. Whatever the explanation may be, several armies had converged on the little town of three thousand souls, which they could leave only by a single road leading to Verrières-Passavant-Commercy. The Germans had to be stopped at the crossroads until the retreat south from Ste. Menehould could be organized—or what they called "organized." The lovely little town, formerly recommended to tourists as a headquarters for visiting the Argonne battlefields, was excellently adapted for a desperate stand. Completely surrounded by the Aisne and the Aisne Canal, Ste. Menehould is a natural fortress, the approaches to which are particularly difficult for tanks. Since the Thirty-fifth Division had been the last to reach Ste. Menehould, it was only natural that it should be chosen to cover the "orderly retreat" of all the troops who had previously passed the town, and to "keep the Germans busy" as long as possible. So far, everything was comprehensible. Any defeated army has its retreat covered by one or several divisions; there was no particular reason why we and not others should not have been sacrificed for this task. The crime of Ste. Menehould is to be sought elsewhere.

Anyone, even a layman, who visualizes the situation of Ste. Menehould will realize that the bridge on the northern end of town should have been blown up, after the last man of the division—or divisions—destined to defend the town had crossed it. The bridge at the southern end should have been kept intact so long as the division—or divisions—assigned to defend Ste. Menehould remained in the town, so that the only avenue of retreat would not be closed to the fighting troops. And what happened? The northern bridge was left intact, providing the Germans with a comfortable and unhoped-for road of entry into the hospitable shelter of Ste. Menehould. By contrast, the southern bridge was blown up by French engineers while most of my division was still in the town—no doubt to cut us off from the possibility of a "premature" retreat.

Since the battle of Ste. Menehould, where our regiment lost half of its effectives, I have often asked myself how this absurd slaughter could have come about. Was it negligence or crime? The memory of my dead comrades has forced this question upon me. In sleepless nights I may have been guilty of treason toward my dead friends, as I tried to find excuses for the slaughter. For the failure to blow up the northern bridge, I thought, an explanation might have been found. Possibly the disorganization and lack of information were so complete that the High Command did not know whether we were the last division retreating; possibly they did not know that the Germans were following close on our heels. But no possible excuse can be found for blowing up the southern bridge. The only possible explanation is that the High Command wanted to keep the Germans busy massacring us, in order to gain as much time as possible for the troops retreating southward. The consequence was that on one single morning, four hundred men of our regiment were killed. They fell in the battles between the Place d'Austerlitz, the Rue Camille Margraine and the Rue Chauteraine. They defended each house. At least two thirds of them were not killed on the spot; they were only wounded. But as the bridge had been blown up, and the only way the unwounded could escape was by swimming across the canal, the wounded were left behind. They bled to death or their bodies were crushed by the German tanks and armored cars.

When I went out of the church with Kohn Gabriel, I heard the first German tanks entering the town.

The panic had started while we were inside. Soldiers ran up and down on the square looking for cover. There were practically no officers left; at least none appeared on the square. Even today I believe that some of the men lost their minds at this moment. I still can see Sergeant Rupin dashing madly about the square on his bicycle, around and around, like a participant in a six-day bike race. Again and again he flitted by my nose, and I couldn't stop him. Adjutant Lesfauries stumbled by me asking, with an infinitely stupid look, whether "there was anything new." He did not wait for my answer. Some lay flat on the pavement, pressing their guns to their shoulders. This gesture—only natural on the battle-field—here seemed grotesque. Men with rifles, with knap-sacks on their backs, lay on the pavement of the main square like toy soldiers on the carpet of a nursery. The first planes appeared. We could no longer distinguish between the sound of the planes and the tanks. A bomb fell in the middle of the square. Stones hurtled through the air. You could hardly tell whether it was day or night. Each bomb that fell spread light and then darkness.

I lay in front of the church. Suddenly I heard a voice: "Take cover in the houses! Stop the tanks!"

No one knew who had cried out. We obeyed mechanically. I slipped under a gate at the corner of the square and the Rue Margraine. At the same moment the German tanks turned into the narrow street. They didn't seem to be moving down the street—the whole street seemed to be moving—moving with the armored cars. They filled the street. They took it with them. The red maws of the tanks drilled their flaming tongues into the walls of the houses. It looked as though nothing could remain in their wake. It was as though each tank peeled a piece off the crust of the earth. But for this very reason we were not frightened. The whole thing seemed unreal. It was more like a bad movie of the future, with warriors from Mars and synthetic men popping out of bottles. Everything moved as on a screen. We felt that it couldn't go on much longer.

Suddenly, in the midst of the deafening noise of the circling bombers and the slowly advancing tanks, I heard a familiar sound—the rattle of a machine gun not far from me. The sound was almost friendly, almost musical. I looked up. From the second or third floor of the adjoining house a machine gun was firing—firing at the approaching tanks. And the same thing happened that always happens when a man turns up in a faint-hearted crowd. Suddenly firing started from all sides. It was a childish effort. Our experience had taught us that even the anti-tank guns were powerless against the heavy German units. Only the seventy-fives obtained some success. And now we were firing our machine guns and old carbines. But what did that matter? There was a sudden patter from all the houses. I quickly ran to the other side of the street. Bullets whistled past me on both sides. Our soldiers had made up their minds to lay a barrage across the street.

I ran up the steps. It was a little old house with wooden stairs. Halfway to the first floor, a door was open: the door to the W.C. Nothing on earth is funnier than a W.C. when the whole world is collapsing.

I did not know the machine-gunners. But at the window of the adjoining room stood a man whom I immediately recognized, even from behind. It gave me a feeling of indescribable joy. I say "indescribable," because a normal human being in his daily routine rises to the joys of his existence from a settled level of mediocrity. One must fall to the depths to understand what it means to find a friend. At the window stood Saint-Brice.

I called him. He made a sign to me with his left hand, but did not turn around. I stepped to his side at the window. His round, good-natured, boyish face, now framed in an unkempt red beard, was calm and collected as usual. His big, round spectacles were exactly in place. He quickly held out his left hand to me, then balled it into a fist to support the barrel of his revolver. I quickly loaded my old Remington, though I had little hope that it would actually fire its single shot.

For some unknown reason, the tank, followed by innumerable others—the street was so narrow that they could move only in single file—halted. At the same time the roar of the airplane motors redoubled in intensity. The tank stood at the northern end of the Rue Camille Margraine. The machine guns stopped rattling. Half hidden in our room, we looked down into the street. Fallen soldiers lay on the asphalt. Blood ran down the gutter. It is so easy to write these words, forgetting what they mean: blood running down the gutter. In writing, everything seems two-dimensional in effect, without background. Blood in the gutter: nothing behind it. No suffering, no pain, no meaning. Red water in the drain. Gurgling red water. You move as in a film, watching yourself. And that is what makes it all bearable.

A few steps from our house a wounded soldier was screaming. From time to time the upper part of his body rose. Each time he fell down again, he stopped crying. Again and again we believed that he was dead. But at regular intervals he sat up. At regular intervals the dead man screamed.

Behind the tank, German motorcyclists appeared. As the street was too narrow, they formed on the sidewalk. Each cycle had a sidecar with two men in it. Each of them was armed with an automatic rifle. But they had not yet started to move. My brain throbbed with the tension. Something seemed to be flying through my temples. Behind street corners and windows a group of desperate men was waiting. How many were they? Were we not alone? Alone with a few dead and the half-dead whose cries rent the air. We did not know. Any sound would have been more bearable than this silence in which you couldn't tell where your comrades were. Even the machine-gunners in the next room did not stir.

At last the motorcyclists started. They emerged at the right and left of the armored car. One of the two men on each motorcycle held his automatic rifle upwards, the other horizontally down the street. They fired without interruption. In less than a fraction of a minute, they were in front of our house. At least fifteen of them arrived at the same time. I was half crouching under a window. Saint-Brice bent forward. I saw that he was taking aim. I made ready to shoot. Saint-Brice pulled the trigger. I followed him immediately. The miracle occurred—my Remington went off! I reloaded in feverish haste. Despite the infernal noise that was suddenly unleashed—motorcycles, armored cars, airplanes, bombs, machine-gun fire, rifles—I distinctly heard orders shouted in German. Somebody cried: "*'Rein ins Haus!*" (Into the house.) Simultaneously the pane splintered. They were firing at our window.

I crawled into the adjoining room for ammunition. A bullet whistled by me. Curious, I thought unconsciously, this shot cannot come from the street. Then I heard somebody saying beside me: "*O, les salauds!*"

I crawled to the three men at the machine gun. And then I saw what, for the first time, struck me with horror. In a window of one of the few undamaged houses on the opposite side of the street—the same house under the gate of which I had been hidden a short time before—a machine gun had been set in place. Behind the machine gun a German steel helmet emerged and quickly disappeared. But the man could not disappear quickly enough: I saw his face. His eyes stared at me. It was probably only my imagination, but it seemed to me that I had never before seen more evil eyes. And though I had never feared all the terrifying things invented by men, I was afraid of this man. Cannon, shells, and bombs are not terrifying. Only man is terrifying.

"*'Rein ins Haus!*" somebody cried out downstairs. I translated quickly. One of our men at the machine gun, a boy with deep, black eyes—must be from the south of France, I thought—made a sign to the two others. Everything happened

with incredible speed, in silence. Half-crawling, they dragged
the machine gun to the stairs. The very next moment it began to rattle: the boys were shooting down the stairs that
the Germans intended to climb.

Saint-Brice still stood behind the window. I could not hear
him, but he signaled to me that he was out of ammunition. A
hand grenade fell in the adjoining room but failed to explode.
The planes circled above us. I still had two cartridges. I held
them in my hand and felt them growing warm.

Suddenly I realized that Saint-Brice had seized me by the
arm. The nasal German voice was roaring.

"We've got to get out of here!" Saint-Brice whispered
into my ear. I followed him. He pushed me forward and covered our retreat with his unloaded revolver. He must have ex-
plored the premises in advance; he took me through a narrow
corridor, through a half-demolished room, down a wooden
staircase, and finally through a store-room. And then we were
outside.

We must have left the house by the back door. We stood
in a little vegetable garden, bordered by an old stone wall.
Suddenly we found ourselves in the midst of a summer
morning. I stood still, breathing deeply. The din of the
battle was muffled.

"Come on," said Saint-Brice.

We ran across a field. What did we care whether planes
spotted us? We breathed. We were alive.

But there was no time to pause. To reach the bridge we
had to go back through the town. Meanwhile the Germans
had moved in everywhere. But our regiments were resisting
desperately. I saw soldiers firing from behind corpses, resting
their guns on the bodies of their dead comrades. The town
stank of corpses, smoke, and sugar. I had a glimpse of Colonel
de Buissy, trying, with a few men, to erect a tank barricade.

The Crime of Ste. Menehould

The whole scene had a toylike effect, comic and tragic at once: on one side a few riflemen, the lieutenant with the revolver, the meager fabric of barbed wire, the forlorn machine gun; on the other side, tanks, armored cars that reached nearly to the second story, motorcyclists, machine guns on wheels. And yet God so orders things that the greatest horrors are bearable by reason of their very absurdity. We had a feeling that the fellows on the other side could not possibly be serious! The disproportion was so striking that hope returned; this irruption of reality into the nursery could be nothing but a nightmare. The pestilential odors rising from the nursery carpet could not dispel this feeling. Then a ghostly apparition rose from the mist of powder smoke. It was Mayer—Mayer-Mayerescu from Bucharest.

I had only a fleeting glance of him as I rushed by. He stood near the bridge. I couldn't tell whether he was able to go on. He stood there leaning on the parapet; he had forgotten to throw himself on the ground. He still had his glittering pot on his back. His steel helmet still sat on his head like a mournful black derby at a funeral. His face was gray with soot. His faded blond hair hung down over his narrow, red nose. I called out to him once again. But his look remained fixed. He stared—I did not know at what.

A single machine gun was holding the south bridge. A young Frenchman of the Eleventh Regiment whom I knew and a Negro of the same regiment were tending the gun. Suddenly the Negro clutched his chest and collapsed. From the bridge I saw Mayer-Mayerescu of Bucharest throw himself on the dead man. He lay on the Negro's body and guided the machine-gun belt.

Soldiers of the engineering corps ran across the bridge with me. Quicker than I could think, with the town still full of our men, they carried out their orders. I had scarcely passed when the bridge blew up. It was the only avenue of retreat. In the cloud of dust and smoke I saw something glitter on the other side of the bridge. It was Mayer's pot, shining in the sun.

France had men. One of them was Pierre Saint-Brice.

We had separated when we saw the colonel. We agreed that I would wait on the other side of the bridge. Unseen to one another, we had crossed it at about the same time. Then suddenly we found ourselves side by side. I told him about little Mayer's exploit. He thought for a while. Then he said: "Come on! Quick!"

We ran along the river bank. At one place the river was particularly narrow. Saint-Brice sat down on the grass and began silently to pull off his boots.

"What are you doing?" I asked.

"I'm going to get little Mayer!"

I said nothing. I sat beside him and tried to unbuckle my puttees.

"What are you doing?" Saint-Brice asked with annoyance.

"I'm going with you."

"What for?"

"So that you won't be alone."

He looked at me, smiling behind his glasses.

"All right," he said. "Let's take a bath."

We both cursed as we pulled off our shoes. It was a real operation to take them off our swollen, bleeding feet.

"I am not tired any more," said the lieutenant.

"Neither am I. I've forgotten all about it."

We hid our shoes and our tunics in the bushes. When we came out, Saint-Brice said: "I'll get little Mayer by myself. But do you see that house over there?"

He pointed to an ancient ruin.

"Yes."

"In the cellar you'll find the scouts of the Second Battalion. I told them to wait there. They're unarmed."

"Right."

"Show them this part of the canal. It's the narrowest. The Germans don't seem to know about it yet."

"*Entendu.*"

He had left his glasses on his nose. Now he took them to the bushes. Then he said: "Have a good bath! *A tout à l'heure!*"

He jumped into the water first.

When I left my watch—a gift from my father, to which I was particularly attached—in my shoes, the time was two o'clock in the afternoon. When I came back with the soldiers whom I had found in the place indicated by Saint-Brice, it was three o'clock. Little Mayer was sitting on the grass. But in the meantime Saint-Brice had returned to the burning town. He had "delivered" Mayer only a short while before, and had immediately gone for another bath. Between two and seven in the evening he made three trips to the town, which had meanwhile been completely occupied by the enemy. Each time he saved seven or eight soldiers from certain death. Around seven o'clock he finally decided to "dry himself." He sat in a clearing by the canal, wiped his glasses, and pulled on his boots. He behaved as though he had just returned to his office after a brief call at the courthouse. He looked at me with round, astonished eyes when I offered to rub his back. Finally he let me do it. When his shirt was half dry, he put on his worn, torn, ragged officer's tunic.

I never saw a man more worthy of his officer's stripes than this notary from Angers.

As regimental intelligence officer and chief of scouts, Saint-Brice had been ordered to stop at the schoolhouse in Verrières to await the divisional instructions which he was to transmit to the regiment. When we reached Verrières, the town was as good as deserted. Though Saint-Brice was sure that the blown-up bridge gave us at least five or six hours' head start on the German motorized units, the French troops had been withdrawn from Verrières.

Having set up our headquarters in the abandoned school-house, we nailed a notice on the door saying: "Back soon!" and went out to look for food and other earthly pleasures. The first earthly pleasure to fall to my lot was a pair of trousers that actually covered my flesh. My own had lost their seat long before, and for some weeks now I had been unable to avail myself of poor Torczynsky's sewing talents. On the main square of the town, near the church, we found a garden where trousers grew like spring flowers. A truck— there were a few of them in the French army—had delivered a load of brand-new equipment to a battalion of engineers stationed at Verrières. This equipment, unlike our own, had all been manufactured during the present war. The consignment included new knee breeches, clean soup containers with lids that worked, warm blankets, knapsacks, canteens, suspenders—and quantities of chocolate, condensed milk, and sardines.

Near the church of Verrières there is a magnificent city park, with an artificial brook, hidden arcades, romantic rose bushes and a broad succulently green lawn. On this lawn, all sorts of luxuries "grew" as in fairyland. In the midst of them there slept a creature who might have been taken for Sleeping Beauty if not for the thick, black beard that framed his square chin. We awakened the man, and he told us that he had come here with his truck the day before; but the battalion of engineers he had been looking for was gone. No one knew what had become of them. He had unloaded and was about to leave when the truck had been requisitioned by some officers. They took the driver with them, but then they had sent him back to "guard" the goods.

"What are you doing here now?" asked Saint-Brice.

"I'm waiting for the Germans," said Sleeping Beauty without getting up. "I've got sore feet and I can't walk. After all the Germans won't eat me."

He lay down again, took up one of the hundreds of cigarette packages that were scattered about him, and prepared to go on with his sunbath. With a silent gesture, he invited us to help ourselves.

The lieutenant and I avoided one another's eyes. Without a word, we went about picking whatever seemed useful, but we avoided overloading. We replaced our torn trousers by new ones, changed shirts and took as much chocolate and cigarettes as we could carry. Then we resumed our explorations.

The village was large and dusty. It reminded me of the villages of eastern Europe, of our villages in the Austro-Hungarian Empire. There, the wooden doors in the little farms were always open. Evenings, when the cows came back from their pastures, they walked slowly through the village, each finding her own warm stable; one by one the whole herd went home. The peasants sat in front of their houses smoking their pipes. Sometimes a young girl sang. The sky was warm and somewhat dusty, too. This village, now, in the heart of France, in the heat of the battle, a few hours before occupation by the enemy, was just like those other villages. The other war, the so-called World War, must have been just like this, I thought; my father, with his cavalry regiment, must have passed through just such villages. Now and then a cavalryman galloped through the streets. These solitary riders, too, were like phantoms from the World War. From time to time a straggling wagon rolled by. The driver stopped to ask the way . . . though he didn't know where he wanted to go. All this reminded me of an army postcard of the years 1914-1918. It was almost impossible to realize that, this time, there were bombers and tanks. From time to time, a ramshackle field kitchen, drawn by two weary horses, would appear, the driver asleep on his box. The kitchen would pass by as though it were painted on a backdrop and pulled by two strings. Behind the receding riders a cloud of dust whirled up.

On our tour of exploration we discovered that the village was not quite so deserted as it seemed. We found—what we were to encounter again and again on our retreat through other villages—old people and halfwits. They had been left behind. The village idiot sat in a barn opposite the school. From time to time he rose to chase the chickens or the dogs, fell down, laughed, and crawled back into the straw. He asked us whether we were the "Boches." There was an insane fear in his eyes. When we convinced him that we were not the Boches, he led us to his mother. She was an old, toothless woman, who lived in a dilapidated hut at the edge of the village. She was at least seventy-five years old and seemed not to have washed for an equal length of time. She complained that "because of this miserable cripple"—meaning her son—she had been unable to leave with the rest; otherwise she seemed quite normal. An old Renault stood in the yard; I asked her whether the car belonged to her. No, she said, but she had been asked to keep an eye on it—did we want it? We said yes. For half an hour she bargained about the price; finally she accepted two loaves of bread. We went to the main square, where Sleeping Beauty was still asleep, took two loaves of bread from the lawn and brought them to the old woman. The hunchbacked idiot, who had conceived a great confidence in us, did not leave us for a minute. Curiously enough, the old woman did not seem to recognize us when we returned. Finally she took the bread and we got the car ready. As we were about to leave, she suddenly pulled me aside with a mysterious look on her face. She put her finger on her lips.

"Tell me," she said, "is it true that the Boches rape young girls?"

"Why?" I countered. "Are there any young girls here?"

She looked down, took her dirty blue apron between her thumb and forefinger, shook her head to the right and left, and whispered to me: "I am a young girl myself!"

And she ran away.

Shuddering with horror, I returned to the car. Saint-Brice was busy trying to get rid of the idiot. The car happened to have a few liters of bad gasoline in its tank. It stank and groaned. But we coddled it like a Packard. At last we rolled out of the yard. The old woman came out of her kitchen and coyly waved her apron at us. The idiot bleated. Night fell over Verrières.

Back in the school we soon learned that no one had been looking for us. We held council. Military discipline had become so natural to us that even now we hesitated before leaving our assigned post without express orders. I vainly tried to convince the lieutenant that we were incapable of holding this village by ourselves; Saint-Brice now put all his trust in the antique, bedraggled Renault.

"The Germans have no reason for marching at night," he said. "They won't leave Ste. Menehould before daybreak. We can get a good night's sleep. If no order comes through until then, I'll be ready to go. With the help of this car we'll quickly get to our regiment."

He coughed. He had apparently caught cold swimming. We decided to wait. In the schoolmaster's kitchen we prepared an omelet of twenty-eight eggs. Eggs were available in all the barns. With the omelet we had a bottle of Burgundy from the cellar. Then we lay down on benches in the classroom.

We lay silent for a few minutes, then Saint-Brice asked: "What are you sighing about?"

"Did I sigh?

"You did."

He, too, sighed. Then he said: "No, it's not a pretty sight."

"What do you think?" I asked. "How long are we going to keep running like this?"

"I've no idea! Maybe till the Germans occupy all France."

"And what about the Maginot Line? And the Daladier Line that's supposed to be waiting somewhere? And the resistance that's being organized on the Loire? Why shouldn't this war have its Marne, too? Don't you believe in it?"

I felt in the darkness that he had turned toward me with his head in his hands.

"No," he said, "I don't believe in it."

I did not want to ask questions, but he went on talking, as he seldom did.

"I have stopped believing," he said. "We had not prepared for this war. No, I don't speak of armaments. We could have caught up in nine months. But no Frenchman knew what he was fighting for. The Germans, over there, wrapped their foulest plans in ideological tissue paper. And we? We did the opposite. We were really fighting for freedom and humanity, and we were ashamed of those two words. We acted as though nothing but territory were at stake. Did we hate the Germans? Our young people didn't even know what the Germans meant. Even today, the blockheads think they'll survive a Hitler victory. Yes, they *will* survive! But as slaves. The purpose of this whole war is to bring slavery back to the world. And the world will regard us as voluntary slaves!"

His voice sounded hoarse. I stretched out on the narrow school bench. Between us lay a desk, with an inkpot and drawer.

"We Frenchmen forgot the meaning of freedom long ago," he went on. "Real freedom. We were in the midst of a civil war when the Germans overran us."

"In times of war," I objected, "Frenchmen always dropped their internal quarrels."

"That was true in the past," said Saint-Brice. "Patriotism is stronger than politics. It always was in our country. But philosophy is stronger than patriotism. The Germans armed themselves with a philosophy for this war. Their philosophy is a skeleton key that lets them into a country without resistance. But God help a country once the Germans have occupied it!"

Never before had he spoken like this. Despite our intimacy, we both had preserved the distance between superior and subordinate, between Frenchman and foreigner. This time Saint-Brice seemed to be speaking to himself.

"Recently," he continued, "a captain told me that he loved France more than he loved Hitler, but that he loved Hitler more than Léon Blum. What more do you want?"

He was interrupted by a fit of coughing.

"Yes," he said at last, "I know the old story of our deficiency in arms. But do you think that was the decisive factor? Didn't we win the World War despite our inferior armament? They say that the greatest part of our aircraft was destroyed on the ground. Do you know what that means? There were officers who prevented our pilots, at the point of a gun, from taking off. Can you conceive of such a thing?"

"No, I can't."

"I am beginning to understand; we were not sold out, but we were betrayed. And that's the worst part of it. A couple of corrupted generals can always be dealt with by a firing squad. But we had no corrupt generals. You can't prove anything against them. There is no *bordereau* as in the Dreyfus case. They betrayed us without having exchanged a single word with the Germans. They did not want to fight against Germany. They liked Germany. Bought by the Germans? If only they had been bought! But they weren't even bought! Once I was told that the people of some Balkan state were always ready to sell their country, but never to deliver it. We did worse than that. We delivered our country, without even getting paid for it."

"Aren't you painting too black a picture?"

I said this without conviction. But he was tormenting me, just as he was tormenting himself. We had loved this country and this people more than anything in the world: each of us in his own way.

"No," he said, "it can't be painted too black."

We tried to sleep. But the day and the conversation had been too much for us. And the thunder of the guns was drawing nearer.

"Artillery preparation," said Saint-Brice. "They still expect resistance."

I took up the thread of his thought.

"On this lousy, clogged road, resistance is unthinkable."

"Right," said the officer. "That's what they want to show us. It's the same men who sabotaged our armament. Always the same. They started the Dreyfus case—and lost it. After that they were dethroned in France. Now they're taking revenge for the Dreyfus case. Now they expect to stage a triumphal comeback on German bayonets. People won't understand that. Not for a long time. Because, by accident, war was declared between Germany and France. Because our generals were not as straightforward as General Franco. He, at least, openly invited the foreigners into his country. Yesterday, in the streets of Ste. Menehould, couldn't you feel that this is not a war between two states, but a civil war? You did feel it, didn't you? And doesn't that explain everything? On the one side, free France. Like free Spain. And against it, a gang of bandits leaning on foreign support! Only here the plot was much more diabolic, the whole thing was much more subtly conceived, much more treacherously carried out. In Spain, civil war was openly proclaimed. The motives were clearly stated. No false slogans, no false banners! You could take one side or the other. Here they all sail under a false banner. They make it look as though Frenchmen are fighting Germans. Never, never, I'm telling you, would France have lost the war against Germany. We would have beaten them even with our medieval guns. But this was a war of Frenchmen against Frenchmen. And no one told us . . ."

He stopped speaking. He could not go on. I felt that his body was shaking. Had his cold made him feverish? Or was he sobbing?

I stood up with my blanket over my shoulders, and then sat down beside him. The cold dawn filled the classroom. An ashen gray covered the walls. From a shelf, a stuffed owl looked down at us with evil glass eyes. The thunder of guns was coming nearer and nearer.

"It was—it was—" I said. "Perhaps it's not yet too late."

As though reminded of time, Saint-Brice rolled out of his blanket to look at the clock.

"Still no word," he said.

We sat silently side by side on the school bench. We both dropped off to sleep. We awoke when the barn across the street was struck. It was day.

"Four o'clock," said Saint-Brice. "There's no sense in waiting any longer."

We silently lighted our cigarettes.

"Are you ready?"

"Yes, *mon lieutenant.*"

We went out to our waiting car. It lurched forward as though unaware that it had cost only two loaves of bread.

CHAPTER SIX: DÉBÂCLE

Can i enumerate the stations of the ordeal that began that morning in Verrières and ended in a German prison camp? After that cool June morning when I drove off with Lieutenant Saint-Brice I never saw the enemy. That was the strange thing about this flight: a nation was fleeing from an invisible foe. And another nation triumphed over an enemy who admitted defeat without having fought.

We found the colonel with the remnants of our regiment eleven kilometers southeast of Verrières, in the elongated, narrow village of Passavant. The survivors of my company were quartered in a barn at the center of the village. For the last day and a half, the same barn had sheltered the remnants of a battalion of the Eighteenth *Chasseurs à Pied*, the *Joyeux*.

On our way into the village, I experienced a happy surprise. I ran into the Breton peasant who, for nearly four weeks, had been stationed beside my observation post with his anti-tank guns. We hailed one another as old friends. He was about to build a "tank trap" with the help of other artillerymen from his regiment, on the basis of alleged orders to halt the enemy in Passavant. The tank trap consisted of some barbed wire that could have been cut with shears, and a few plows taken from abandoned farms. These plows were so arranged that the tank driver would have had to be an obstacle racer to drive through them—unless he got down from his tank and simply pushed them aside. The anti-tank guns had fallen into enemy hands north of Ste. Menehould.

A company of Arabs was just moving out of a farm near our barn. They sat in the yard wearing their steel helmets on top of their artistically wrapped turbans, and ate stewed fruit with great relish. Each one of them held a bottle with a broken neck, and fished cherries, plums or gooseberries out of it with his fingers. Four or five beheaded bottles stood on the ground around each soldier; they had been broken for the sake of three or four pieces of fruit. In this region, between the Meuse and the Marne, there is a great abundance of fruit and the peasant women commonly put them up in wine bottles. I don't know how they squeeze the fruit through the narrow bottle necks; at any rate, you had to behead the wine bottles to take out their delicious contents. There were hundreds of these bottles of stewed fruit in the cellars, and the Moroccans helped themselves to an "assorted fruit compote." They sat around the yard getting ready to march. The house itself was in a state hard to imagine. The mattresses had been torn off the beds, the large grandfather's clock in the dining room had been split up into its component parts; on the dining-room table lay letters, pictures, calendars, sheets, towels, spools of thread; the beds were full of broken bottles; everywhere there was a smell of tobacco and sugar, everything was sticky from the spilled syrup of the stewed fruit. None of the Arab soldiers understood French. At last I found a corporal and asked him where the officer was. The corporal was an elderly man with a large, black beard, a handsome, narrow nose and a bright yellow turban. As the stewed fruit was mostly preserved in alcohol, he had the sweet, pungent smell of a drugstore. At my question he shook his head, smiling.

"Officer took car," he said. "Away day before yesterday.

Said, come back in hour. No more come back. Away like bird." He gaily imitated the wing beat of a bird. "We alone. We no more count hours. We stop clock." He pointed at the disemboweled clock. "Now we, too, birds. Now we, too, away."

"Why are you leaving now?"

He pointed at the table.

"We nothing more eat. And we nothing more drink."

"Where are you going?"

He pretended not to understand my question. He suddenly became deaf and mute. But his long, narrow eyes were tense. I had a feeling that he could hear something that had not yet reached my ears.

He went out into the yard and looked about the sky. The next moment he said something in Arabic to his comrades. I did not understand what he said, but I saw them all throw themselves on the ground. They remained in a kneeling attitude, and suddenly began to bend the upper parts of their bodies rhythmically in an oriental prayer. They alternately crossed their arms on their chests, and stretched them out in front of them.

"Get into the house!" I cried, myself returning to the desolate dining room.

But no one followed me. Nine German planes in three regular V-formations cruised over us. The praying Arabs betrayed not only themselves but all the other troops stationed in Passavant. But they did not budge. They lay on the ground and said their prayers. From time to time they interrupted their ritual gestures and placed their long, slender hands over their ears. Then again they implored Allah the Almighty. In their haste they spilled a few bottles of preserved fruit. Their knees were in the glass splinters and their faces were smeared with the oily, sweet liquid. They lamented and murmured a prayer. The glittering, silvery German planes flew over us, and the monotonous roar of the motors mingled with the monotonous chant of the Arabs.

The planes passed, having taken little notice of us. The soldiers rose and went on packing with redoubled haste. All of a sudden three or four baby carriages appeared. They were white, pink and bright blue; one of them was so tiny and pretty that it was more like a doll carriage. In these perambulators the Arabs had stored their provisions. Bottles of preserved fruit, wine bottles, several boxes of cheese, one or two blankets, and all sorts of other worthless but glittering objects had been packed in. The bearded corporal, apparently the only remaining "officer" in the group, gave the order to march. At the same time umbrellas were opened. I noticed them only then. Apparently, the Moroccan warriors had collected all the umbrellas they could lay hands on in the village and now they used them as a protection against the sun. (Oddly enough, as I have often observed, Spaniards, Africans, and other inhabitants of the South are particularly sensitive to sunlight.) Thus did the Arabian soldiers of the French colonial empire leave Passavant; without commissioned or non-commissioned officers, led by a bearded corporal with a yellow turban under his steel helmet, bearing his carbine in his right hand and an umbrella in his left. In single file, the swarthy soldiers moved along the walls, pushing their bright baby carriages before them. They walked with the catlike tread peculiar to the Moors. Beside each soldier you could almost visualize a gaudily dressed, high-bosomed, tender, and festive "ma'm." It looked as though the presence of the guns was quite incidental, while the umbrellas served the actual purpose of protecting the soldiers' wives. Bottles of fruit jiggled in the baby carriages. . . .

Filled with disgust, I returned to my barn. Dési, little red-headed Dési, who had luckily survived Ste. Menehould, received me with the news that we were probably going to spend the night in the village. For the last hour a rumor had been current that our colonel had suddenly been dismissed, and that a new colonel was due to arrive the same day. I lay down in the straw beside Dési.

Around us, the *Joyeux* were resting, sleeping or playing. Right beside me their lieutenant sat in the straw writing. He was a thin man with a delicate, hard head and eyes so blue that they seemed transparent. The white of his eyes was almost dissolved in the blue, as in blind eyes—you couldn't tell in what direction the man was looking, or whether he saw anyone at all. His uniform with the two silver stripes—the officers' stripes in the Chasseurs' regiments are silver instead of the usual gold—was painfully clean. His lips were a single thin line. He did not say a word. From time to time he looked up from his writing and observed his men. There was something watchful, distrustful in his look. When someone spoke to him, he only nodded or shook his head like a man afraid of betraying some secret by an imprudent word. I never saw a greater distance between privates and officers than between these men and their lieutenant, who—like them, declassed and punished—had to live and eat with them.

Hours passed and the lieutenant kept writing without interruption. He wrote one letter after another—who could tell to whom? He folded and sealed them carefully and traced the address on the envelopes in a clean, elegant hand. He distinctly wrote the letters F.M.—*Franchise Militaire*—on the spot reserved for the stamp. For weeks we had been receiving no mail; for days no mail had been going out. Who was to take his letters—and where . . . ? The lieutenant knew this as well as I did. Why he wrote, I never found out. A whole pile of letters had accumulated by his side. When a soldier in his battalion left the barn, he looked up with his strange, sharp, and yet blind eyes. I felt that he was thinking: I won't ever see that one again. . . . But a moment later his fountain pen would again be racing over his letter paper.

Behind me one of the *Joyeux* lay in the straw. We struck up a conversation; the man had previously been talking with Dési. We spoke softly so as not to disturb the lieutenant. The man was thin and pale and had a peculiar, tiny, coquettish mustache, which seemed foreign to his face. It was hard to believe that this man was a convict; he looked more like a marriage swindler who had lost his sex appeal. His uniform was torn and full of holes; around his neck he wore a dirty cloth which had once been white; and he coughed almost without interruption. From time to time he said with a sigh:

"I am glad my poor wife didn't have to live through this!"

I offered him a cigarette. For a while he smoked in silence. Then he said: "My wife would never have survived the fall of Paris. I myself am from the provinces. From the north. From Douai. But she was a real Parisian. She couldn't have stood the sight of a Boche in Paris. . . . Sundays, when we went to the city, to the Tuileries, she was half crazy. She hung on to my arm as though she were drunk. I never saw anyone who could get so drunk on air . . ."

I couldn't see him while he talked. He lay in the straw behind me; I myself was stretched out. We both lay on our backs; our heads almost touched one another.

He took a few puffs at his cigarette.

"Yes, she was like Paris," he said. "She was delicate and tender. She was a real one. She could dress with nothing, she could make something out of nothing." He laughed softly to himself. "I remember one hat. A bit of straw, a rose made of tissue paper, a ribbon. But how she wore it!" And he suddenly added: "No, it's better for her like this."

The lieutenant looked at us with hard, absent eyes.

I asked in a muffled voice: "What happened to your wife?"

The answer was hoarse but without hesitation: "I killed her."

After this he did not speak. The lieutenant's pen kept scratching.

I rose and, though it was forbidden, went out in front of the barn to see if there was any news. A motorcyclist was just pulling in from the direction of Ste. Menehould.

"Do you know where the Eighteenth Chasseurs are stationed?" he asked.

"Yes. They're right here in the barn."

"Is there an officer with them?"

"Yes. A first lieutenant."

"Please ask him to come out. I am dead tired and I'm in a hurry."

"*D'accord!*"

I went back to the barn. The lieutenant finished the sentence he was writing, screwed the cap on his fountain pen, and carefully arranged his letters under his coat which lay on the straw. Then he followed me. The motorcyclist handed him a sealed envelope. The officer tore it open, quickly read the order, and returned to the barn with firm steps. In the doorway he stopped. He leaned against the wooden jamb and looked around. His eyes were again full of distrust—as though he were looking for someone to cover his rear. Then, with a gesture of quick decision, he clapped his hands.

"*Allons-y, messieurs!* Get going!"

A murmur echoed his words. The murmur crept along the straw. The thin man in his spotless uniform looked like a lion tamer surrounded by beasts in a cage.

"Where to?" someone asked.

The officer hesitated before making up his mind to answer. Then he said: *"On monte au feu.* We're going to defend the village."

A few had risen. Several took their guns in silence. A huge, broad-shouldered fellow with a plaster on his nose lay where he was. The lieutenant came close to him and stepped over his extended feet. Still he said nothing. Then he went back to his place in the straw. He put on his coat, buckled his belt, and tested his revolver. Then he gathered his letters in a pile which he carefully placed on a cart wheel that lay near by. He put his letters on the wheel as if it were a mail box. He was silent as a corpse.

Now everyone was looking toward the officer. Dési and I stood in the doorway. The lieutenant approached us. He stood silently with his revolver in hand, as though he had forgotten to put it back in its holster. The huge long-legged fellow rose with a curse.

"Follow me in single file!" cried the lieutenant. His voice was metallic, as bright and unreal as his eyes. He turned around and stepped out of the barn. Slowly the *Joyeux* began to move.

And thus they passed by me, a hundred or more of the Eighteenth *Chasseurs à Pied*, condemned to die. These men had nothing to lose. They had killed their wives, cracked safes, assaulted people. Earthly justice had dealt mercilessly with them. For years they had eaten out of tin pots, worn striped uniforms, obeyed tyrannical commands. For a long time they had seen nothing of the sky but a barred square. If they refused to face danger now, they would go back to their tin pots, uniforms, hard labor, and bars. They had nothing to lose. And everything to gain. Everything that man can ultimately possess: freedom. And yet I never saw terror so clearly written on a face as I saw it on the faces of these lost men. Never were men less willing to die than these hundred or more of the Eighteenth *Chasseurs à Pied*. Never, to any living being, did life appear so worth living as to these men who had gambled away their lives.

Thus they passed before me:

A swollen head, with puffed lips and tiny eyes. Brutal eyes full of terror. Frightened brutality is a terrible thing.

The next. A small, haggard bit of a man, right after the big, strong one. His eyes looked up at me seeking for help. A comical little fellow—a bookkeeper, perhaps, who had met a merry blonde suburban widow and embezzled his receipts. A flickering glance turned upwards in search of a God.

The next. Straight out of the rogues' gallery. Protruding ears, pop eyes, two yellow teeth. White as chalk, trembling throughout his whole emaciated frame. I can still see his face: front, profile, front, profile. A page out of a rogues' gallery.

The next. A young fellow. A harmless face, soft, blond, girlish. A smile, expressing not pleasure, but everything that can be expressed. Behind that smile lurked everything that had to be hidden. A soft, red mouth, smiling. The face did not follow the smile. And so much terror in the eyes—as though death were at the smiling man's throat.

The next. A ruined old face, framed in a gray beard. An old face, but without age. A large head, with wrinkles on the forehead like sea waves drawn by a childish hand. His gaze met mine. He lowered his eyes. With downcast eyes he passed me.

I stepped aside. Intolerable, these enormous heads, one quickly following the next. Intolerable, their likeness despite their diversity. Fear made them alike. And the seal of death. But something else, too: hatred toward the living. So many men passed before me, and so many wished my death. Why me? and not you? each rebellious look seemed to say. Every head was a death sentence.

They were a long file now. They all turned to the left, toward the "tank trap" at the entrance of the village. But suddenly one spun around near the door, and began to run. He ran to the right, southward. He was my neighbor, the one who had killed his wife.

The lieutenant, far ahead, did not notice him. Nobody noticed him. The *Joyeux* were marching forth to defend Passavant.

We lost thirty-six hours in Passavant.

I owe the authentic story of those thirty-six hours to an eyewitness. I shall relate it briefly, adding and subtracting nothing.

Colonel de Buissy, at the head of his regiment, had defended Ste. Menehould with heroism. De Buissy was nearly sixty years old. He had been wounded seven times in the World War. He had spent eighteen years in Africa, commanding the Fourth Foreign Legion, the most famous of all the famous regiments of the Foreign Legion. He had distinguished himself in the great Moroccan battles. At the outbreak of the present war, the colonel, who had been pensioned shortly before, left his home in Lille and offered his services to France. In consideration of his particular abilities and merits, he was immediately appointed commander of the First Foreign Volunteer Regiment, which was later renamed the Twenty-first. He was an officer of the Legion of Honor and bearer of almost every high distinction that a French officer can achieve.

Colonel de Buissy was ordered to appear at Passavant at nine o'clock on the night before Saint-Brice and myself reached that village. The general commanding our brigade waited for the colonel in the notary's house. It proved impossible, however, to interrupt the battle of Ste. Menehould according to a prearranged schedule. If the retreat of the innumerable regiments streaming southward was to be even partly covered, we had to hold the enemy in and around Ste. Menehould. Colonel de Buissy reached Passavant at five in the morning, on foot, totally exhausted, having escaped death by a miracle. Lieutenant Costa, a brave Corsican who commanded our motorcyclists—motorcyclists without motorcycles, mind you—had fallen on the battlefield only a few steps from the colonel.

The following conversation took place between the general and the colonel.

The General: Why are you so late, Colonel de Buissy?

The Colonel: We held Ste. Menehould as long as we could.

The General: You could have retreated long ago. I have been waiting here for twenty-one hours.

The Colonel: I am sorry. We tried to resist. Unfortunately, *mon général,* our arms were more than deficient, as you well know.

The General: How many men were killed?

The Colonel: At least five hundred. With normal equipment we would have had four hundred less casualties.

The General: Five hundred Jews the less.

The Colonel: The Jews fought like the rest. Moreover, there were at least as many Christians as Jews.

The General: You don't look well, Colonel.

The Colonel: I am somewhat tired.

The General: Excellent! Madame de Buissy will be very glad to have you back.

The Colonel: Do you mean that I am relieved of my command?

The General: I mean that within one hour you will be taken to the peaceful south in an ambulance.

The Colonel: Thank you! But I am neither sick nor injured. I have been with this regiment from the first minute of its existence and I intend to remain at the head of my men to my last breath. My regiment has fought heroically. I deserve—

The General: How old are you, Colonel de Buissy?

The Colonel: Fifty-eight.

The General: You deserve a rest, my dear de Buissy. Your nerves are frayed. You'll be taken to the rear in one hour. At the same time Lieutenant Colonel Landry will arrive here.

The Colonel: You mean that my successor has already been appointed?

The General: Yes! And I hope you enjoy your well-deserved rest.

The Colonel: Is that an order?

The General: Yes.

The Colonel: I accept under protest.

The General: I am convinced that Madame de Buissy will not protest having you back with her.

One hour later, our colonel was loaded on an ambulance sent by the High Command and was taken to Divisional Headquarters at Commercy. The colonel on his stretcher was brought to a hall where two generals—the commanders of the brigade and the division—were engaged in a conversation. The hall was large and the two generals apparently thought that the colonel would not hear their whispering. Besides, Colonel de Buissy pretended to be asleep.

This is what he heard:

✦

The Brigade Commander: Colonel Landry has taken over his post.

The Divisional Commander: This de Buissy has given me enough trouble.

The Brigade Commander: He wanted to resist at any cost.

The Divisional Commander: These Foreign Legionnaires are intriguing politicians, all of them.

The Brigade Commander: What shall I write in my report?

The Divisional Commander: I don't know.

The Brigade Commander: He told me he would protest against his dismissal on the ground of sickness.

The Divisional Commander: I'm telling you, the man has caused us nothing but trouble. He has completely adapted himself to the rabble he commanded. Can't you find something? Something incriminating in his record?

The Brigade Commander: No. I went through all his belongings. But there was nothing, except—

The Divisional Commander: Except—

The Brigade Commander: Except an empty bottle.

The Divisional Commander: Was there liquor in it?

The Brigade Commander: Perhaps.

The Divisional Commander: Excellent! Report that his alcoholic excesses necessitated his summary dismissal.

Colonel de Buissy had overheard this whole conversation. He opened his eyes. The Brigade Commander approached the stretcher. He assured de Buissy that he was happy to have been able to put through his well-deserved retirement. He asked whether Madame de Buissy had succeeded in reaching Perpignan. He whispered that he intended to propose the colonel for a high distinction, on account of his regiment's magnificent bravery. The colonel did not answer. When the general had finished, de Buissy inquired: "Has a bottle been found among my belongings—a bottle of iodine? It's a habit I acquired in Africa. I always carry a bottle of iodine."

The general said with embarrassment that the colonel would have no further need for iodine.

The same day, Colonel Paul de Buissy was sent south. We were given a new commander. Subsequent events demonstrated that the new chief was a man of his word, and that his superiors had no reason to regret his appointment. He offered the Germans no resistance.

We marched for two days, almost without rest, and ended up in a village ten kilometers from Commercy.

I was on foot again. Colonel Landry's first official act had been to confiscate our car for his field kitchen. Nicola, the Hungarian cook, was given instructions to prepare two warm meals a day; the colonel attached extreme importance to an adequate cuisine.

All along the road we encountered floods of civilians. The villages were burning. The cavalrymen tried to race their horses through the towns, but the horses shied and filled the air with their neighing. Rearing horses landed on top of wagons and carts; women screamed, babies were dropped, soldiers fell to the road, unable to go on. Everywhere we heard the same words: the Germans are coming! They were always two kilometers behind us, ahead of us, to the right or the left of us; no one saw them, no one had seen them. Dozens of cars that had run out of gas stood abandoned by the roadside. Many were piled high with mattresses and bedding, all the fugitives' earthly goods. In one village a transport truck had run into a house wall; the dead soldiers hung out like marionettes with no one to guide their strings, or like hanged men that no one had remembered to cut down. The horn had been jammed, and blew without interruption,

as though the dead driver and his dead passengers were impatient for the stone wall to move aside. Burning ashes were
borne on the wind. How we managed not to lose one
another—or rather, how we kept finding one another again
—remains a mystery. We were no longer a closed rank; we
were only single soldiers limping along highways without
end.

The German bombers had failed to set the earth on fire.
As you emerged from the hell of a burning village, the spring
suddenly struck you in the face. All at once the horror you
had experienced but two minutes before seemed like a distant nightmare. The sky was light blue, and little white
clouds burst in the air. When the road was free of dead
horses for a few yards, there was a sweet smell that reminded
you of life. You could almost imagine a peasant, without a
uniform, coming across the field, guiding a plow, halting
from time to time and gazing toward the distant church
steeple, thanking God for all his blessings. You could catch
the smell of the earth, the smell of a good June rain, the
smell of sweating horses, the smell of the starched white
blouses of the peasant girls. And then your eyes turned back
to the flood of limping soldiers, trying in vain to look like
men in the presence of the fleeing women. You saw children
screaming desperately or still as death; officers' automobiles
blowing their strident horns and trying to open a path; bright
cavalry uniforms on shy, weary horses; wagons with their
sleeping drivers; cannon without ammunition: the whole dis-
ordered funeral procession of a disintegrated army. Sometimes it seemed as though, far up in front, they must be
carrying a coffin, and as though we were limping after it, a
procession of invalids; sometimes it seemed as though we
were our own grieving survivors, mourning for ourselves and
burying ourselves. Nothing was lacking that might have

made the procession more funereal. Once a hearse rolled by, bearing living women, children, soldiers in place of a coffin, with mattresses on the roof and a baby carriage on the hood. Even this vehicle of death served to carry people away from where they were—away, though no one knew where to.

Our imagination was not active at this time: it too had forsaken us. Even to wish was impossible. The most we wished for was to be dead, or to lie gravely wounded in an ambulance, in one of those cars with a death bell, which raced by us vainly, senselessly seeking a hospital for men who had lost all need of earthly hospitals. I couldn't help thinking of the American short story about the woman who brings her dead husband home in the stagecoach, without admitting that he is dead.

The German bombers had ceased to waste their bombs on us; even the Messerschmitts rarely subjected our columns to the fire of their machine guns. Nothing was more gruesome than the way they "let us go." No death could have been worse than this ironic chase. We were the game, but at every moment we could feel that the hunters were out to catch us alive. What greater contempt could they have shown than to let us live! Very occasionally, the Messerschmitts dropped to two or three hundred yards and swept our column with their machine guns, like a gardener spraying a garden with his hose—except that where the rain of bullets fell, no life sprang up. There was nothing tragic in this flying death, only an intolerable scorn. We were a human mass, fleeing by broad daylight; the bombers accompanied us, and their missiles would have fallen amid the throng as in a soft, thick porridge. From time to time we looked up into the sky, but furtively—as though in fear of attracting the attention of the aviators by our glances. We knew they were playing cat-and-mouse with us. From time to time the hounds made it clear that they could tear us to pieces at will; but alive we were more amusing than dead. All along the highways of France they were playing the same game.

In a village ten kilometers from the city of Commercy we were at last allowed to rest. The village lay somewhat to the side of the main road, and some of the local inhabitants had not yet been evacuated. We were the first troops to enter. Two old women stood in front of their house, waiting for someone to give them a ride. An artilleryman, who had attached an empty gun-carriage to his wagon, called to them: "Come on, *les petites mères,* jump on quick!"

The two old women tripped across the street to the wagon. They had on black straw hats, touchingly festive with pink flowers that looked like the faded artificial wreaths people lay on graves in the south of France. In their hands they carried marketing bags of cracked black patent leather, filled with a few neatly packed provisions, a few towels, and perhaps a beloved old madonna. The soldiers helped them up on the carriage; there they sat, holding on convulsively, squeezing their shopping bags under their arms, with wide eyes in their wrinkled old faces. But they did not complain. That was the amazing thing that struck you everywhere: the patience of the French men, and even more so of the women, was so great that it was almost sickening. There was much heroism in this resignation, but just as much weariness, and above all an almost oriental belief in miracles. I have often thought that one more reason why the French lost the war against the storming German heathen, was perhaps that their profound Christian faith had given rise to a great misunderstanding: they had lost the militant reality of Catholicism and transformed Christian humility, which is never passive, into an oriental fatalism. *"On verra bien . . ."* How often have I heard those words! Up to the last, the very last moment they thought they would "see" something, something that would save them. The women in particular bore everything without the slightest complaint. And there was much greatness in their renunciation. Never shall I forget an old peasant woman whom Saint-Brice and I picked up between Ste. Menehould and Passavant. She knew that her son was somewhere on the front. Her house had been destroyed by a bomb. Her daughter and her two-year-old grandchild had fled with her, and she had lost them on the road. But she was sure that she would find them all again: her daughter, her son, her grandchild—somewhere in the broad French land. There was an almost classic greatness in these French peasant women. It was not to their little plot of land that they clung; they were rooted in the whole breadth of France. To uproot them, the Germans would have had to drive them out of France.

The two old women vanished on the swaying gun-carriage. We went looking for shelter. Everywhere we found provisions in great abundance. From a cheese factory we took hundreds of boxes of cheese, wine from the postmaster's cellars, eggs from a poultry farm. I established myself in the postmaster's house. In his office he had left everything in a painful state of order, though the last mail had not been delivered. I untied the string that held the bundle. A few newspapers fell out. These were from the first days of May and announced that a German patrol had fallen into our hands, but that otherwise there was *"calme sur l'ensemble du front."* I took up the phone, with the superstitious feeling that someone would answer at the other end of the wire. I would call my wife and tell her that the whole thing was a joke and that I would be home next day. I would tell her to lay out my best suit, the light gray one with the stripes. The telegraph set glared at me with hostility. The rubber stamps were lined up on the table like a well-drilled army. The whole post-office breathed a ghostlike silence.

Then Dési and I went to the barbershop across the street. Dési was the only one of my friends who was still with us. The scouts had disappeared between Ste. Menehould and Passavant; I never saw Kellenberger, Imoudsky, Dr. Barati, or Ouchakoff again. But nothing was less surprising than a few missing men. Anyway, Dési and I went over to the barbershop. One of our favorite games was to go into an abandoned house and guess what its occupants had been like. As a take-off on graphology, Dési called this cynical activity "murology," the science of walls. Dési would go into a house and say that its former occupant had had a blonde wife, three children, and heart trouble. Such jokes were our only refuge from despair.

But quite aside from murology, the master barber could not have had very noble sentiments. We had hoped to find some soothing lotion to massage one another with, but the stingy fellow had emptied his bottles to the last drop. Not a single piece of soap was in sight, and even the shaving paper had been removed from the backs of the chairs. All that the avaricious *coiffeur* left behind was a few advertisements for shaving creams and razor blades, a broken atomizer, and a sign saying that the price of a hair-cut was higher on Saturday.

As we stepped out into the street on our way back to the cellars of the more generous postmaster, we suddenly saw the two old women climbing painfully down from their gun-carriage. A moment later, horsemen and wagons began to stream in from the direction of Commercy, the place we thought we were going to. I felt my heart hammering in my throat. Someone was tightening a cord around my middle.

"The road is cut off," said one of the cavalrymen. "The bridges have been blasted. They sent us back."

"Who sent you back?"

"The *Gardes Mobiles*."

"Why have the roads been shut off?"

"The Germans are coming. We're surrounded."

The cavalryman disappeared. We heard the same story from artillerymen, lone officers, and infantrymen who poured back. From that moment on, everything reminded you of a mousetrap, with the mouse running back and forth, beating its nose against the bars, though its doom had long ago been sealed. From that hour the kilometers had to be counted double. We ran in one direction until we met people who told us that that was just where the Germans were coming from. Our officers took their lead from women, gendarmes, even children. All connection with headquarters had been lost ages ago. We ran about in circles, like confused tourists in search of information. Everywhere the same picture. Soldiers passed us in single file, and came back at the end of an hour. No one knew why they came back; they themselves didn't know. They had fled, now they were fleeing back again. Each time someone said: The enemy is coming. He came from the south, he came from the north. No one saw him. The cannon were silent; even the planes grew rarer. Here and there a solitary machine gun rattled. But the enemy was everywhere. You never saw him yourself, but someone had seen him. You turned around. You ran away in the very direction from which you had just fled in terror. Wherever you went, there was someone who knew everything. Usually it was an isolated *Garde Mobile*, but it might just as well be a civilian, even a child. They knew that the Germans were two kilometers away. Always two kilometers away. Always in the next village. And always unconquerable.

Imbach, the Alsatian lieutenant, was sitting in the postmaster's room writing a letter when I reported what I had heard on the street.

"If that's the case," he said, "I'll just address my letter: via Red Cross, Geneva." And he kept on writing.

An hour later we left for Commercy after all. Beside me tottered Vago, the little architect with the well-tended beard. He smelled of perfume like one of Coty's shops. "Where did you get the perfume?" I asked him. He looked at me with bleary eyes, then he breathed into my face. His breath smelled of perfume.

"Fooey!" I said. "What have you been doing?"

He pointed toward the barbershop. "In the cellar," he stammered.

I understood. The stingy barber had hidden his sweet-smelling spirits in the cellar. Vago had mistaken the perfume for wine.

Suddenly Captain Billerot stood beside me.

"We are marching only three kilometers," he said. "Westward. There is a village on the mountain ridge. The Germans would have to pass through and we have orders to stop them off at any price."

I nodded. Dési and I took Vago between us. We marched off in a cloud of perfume to meet the Germans.

This was the beginning of the end.

The village—I have forgotten its name and can find it on none of the maps—was four or five kilometers to the west of Commercy, on a hill about twelve hundred feet high. Its forty or fifty houses were situated in a hollow between two hills, and all were inhabited. The place seemed almost undisturbed by the war. We knew nothing about the village except that it guarded the chief crossing for the Germans advancing from the west toward Commercy and Ligny-en-Barrois. The latter city, one of the most important railroad junctions in the region, had to be defended at any price.

We reached the village in a sorry state. Our reception there was the more welcome. The rain was coming down in streams. Since leaving the main highway, we had been ankle-deep in mud. The mud clung to our tattered boots. Our wet coats, our dripping gas-masks, our soaking knapsacks dragged us down. In my weariness I felt as though my head were a mile away from my feet. I tried to establish a connection between my limbs, but it was too far. I tried a new marching technique: I slid through the mud without raising my feet. But it was a poor way to get through puddles.

We marched into the village, expecting the usual picture of abandoned houses, fugitives, suspicious looks, children crying out for help, plundered farms. Instead we found the place in a festive mood. For this there were two reasons. The first and main reason was that the inhabitants, who had only heard of the rapid German advance a few days before, had been waiting ever since for French troops who would come to defend them. They looked on us as their saviors. The only danger, they thought, was that we might come too late. Once we were there, they were sure we could hold the village. They welcomed us as though we had already won the battle. The second reason for the festive mood was that the mayor's daughter was celebrating her wedding.

Among all my ghastly memories of this most disgraceful retreat in history, my memory of this little mountain village above Commercy remains the most ghastly.

I was marching at the head of the column with Dési, Vago, and a Pole by the name of Sienkiewitz, who had been assigned to me to replace my missing scouts. Suddenly, behind a little pine forest, the village emerged. At the entrance stood ten or twelve men and as many women, bareheaded in the rain. For a moment we stood still in amazement. We thought they were hostile. Then we saw that they were holding their hats in their hands. And as we approached, the hats flew into the air. At the head of the reception committee stood the mayor. He was an old man with gray hair and a longish face, refined by age. He wore a gleaming white shirt, a Sunday tie, and a Sunday jacket. On his lapel he wore World War decorations in all possible colors.

Involuntarily we stopped. The column stopped behind us. Without a command the men stood presenting arms.

The old man spoke. His words were few, but they so moved me that I experienced a pain that was almost physical. We could count on the civilian population of the village, he said. Every single man would do his duty.

"The old soldiers greet the young," he said in conclusion.

Again the hats flew into the air. The rain fell without interruption. I was glad of that, for tears were running down my cheeks; as it was, they might be taken for rain water.

Then the mayor popped his big surprise. The villagers, he said, had foreseen that we should be tired when we arrived to defend the village—their village. Most of them were World War veterans—they had dug trenches on the west side of town; all we had to do was to step into them.

The whole population escorted us to the trenches. They were expertly dug, about nine feet deep, placed at the edge of the wood, designed according to all the rules of military art. The old mayor was the first to jump into a trench. With paternal benevolence he pointed out to us the advantage of trenches laid out at an angle. He was as proud of his work as if it had been a new church. The women stood there,

177

noisily blowing their noses into their aprons. There was not a one of us but would have gladly given his life for the nameless village.

My company was to man the trench for two hours, then another company was to relieve us. My company consisted of observers, telegraphers, telephonists, signal corps, and scouts; actually we understood very little about trenches. But this was no time for subtleties. We installed ourselves in the trench, set our rifles in position, and waited for the enemy. The rain continued to beat down on us, and we stood deep in the mud that had collected on the trench floor; our eyes tried desperately to pierce the mists rising from the fields, where the first field-gray uniform might appear at any moment. The hill across from us was bare, and we wondered whether the Germans would come rushing down it with their tanks. Captain Billerot came down into our trench with a compass in his hand. His mouse-gray features looked even grayer in the rain. He showed us where the enemy would presumably appear. He held a whistle in his hand.

"We shall resist as long as we can," he said. "No one will move from the spot before I whistle. When the whistle blows, we shall beat an orderly retreat in this direction."

He pointed toward the village. But no one believed that the whistle would blow. A few stout-hearted men and an old soldier with faith in the young had sufficed to turn a demoralized horde into heroes of the Marne. Not a man of us contemplated retreating as long as he drew breath. Beside me stood Mayer-Mayerescu of Bucharest. His head seemed to have grown even smaller, and his steel helmet was sliding down over his ears. He had finally lost his cook-pot. He clung to his gun as though in need of support. His hair seemed even more straw-colored than usual, like the Russian actor in *The Root of All Evil*. Mayer, the Tolstoyan hero,

had grown even thinner and more emaciated. Amid all our
plundering Mayer had refused to eat anything. His eyes
stood out of his head as he watched us diving into the cheese;
his mouth watered as we wallowed in compote. But he ate
only the miserable biscuits handed out by the "kitchen."
Now he stood beside me and asked: "Do you hear?"

I turned around. Yes, I could hear it. In the village someone was playing an accordion.

For two hours we stood motionless at our posts. Twice
women came out of the village and brought us hot tea. We
received them with cries of joy. "*Ce sont les hommes qui ne
sont pas capables de réfléchir sur la vie, qui réfléchissent sur
la mort,*" wrote a historian of the World War. We did not
think of death. We thought only that when the two hours
were ended, we could go and see where the accordion was
playing.

At last our two hours were up. We were relieved. Dési,
Vago, Sienkiewitz and I went straight to the inn, the local
café where the wedding was at its height. The mayor owned
the café, and nothing was lacking. The bride was no longer
young. She seemed to be about forty, with a tired face, and
you could see what exertion it cost her to smile. She held the
hand of the bridegroom, who sat beside her in silence. He
was a man of fifty, a widower, they told us, from Amiens in
the north; he owned a good farm and had fled from the
Germans. Suddenly his whole life seemed very important to
us, and we urgently inquired about all the details. As it happened, he was the only one present who took no part in the
general rejoicing. He sat beside his bride like a photograph
in his starched shirt-front, and spoke not a word. Clouds
passed across his square protruding forehead like the clouds
in the heavy June sky.

But the happy couple were no longer the center of the

celebration. Now it was the soldiers who were being feted.
They filled the room. As we came in from the trenches the
mayor took us in charge. Our coats were hung up to dry
and a young girl brought me a big glass of rum. Never has
a woman made a profounder impression on me than this girl.
Her name was Jeanne, like Jeanne d'Arc, who was also a
peasant girl, born not very far from this very village. Such
was the pain within me that a woman's glance seemed to
me the tenderest tenderness. In my overflowing need for
warmth, I held fast to her hand.

"Please stay with me a moment," I begged her.

"What for?" she answered, laughing. She was not beautiful, but she had white teeth, and her form had a gentleness
that belonged to another world—a warm, gentle, forgotten
world.

I could think of no good reason to give her. But she stayed
for a moment and held my hand. Then she said, but this too
with a laugh: "Will you defend me when the Boches come?"

"Certainly!"

How could I have helped defending her? I went up to
Vago, who was standing at the bar with cheeks aflame,
combing his beard. He was engaged in earnest conversation
with a bearded peasant; they were exchanging expert pointers
about the care of beards.

The mayor—host and father—was now sitting at the long
table, beneath two oil paintings. The smaller showed the
Mother of God appearing to the Maid of Orleans, the larger
President Sadi Carnot delivering his acceptance speech before
the national assembly. The mayor was telling about his war
experiences, with that slightly ironic but eloquent tone which
the *anciens combattants* affect in speaking to the younger
generation of soldiers. From time to time the mayor's sister,
a high-bosomed matron with a gigantic coiffure, who had

been keeping house for him since the death of his wife, wove
in a few of her own memories. Again and again the conversation turned to the trench which the villagers had dug
for us.

"I told you," said a little old man with an improbably thin
voice, "that the boys would come in time."

He coughed and slapped our red-headed Dési on the back.
Everyone applauded.

I stepped out of the house. Suddenly I felt strangled. I
didn't know why, but I was at the end of my strength.

Across the street stood an old stone well. I sat down on the
rim. The rain splashed into the dipper. My face burned, my
ears burned. My hands were ice-cold. I looked toward the
trench. I saw the backs of the soldiers. Behind the trench sat
Captain Billerot, hunched over, smoking his pipe. The hills
round about had vanished in mist.

The peasant woman with the blue apron came out with
another pailful of tea. She shoved me back into the house
just as the accordion player was starting in again. Everyone
was silent. The bride and bridegroom sat as though framed,
as though they had been hanging over the dining-room table
for the last forty years. The accordion player was a young
hunchback exempted from military service because of his
deformity. Even the mayor had stopped talking. Only the
blue-white-and-red garlands around the picture of Jeanne
d'Arc swayed gently.

And then a whistle blew.

The accordion player stopped on a painful, long-drawn-
out note. A few of the people jumped up. A woman tore
open the door. We grabbed our coats off the hook, buckled
on our belts, and ran for our guns, getting them mixed up
in our hurry. Everything happened convulsively, incoher-
ently, in mad haste. The mayor called out something to me

that I didn't understand. Only the newlyweds sat there motionless, hand in hand.

And then someone uttered the word "retreat."

All of us knew what the whistle meant. But I don't know who was so incautious as to utter the truth. Nor do I know how the people understood, all in a flash, that we were leaving them in the lurch. All I know is that suddenly two women were hanging on my arm. One of them was Jeanne. But I could scarcely recognize her now. The wild horror in her eyes changed her whole face. Her lips were as white as her teeth. The bearded old man held one end of Vago's rifle and they tugged at it like two dogs fighting over a bone. The hunchback stood by the door with his accordion as though to block the way.

We forced our way out. The men from the trenches stood three abreast, ready to march. Adjutant Daroussat ran past me and said: "We're running away again. I could vomit my soul."

The rain dripped from his white cap.

I shook Jeanne off my arm. I tried to say something. But I couldn't. The old woman had let me go and was running into the house.

We marched off. We hadn't seen the enemy. We were running away from a ghost. With downcast eyes we left the village on the mountainside. No one dared to raise his head. By the roadside stood the people we were leaving behind. Old men, women, children. They were all speechless, paralyzed like ourselves. Only when the first officer passed did a woman begin to scream: "So you're handing us over to the Boches?"

And then they all awoke from their lethargy. A flood of curses rained down on us. No steel helmet could ward them off. The women screamed: "Save yourselves, cowards!" And

mild little Jeanne screamed the loudest. The bride had come
out too. She ran beside the soldiers in her shiny black silk
dress, dragging her train in the mud. She spat, she screamed
obscenities, she balled her red hands into fists. The bridegroom ran behind her trying to quiet her, but she paid no
attention to him. The peasant woman with the blue apron
poured out a pailful of tea before our feet. The hunchback
laughed so hard that the wrinkles in his thin face danced,
as though to the rhythm of his accordion. Only the mayor
stood leaning against the well, speechless, his hat in hand. I
think I have never seen such sadness in a human face.

And I think I shall never again be so ashamed as long as
I live.

We had lived through days of agony. But that was not the
worst. The worst was the orgy which now began.

Near the village we had just left, five of us—Vago, Dési,
Sienkiewitz, a Turk named Raphael Adatto, and myself—
found an abandoned truck. Adatto, an automobile mechanic,
succeeded in making it work. Despite the protests of Colonel
Landry, who insisted that both the hale and the sick should
go on foot, we kept the old delivery wagon and coddled it
like a treasure. We always took fifteen or twenty sick men
aboard, though of course there were many more. The truck
had long passed its prime, and it was intended for six or seven
passengers at most. It creaked beneath the weight. The tires
were so old and worn that even on the paved road they
skidded as on ice; when it rained, we could advance only
at a snail's pace. Adatto, who drove this medieval steed, won
power over our life and death. We could never have advanced without him, for the old wreck went on strike again
and again, and it took all the persuasive gifts of the inde-
fatigable little Turk to set her in motion again. Ours was the

only functioning vehicle in our company, and at every stop there was a heart-rending struggle for every space in it. (The only army truck, after the natural death of the Renault found by Saint-Brice and myself, had been commandeered by the colonel for his kitchen.) Men's feet were bleeding so freely that the blood oozed through their stockings and shoes. Many were sick and lay pale as death by the roadside. But none had entirely given up hope. And everything that is understood by human hope, all the delusion and faith, all the self-deception and trust in God, all the clinging and self-justification, was centered on this abject, once blue delicatessen truck, driving through the tortured countryside. When we passed a group of despairing marchers, a sudden gleam of hope came into their spent eyes. They called to us, and those who had painfully dropped to rest arose and hobbled along behind us, raised their arms beseechingly, or with their last strength hung on behind and let themselves be dragged until they fell from exhaustion. They knew that they were lost if they had to go on by foot. But when they tried to clamber up, our passengers shoved them off.

The faces of the soldiers on the road were convulsed with horror. You could scarcely recognize them. With raised arms they ran after the miserable truck, then fell back exhausted and at length vanished, like the lepers in the Bible, pleading in vain for succor. We drove through lanes of glances burning with hate. Every five or ten kilometers we tried to unload a few of our passengers and take on others. But each man defended his place with the utmost desperation.

Adatto drove the car and repaired it; my job was to get gasoline. On the road from Commercy to Ligny—suddenly we drove senselessly westward, only to turn around near Ligny and dash on in a southeasterly direction—the great gas tanks were in flames. The engineering corps had orders to blow up all gasoline dumps on their way, to prevent them from falling into the hands of the Germans. Thousands of gallons were burning—the heavens were red with the flames —yet often we spent hours vainly searching for two gallons for our Flying Dutchman. Shortly before Ligny, I found a gasoline pump on the road and saw a man in the house behind it. We stopped. The pump was locked. I asked the man if he had any gas. He was a man in his fifties, with a little black mustache and a high black collar. He said yes, there were about twenty gallons in the pump. I let out a cry of joy.

"But the gasoline stays here," the man added at once.

"What do you mean?"

"I mean that the gasoline stays here unless you bring me a stamped order from the captain."

"My captain?"

"Oh, no. The *commandant de la place*."

"Where is he?"

With a smile the man pointed to a burning house at the end of the village.

"There!"

I asked him if he was trying to kid me. He said no. And I don't think he was, any more than I think that in the literal sense of the word he belonged to the Fifth Column. He belonged to it unconsciously, like all Frenchmen whose souls had been destroyed by their bureaucratic training. He knew that tons of gasoline had been set on fire in the region. He knew that the Germans were at our heels. But in the bottom of his heart, he believed neither in the fire nor in the Germans nor in the war. He believed only in a piece of paper and a stamp. It pained me to have to shake his whole neatly ordered world, but without hesitation I leveled my rifle at his breast.

"Give me the key!"

Like all bureaucrats, he immediately acceded to a show of force. He gave me the key, we filled up our tank, took out all the cans we found in the man's office, filled them to the brim, and left the fellow alone with his empty reservoir.

We drove on. We were often the first to arrive in a village, but always the last to leave it. We always waited until all the troops had passed us. Our colonel usually sent the light truck with the *popote*, the officers' mess, ahead; then he followed in his light gray Renault which he had when he came to our regiment. He had his own driver, a young Frenchman; most likely he did not want to be driven by a volunteer. When we arrived in a village, Colonel Landry was already sitting at table, and only long after the other soldiers had drawn by was the *popote* packed up again. It never ran out of provisions, for in every village it had first rights. Two or three officers of the staff were kept busy maintaining the *popote* at its high level. The *popote* triumphed over all the horrors of the retreat.

Ligny-en-Barrois has 4,612 inhabitants and a railroad station. We found the city empty and the station full.

Our brave chariot hobbled along the highway. About a hundred yards from Ligny four or five officers blocked our way. They were all shouting at once, and I couldn't understand them at first. I leaned my head out of the car. A captain whom I did not know and who did not belong to our regiment seized me by the arm.

"Hey, sergeant. Don't forget to stop at the station. The station is full. Take what you find. If you can't take it with you, set it on fire."

He hiccupped. He reeked of liquor. His eyes were bleary, and it cost him an effort to form his words.

"There's plenty to drink too."

He pinched my arm.

"Whatever you do, don't leave anything. What you can't take with you, set on fire. Understand? The Germans will be here right away. Whatever you do, don't leave anything."

He waved his riding crop at us until we turned into the street leading to the station.

Many cars were standing in front of the station: some belonging to officers, one or two army trucks, three or four "commandeered" delivery wagons like our blue Renault. Each car was guarded by a single man. The other passengers were apparently out on the tracks. I jumped off and went into the station with a few comrades. Adatto remained behind to guard our precious truck. I gave him a revolver, for I knew that some of the men here were desperate enough to attempt to seize our truck by force.

This was the largest freight station in the vicinity. The last consignments of goods had not been forwarded, and there were three spurs full of loaded cars. The men were breaking into the cars, opening up packing cases by the hundreds.

Ligny-en-Barrois is in the middle of the Champagne country. There was an entire train, at least fifteen or twenty cars long, full of cognac and the noble, bubbly drink known throughout the world as champagne, in honor of this country: the symbol and taboo of luxury, love, and the things that happen but once in a lifetime. The officers outside the city had apparently directed all the arriving regiments toward the station, for innumerable champagne and cognac bottles were strewn about. To reach the platform from the second track, where the champagne train stood, you had to wade through a field of broken glass: hundreds of bottles had been emptied and smashed on the spot. Countless bottles had been half-emptied and abandoned; a sticky, light brown mixture of cognac and champagne oozed out of the cars. Civilian fugitives had also taken part in the orgy. I stumbled over a drunken old woman who had slipped off a champagne crate and fallen face downward in the broken glass. Champagne, blood and cognac flowed all around her wretched, writhing body. A soldier with an unforgettably foolish look sat precariously on a crate humming a tune and brandishing a champagne bottle in either hand. At every instant I expected him to fall into the sea of broken glass. An officer stood beside him but said nothing. He was too busy trying to load a crate labeled *Grand Marnier* on his back. A horde of soldiers, among them an officer and at least two non-coms, had devised a vandals' sport. Along the tracks they set up nine champagne bottles like nine-pins and bowled at them with other bottles. Each time glass struck glass and both bottles crashed, the players let out a bloodcurdling yell, joined hands, and danced about in a ring, kissing one another and emptying a few more bottles.

Yet there are some whom alcohol affects differently. Beside one of the railroad cars a captain was sitting on a crate, with his head buried in his hands. *"La ligne Daladier! La ligne Daladier!"* he kept repeating. He was past middle age and liberally decorated, obviously a reservist who had served in the World War. He sighed so loud that it sounded like a moan. He repeated the words without looking up. I doubt whether he himself knew what he meant. A little old man, a sort of municipal clerk, came up to me, plucked my sleeve, and asked: "When is the next train home?" Just to be saying something, I asked him where his home was. But he only looked at me without comprehension and repeated: "When is the next train home?"

I kept stumbling over soldiers who lay sleeping between

188

the rails. Many of them snored or hummed in their sleep.
A bedouin in a bright-colored turban leaned out of the
station-master's office and vomited on the platform. The
whole station reeked of alcohol.

I barely managed to dissuade my men from taking part in
this tragic orgy. But I did not have the strength to prevent
them from each taking two bottles of champagne and loading
a case containing fifty small bottles of *Grand Marnier* onto
our truck. Then at last they were ready, though still reluc-
tant, to drive off.

South of Ligny, all the regiments we passed had followed
the order to leave the Germans nothing. Whole columns of
infantry marched by with champagne bottles in their
pockets. Some of the officers—among them Captain Billerot
of my own company—marched at the head of their columns
with downcast eyes, never looking up, overcome by a profound disgust and an unspeakable sadness. But these officers
were in the minority. A man needs a good deal of strength
to accept misfortune and refuse to take refuge in drink and
forgetfulness. More and more cars full of fleeing officers
passed us, and every last one of them was piled high with
bottles, packing cases, food. We passed innumerable columns
without officers. For several days now the highways had
been full of stray soldiers who claimed to have lost their
regiments. No one thought of stopping them, questioning
them, fitting them into a regiment. Desertion was taken for
granted: officers left their companies, companies left their
regiments, regiments dwindled to the vanishing point.

The drama of Ligny was repeated at nearly every town
we passed through later. Officers, non-coms, privates stood
at the gate and invited those who followed to plunder:
"Don't let anything fall into the hands of the Germans."
Outside each town stood the tempter. And in every town

the same drama was repeated. The shops—abandoned in haste by their owners a few hours before—were plundered. But never was plundering more senseless. The soldiers stole whatever came to their hands, just for the sake of stealing. Thousands of soldiers hobbled along the highway, and out of their pockets hung bottles, women's shoes, neckties, ribbons, toys. A Negro soldier was carrying three or four women's corsets. The ribbons hung down and twisted around his legs. Baby carriages rolled along, bearing champagne, cognac, shirts, clocks, umbrellas, coffee-mills. Scarcely any of the soldiers had retained their steel helmets or khaki *bonnets de police*. Most had found hats in some store: there were gray, black, brown felt hats; blue, green, and white berets; a few of the Arabs had pinned flowery women's hats to their fezzes.

The witches' sabbath increased in horror and absurdity. Since every town and village offered new luxuries, the officers in the fleeing cars threw overboard the loot from the last town to make room for new merchandise. The loot from a whole town would be lying on the highway five kilometers further on. Several big cheese stores had been completely plundered. Soon afterward, other delicacies were found, and now the *Port de Salut, Roblechons, Roqueforts*, lay on the road by the hundreds. For several minutes our car drove through cheese. The wheels sank into the soft yellow mass. Adatto cursed because the cheese soup made us skid. The best things that the best men of France, the peasants of this peasant country, had created in the sweat of their brow, were thrown on the road and trampled on. Champagne, the product of hundreds of years of diligence and skill, flowed in the ditches.

And so we dashed through the provinces of the Marne, the Meuse, the Vosges, the cities of Void and Vaucouleurs, and through the village of Domrémy-la-Pucelle where the French

national saint, Jeanne d'Arc, was born. In front of the house
where St. Joan was born, two soldiers were fighting over a
bicycle. When we came to the little city of Vaucouleurs, in
the heart of Lorraine, the inhabitants were still in their
houses. From here there was no possibility of evacuation. I
stepped into an inn and asked the landlord to give each of us
a glass of pernod. We sat for ten minutes at the little round
tables of imitation marble, like real guests in a real café. The
landlord was a fat man with an open vest and a big watch-
chain; the *patron de bistro* that I had always loved in France.
He said he was not afraid of the Germans, the worst they
could do would be to kill him. He said that we soldiers were
not to blame; France had been betrayed. With a few old
veterans and a handful of women he himself was prepared
to hold the city—"But what for?" he asked. "You fellows
will just take us from behind." Despite the bitterness of his
words, they did me good: out of his mouth spoke a France
that would have been worth dying for. In those ten minutes,
I took my leave of many things. I caressed the "zinc," sat
down for a moment on the high chair behind the bar, laid
my hand on the cash register. I even went out to the W.C.,
to give myself the illusion of civil life. I took a quick look
at the mirror, failed to recognize myself, and came out. It
gave me a childlike pleasure to pay the check; the host was
surprised and took the money reluctantly. He did not understand that in paying I was trying to conjure up the spirit of
order; he only said that the francs would be worthless anyway.

Out on the street the soldiers were staggering along between rows of hostile women and girls. In the bakery hot
bread was being given out. I took a piece and soon had a
good case of stomach cramps. In a pastry shop a dark-haired
girl gave me a cake of chocolate. She said I was not to blame

for the whole débâcle. I stroked her hand and gave her a picture of myself . . . I don't know why. Then I had the mad idea of going into a drugstore and buying some cologne. I went into the *Pharmacie de la Croix Lorraine*, beside the *Confiserie Jeanne d'Arc*, and bought a little bottle of cologne. It filled me with indescribable happiness to be able to pay for it. In the drugstore a man in a white smock stood behind the counter; on the wall hung advertisements for cough drops. The whole place was like a dream, with its colored bottles and neat vignettes. It crossed my mind that I should wake up in my bed next day, and that Mamma would stand by my bedside with "Uncle Doctor," and that I would have to take a bitter medicine, but that I should get well because I was a good child and because Mamma laid her lovely white hands on my forehead.

I do not know whether it is biologically possible for a man to get drunk from eating. Yet I know it was the fresh hot bread that clouded my mind. I had all the symptoms of intoxication: the high spirits in the beginning, the subsequent hangover. We drove out of the village; soldiers, girls, men, women, were sitting in the streets, screaming, drinking, falling down, brawling, laughing, weeping. My head began to turn and everything became confused: the girl in the pastry shop was wearing the druggist's white smock, and out of the mirror in the café the face of the drunken woman in the station at Ligny glared at me. The only thing that was clear to me in all this muddle was the burning pain in my stomach.

I remember that we were driven in the direction of Toul and that the bridge at Vaucouleurs flew into the air behind us. We drove all next day until we were stopped near the little village of Alain on the road between Nancy and Neufchâteau. Saint-Brice stood by the roadside and gave us the signal to halt.

"Get out," he said to me, "and send the car forward." Then to Adatto: "About five hundred yards from here, in the woods, you'll find the colonel. Stop there. The sergeant and I will follow."

I got out, and the car drove off. I stood beside Saint-Brice and looked into his good calm face.

"I want to speak with you," he said, and sat down in the grass.

I sat down beside him and waited. He was playing with a blade of grass.

Then he said: "We can be proud of the Twenty-first. Not a man of the survivors is missing. The regiment has managed to get here—God knows how. They're asleep up there in the woods."

I listened to him, but I knew that wasn't what he wanted to tell me. He was just talking for the sake of talking.

"Are we going on?" I asked.

Then he turned to me, looked into my eyes, and seized my hands. "No," he said simply. "We aren't going on. We have received orders to lay down our arms. We are entirely surrounded. France has sued for an armistice."

He stood up and turned away. I too stood up. I looked around. We were standing in a broad field, slanting up to the woods. The noonday sun blazed in the sky. The meadow was yellow in the sun, and gave off a peaceful summer smell. The grasshoppers chirped, and a soft breeze stirred the blades of grass. Everything about us was large and still. And before us on the road stood the image of the Mother of God.

We exchanged a fleeting glance. Then we went down to the little chapel, with the grating before the altar. A few faded flowers lay on a white cloth, beneath the statue of the Virgin.

Then we knelt down and prayed.

193

Part Two

IMPRISONMENT AND FLIGHT

CHAPTER SEVEN: FAREWELL FROM LIFE

ON JUNE 21ST, 1940, LIEUTENANT SAINT-BRICE SAVED MY life.

We spent two days in the dense forest of Alain. General Weygand later explained that of those divisions which had formed "islands of resistance," nine had been completely wiped out, two had lost half of their effectives, and twelve had fallen into German hands with one fourth of their men. The Thirty-fifth Division was one of the twelve that lost seventy-five per cent of their men. When we encamped in the forest of Alain, only one-quarter of our regiment was still alive. The survivors, numbering about six hundred, were completely exhausted after their hardships and privations. In the forest itself no food was obtainable; to send it in was out of the question. Our only remaining car was now used to tow the colonel's *popote*, abundantly supplied with champagne, cognac, and fowl; my old truck had gone on strike for good. We remained in the forest in a state of brooding stupor. I don't remember what I thought about during the forty hours I spent in the forest of Alain; I believe that God so numbed my senses that I was unable to think at all. I had always known that to be taken prisoner by the Germans would mean a quick death for me at best; at worst, it would mean concentration camp, torture, sickness, and interminable agony. The very first day of the war I resolved to put an end to my life rather than fall into German hands. This resolution inspired a certain calm. But now I could think of nothing. I knew only that my hours were numbered. Now and then German planes dropped a few bombs on our forest. Their purpose was not to cause destruction, but only to remind us that no armistice had yet been granted to defeated France.

June 21st was a radiant day; the sun penetrated the densest foliage, scattering little golden coins on the mossy forest floor. At seven o'clock in the morning, Lieutenant Saint-Brice sent for me.

He was leaning over a map.

"Your orders," he said coolly, "are to find a road leading to Charmes. Another scout will go with you. I hear that there's still a chance of getting through to Charmes."

I looked at him with astonishment. Captain Guy, who had been standing beside him, finally went away.

"Of course it's absurd," he said when Guy was out of earshot. "No one can get through. We're completely surrounded. But—" He hesitated. He was not looking at me.

"But I don't want you to be killed," he said quickly. "If you're caught with us, you won't be able to conceal your true identity—even if you throw away your documents and your tag. Someone will give you away, willingly or unwillingly."

"And you?" I asked.

He still avoided my eyes.

"I am French," he said. "Nothing will happen to me. At the most I'll be a German slave for a while. But that can't be helped. After this war there will be nothing but slaves. Slaves in uniform."

He turned to me and added calmly: "Try to put as many kilometers as possible between you and ourselves. Get rid of your army book and your arm-band. Take the Twenty-one off your collar. You have about twelve hours left. Make the best of them."

I thought it over. Then I said: "I can't do it. I can't desert the regiment."

"Nonsense! I give you my word of honor that the war is over—for us. We are under strict orders not to shoot. What are you waiting for? When the Germans come, we'll disband the army, and that'll be the end of it."

I had never seen Saint-Brice so bitter.

Captain Guy reappeared.

"You are still here?" he asked.

"Yes, *mon capitaine*. And I'd like to stay."

"What do you mean?"

I did not answer. Guy said: "Get going right away. There may still be a chance."

I saluted and returned to my comrades. I told Sienkiewitz to get ready. I packed my few belongings, handed my gun to Adjutant Daroussat, put my revolver in my holster, stuck three hand grenades into my belt, and returned to Saint-Brice.

I shed no tears as I bade good-by to my 1891 gun. And yet I had remained loyal to it until that day. I still don't know whether it was apathy, resulting from demoralization, that throughout the retreat prevented me from throwing away my old hunk of hardware and exchanging it for one of the modern Mousquetons that were lying around in various places. I like to think that I kept my 1891 Remington out of a certain sentimentality.

I found Saint-Brice at the same spot where I had left him.

"You see," he said. "Guy really thinks there's still a chance. Maybe he's right. Maybe you'll be back in a couple of hours and get us out of here."

"I hope so, *mon lieutenant*."

We took a few steps together toward the edge of the woods.

"Courage, *alors!*" said Saint-Brice as he shook my hand. "No long farewells! We'll meet soon again."

We looked at one another, we embraced; then, as though moved by the same thought, we quickly turned around and walked in opposite directions. Neither of us wanted to show the tears in his eyes.

I said good-by to a few comrades. Nicola, the colonel's good fat cook, gave me a piece of sausage from the *popote*. I talked a little with Daroussat, Dési, Heguedes the tailor, Pap the truck-driver. Not a one of the scouts remained. I looked for Malagrida, the little Portuguese, but apparently he had fallen in the last battle. I also looked for Désiré Weiss, who had once accompanied me on my expedition to the field kitchen. But I was told that he had been severely wounded somewhere; nothing more definite was known about him. I wanted to report to Captain Ravel, the handsome, elegant Ravel whose boots were always so shiny, but I was informed that he had died a hero's death at the head of his Eleventh Company. At length, I found Mayer-Mayerescu, but he looked so exhausted as he slept with his back to a tree trunk that I had no heart to wake him. Old Daroussat took a few steps with me. His face was drawn, and his hair had become entirely gray, but still he had a word of advice for my journey. He tried to joke. I got the impression that he really thought I might find a way out of the mousetrap. Dési took us as far as the village, and there Sienkiewitz and I set out. Dési's red head shone for a long time in the green meadow, as we went down the road to Charmes. I myself began to believe that our task was feasible. But why had Saint-Brice—

the eternally optimistic, self-assured, self-possessed Saint-Brice—why had he abandoned all hope?

That day we drove and walked sixty kilometers. Alfred Sienkiewitz was a Polish Jew of a type remarkable for its unbelievable tenacity. He was twenty-three or twenty-four years old, slender and sensitive, and even in his shoddy uniform he looked like a Polish aristocrat. All the racial melancholy of the Pole was in his large, oval, chestnut-brown eyes.

We resolved to push forward to Charmes regardless of what we heard along the way. Once in Charmes, where a number of roads intersect, we would seek an avenue of retreat for our regiment. I had in my pocket an *ordre de mission*, a regimental order, and had no fear of being stopped by an officer. Of course, the document proved unnecessary. Hundreds of deserters thronged the highways, and they would doubtless have been vastly amused by our "regimental order."

Our initial euphoria had given place to complete apathy. Numerous soldiers were simply sleeping in the ditches, and to our questions they all gave the stereotyped reply: *"On attend les Allemands."* Many wondered whether they would be allowed to keep their bicycles after being taken prisoner. There were no longer any complete units. The soldiers walked as placidly as in peacetime. For hours not a shot was heard. A heavy army truck, transporting munitions to Charmes, gave us a lift for about fifteen kilometers. Suddenly the drivers stopped, declaring that they planned to rest for two hours: it was time for their *casse-croûte*, the mid-morning luncheon, they said, and there was no danger of being late. Both were men over forty, such as were often employed in the *train d'équipage*. They sat down under a tree, took their luncheon from a carefully folded napkin, spread the napkin on the grass, placed the bottle of red wine in the sun, and prepared for a cozy family picnic. I attempted to explain that Charmes was the only way to freedom, that they could help not only us and themselves but six hundred soldiers; they replied that they would arrive in plenty of time, and that anyway the Germans wouldn't eat anyone. At last they thought the wine was the right temperature and they wished us a senseless *bon voyage* as we walked away. Those who had feared to fight the Germans were not afraid of living with the Germans: a tragic error, which the sons of France realize only today. But the French were not entirely to blame for this attitude. *"Enfin . . . on était fatigué,"* says Sergeant Pierre Seraphin Flambeau in Rostand's *L'Aiglon.* This army, too, was above all tired. It had but one desire—to stop running.

We boarded trucks, we drove a few kilometers with tired artillerymen on their horse-drawn wagons, we stole bicycles and abandoned them, we marched, we ran—and we witnessed the last convulsions of the French army. A group of artillerymen with a radio said Paris had broadcast that we were entirely encircled. They stood around their field kitchen and covered us with abuse when we declined to wait for hot soup. It is true that the word "encirclement" had never been more physically tangible; we must have been regarded as madmen for refusing to recognize its reality. What made the encirclement so palpable was that cars moving in opposite directions became entangled in the streets. The artillery, the *train d'équipage,* the engineering corps still had their automobiles. Regiments, or what remained of them, were fleeing from both the south and the north. Both had the enemy in their rear; now they collided with one another. Again and again the same incident occurred. A car came up the road, another car came down the road. When they met, they stopped.

202

"Where are the Germans?"

"Behind us."

"Behind us, too!"

At first neither trusted the other. Each attempted to move in the direction the other had come from. Finally each gave it up. In the end, the soldiers abandoned their wagons, lighted fires, played cards. Officers' cars that tried to clear the road by blowing their horns were stopped, and the officers taken out. Their old explanations—"We're going to find divisional headquarters!" or "We're going to get reinforcements," or "We're following our regiment"—were received with hoots and jeers. Some officers, mostly young ones, put a good face on their misfortune, left their requisitioned Peugeots, Renaults, Citroëns, or Hotchkisses, and proceeded to smash the motors with hammers, gun butts, and hatchets. Then the officers were admitted to a game of belotte.

Only we two continued running, as if chased by a demon. We felt men grinning behind our backs. They threw their jeers after us like stones.

We spoke little—we were too tired to speak. I am convinced that in these hours we were sustained by our fatigue. We simply could not stop. As we walked we gradually divested ourselves of everything we carried: our cartridge belts, bread bags, gas-masks. Piles of foodstuffs lay by the roadside waiting only to be picked up. Why weight yourself down with a sausage when you could find another a few hundred paces further on? One by one, we got rid of our weapons. Sienkiewitz threw his gun on a pile of other guns, and I tossed my hand grenades into an open field. We marched on and on. We stumbled over stones, guns, sacks, and over hundreds of scattered rubber pipes from gas-masks. We took hope at the most nebulous indications. Again and again we found something that proved to us the existence of a path to freedom beyond Charmes. Even Sienkiewitz's faint-heartedness helped; it inspired me to quick counter-arguments, which, in the end, he always accepted. We abandoned the very thought of resting—we had passed the limits of human fatigue. We were crushed with the heat. The sun was no hotter than usual, though the day was sultry enough. It was not the sun, nor the march, nor the sweat of our bodies. But somewhere a million fires seemed to be burning; and the heat of a thousand blazing ovens was moving toward us. Invisible tongues of flame licked at our faces. I looked at Sienkiewitz, and his face was red, as though reflecting a hundred blazing hearths. Perhaps we were dead and in Purgatory, I thought. But I looked in vain for the rainbow on the horizon, the bridge leading to Heaven.

And thus we came into the zone of silence.

The zone of silence began about four or five kilometers west of Charmes.

Coming from the west along the wide highway from Mirecourt, we had reached the outskirts of the town indicated to us by Saint-Brice. We had been ordered to go to headquarters in Charmes and find out whether the road to St. Dié was still open. The idea behind this plan, which had naturally been withheld from us, was obviously to take the road leading through St. Dié to Colmar, to proceed under the protection afforded by the Maginot Line, and to cross the Swiss border near Ferrette. Our faith in the impregnability of the Maginot Line was still strong, though actually the Germans had crossed the Rhine on June 16th, five days before.

Suddenly we found ourselves alone on the broad highway. Apparently there were no more troops between us and the Germans—wherever they were. A soft wind arose and leaped from one treetop to the next. The rustling of the leaves was like a woman softly humming a few bars while hanging out her wash. Here and there a leaf stuck to a branch like the oval head of a music note. Sometimes a leaf dropped to the ground, and it seemed surprising that it gave off no sound.

A short distance from Charmes a few cyclists came toward us. As they approached we distinguished two men and two women. Both men wore the uniforms of postal employees.

"The Germans are there!" both men called to us. "The Germans are in Charmes!"

As though to confirm their words, the droning of airplane motors, which we had not heard for a long time, suddenly filled the air. German bombers were flying over the town.

I don't know why we kept on going forward. But the idea that our purpose would be accomplished if only we reached Charmes had become an obsession. Actually, we found no Germans in Charmes. It is true that on our side of the Canal de l'Est and the Moselle, which cut Charmes in two, the town was already deserted. A few stray civilians stood in front of their houses staring at the sky. In the numerous inns where we desperately begged for a glass of beer we were refused. The dusty, ugly town, with its bare half-modern houses built in the terrible pre-World War style, deserves less than any other the name which adorns it. On the mighty *Grand Pont*, the enormously long bridge spanning both the canal and the Moselle, Senegalese soldiers stood guard. The whole bridge was plastered with those familiar small gray packages which meant that the bridge was mined.

I asked the Negro corporal where headquarters was. He pointed at a building on the other side of the bridge.

"Are you going to blow up the bridge?" I inquired, just to be saying something.

He laughed, showing his glittering white teeth.

"Someone will blow it up," he said. "If we don't, they will."

He pointed at his black comrades guarding the other end.

"It depends on which side the Germans come from first."

We crossed the bridge. Beneath us the Moselle flowed in summery peace. Between the canal and the Moselle grew innumerable green and yellow bushes. The bombers gleamed like silver in the sun.

No one was to be found at headquarters. The rooms were empty. At last we ran across a lieutenant who declared that the General Staff were in an air-raid shelter belonging to a neighboring wine-grower. He took us to the farm. The door to the cellar was open and a major sat on the staircase. Even at this moment I was painfully aware of the grotesqueness of the situation. I stood before the door to Hades, and the major sat on the top stair. His protruding head was at the exact level of my feet. I looked downward, and he looked upward.

"What's your business?"

"I've come for instructions, *mon commandant!*"

I briefly explained my request. The major listened to me. We both craned our necks. The major was an elderly gentleman with the long hairy neck of a turkey-cock. His enormous Adam's apple stood out on his scrawny throat, reminding you of a snake that has swallowed a hare. After I had finished speaking, the major first called a captain, who apparently was somewhere in the depths of the wine-grower's cellar. But no sooner had the second head, the captain's, sprouted from the ground like a mushroom than the major was seized with convulsive laughter. His laughter shook him so hard, his turkey's head grew so red, that I seriously feared his throat would burst and his Adam's apple would jump out on my shoes. Finally he calmed down. Still coughing, with tears in his eyes, he said: "Look at that specimen! The sergeant wants instructions!"

Suddenly he was silent and eyed me with distrust, as though he suspected me of playing a joke on him. In the end, the head on the ground became enraged, probably just to complete the gamut of human emotions.

"Just go to the big house over there on the square and have a beer. That's the only instruction I can give you, you imbecile!"

I turned around and went to join Alfred, who was waiting for me on the square. Guided by his infallible instinct for the useful, Alfred Sienkiewitz had already discovered the beerhouse and had gulped down two glasses of beer. I followed his example. Several barrels of beer had been set up in an enormous barn and a stout blonde was serving it. The beer was superb and cool, and cost nothing. In front of the barn, on the main square, the four principal roads converged: the roads leading to the bridge and to the railway station, the highway from St. Dié to Paris, and the road to Lunéville. A machine gun pointed down each of these roads, and the St. Dié highway was even defended by an anti-tank gun. Beside each gun stood a pot of beer.

Sleeping soldiers lay in the street. Women and children sat on benches or on the curb. We paced cautiously up and down, trying not to stumble over the sleeping people.

Suddenly three magnificent automobiles emerged on the narrow road by the station building. Two of the cars were black, the third was red. Near the railway barrier the cars braked for a second. I seized Alfred by the arm. In each car sat a general accompanied by four or five colonels. The cars disappeared in a cloud of dust.

"Come on, Alfred!" I said. "Let's follow them. I never heard of a general being taken prisoner!" We started out.

"They must know the right way," I said. "We are on foot and we won't get there as quickly, but we are on the right track."

We felt completely rested, as though rejuvenated. We marched briskly. The road led to Baccarat and was called *Route de Grande Circulation No. 9.* The cloud of dust ahead of us showed the direction the generals' cars had taken. Aside from that, nothing stirred. A few days before there must have been a terrible bombing. The air was filled with the stench of corpses. It was like walking through a field of rotting salad. Dead men and horses lay beside the road. Loaded carriages were half overturned; horses lay there with bellies torn wide open. An immense truck full of ammunition had fallen into the ditch. The hand of death had passed over.

To the left of the road, we saw a white farmhouse with a red roof. On it stood an angular red brick chimney, such as children might draw. The chimney was smoking. A lovely, tranquil white vapor rose from the house. A young girl stood in the yard. We saw only her back. The girl was shoveling garbage onto the dung pile. We called out to her. She turned around, came to the fence, and smiled at us. She had a soft red mouth and smelled of fresh dung.

"Is the road open?" Alfred asked.

"Why not?"

"Have the Germans been here?" Alfred inquired.

"Of course not!"

She laughed.

"Won't you come in and have a glass of milk?"

We refused with thanks. She wiped her hands on her apron.

"Did you see three cars pass by?"

She had seen them. The cars had passed a few minutes before.

We thanked her and walked on. The road passed through a dense forest. We gathered that batteries were concealed in the woods, for now and then an artilleryman would come out, looking in a northerly direction. Then all of a sudden we saw the three cars. Our hearts stopped beating. We knew what those cars meant. The generals had not found a way out; they had gone only a few kilometers beyond the town.

There was a small graveyard in the woods. It was a soldiers' graveyard from the World War, with pink tombstones. Only France could have such graveyards. This one was like a perfumed boudoir. The tombstones were as tender and graceful as powder boxes on the dressing table of a pretty woman. Smoke rose from a few graves. The generals and colonels stood around the tombstones throwing papers into a fire they had fanned to a blaze. A young major walked back and forth, and with the help of the chauffeurs removed papers and folders from the inside of the cars. But the strangest thing of all was this: a German soldier stood by the open fire, apparently warming his hands.

We stopped behind the car and asked the chauffeur what was going on.

"We're burning everything before the Germans come," he answered.

"And what's he?"

I pointed at the German soldier who now had his face turned to us. It was a square face with bloodshot eyes. He could not have been more than twenty years old. He grinned from ear to ear. When I kept staring at him, he suddenly stuck out his tongue and uttered a long "ba-a-a-ah!"

The chauffeur laughed.

"Our prisoner!" he said. "An outpost who lost his way. Captured by the general in person. Now the general doesn't know what to do with him. The German is having the time of his life. In an hour the general will be *his* prisoner."

The generals were silently throwing papers into the fire. A colonel stood by the side of the grinning German, guarding him with a soldier's gun. There was something irresistibly comical in this tragic scene.

We hastened forward. Again we were enveloped in silence. For at least one kilometer we marched without encountering a living being. We gathered new hope. Then we saw a cart behind us, drawn by a weary old nag. There was no driver. The cart rolled on because the horse was like us—he was so tired he could not stop. Inside, a little man with eyeglasses sat on a plank dangling his legs. He wore a lieutenant's uniform with the red velvet facings of the medical corps. It was not possible to see who was lying on the floor, but you could hear the sound of weeping, and from time to time the râles of a dying man: someone seemed to be making a last attempt to breathe.

Alfred found encouragement even in the presence of the hearse.

"If they're still evacuating the wounded in this direction," he declared, "there must be a way out."

I asked the physician: "Where are you going, *mon lieutenant?*"

He shrugged his shoulders and said nothing. The face of a Negro appeared above the side of the cart. Heavy tears rolled down his cheeks. Even his tears looked black.

"Are you wounded?" I asked the soldier.

"No," he said. "My brother is dead."

The wheezing had stopped.

At the same moment two cyclists passed us from the front. They were German soldiers.

We looked at one another. My brain was as numb as if my blood had frozen in my veins.

The two Germans took no notice of us or the cart. Both had automatic rifles, but they kept them on their shoulder straps, as if it hadn't occurred to them that they might have to use them. They were freshly shaven and their blond hair was carefully combed. The handle bars glittered like silver.

Alfred and I deliberated for a moment. To go on ahead was absurd. I suggested that we go back to the farm and try to get civilian clothes. We knew that according to the laws of war, soldiers in civilian garb were shot on the spot if they fell into enemy hands, but we had nothing to lose. We turned back and skirted the woods till we came to the farmhouse. As we passed the pink graveyard, we looked through the bushes and saw the prisoner talking with the two cyclists. He pointed in the direction of Charmes. We saw only a cloud of dust in which the generals' cars had disappeared.

We reached the house without incident, pushed open the gate, and entered. But the girl was no longer alone. Two French soldiers were sitting in the kitchen. One of them was drinking milk, the other wine. The one drinking milk was a huge, blond, Alsatian sergeant. He had the red cheeks of the Alsatians, and his blue eyes took stock of the girl. He reminded me of Gerber and I began to feel uneasy. The second soldier was dead drunk. He banged the table, cursed, muttered to himself, demanding with the incomparable logic of the drunk that Hitler should mend the torn seat of his trousers. "Isn't Hitler a paperhanger or something?" The girl kept trying to make him stop drinking, but as soon as she came near him, he laid his heavy hand on the pot-bellied bowl he was drinking from.

I took the girl aside.

Certainly, she said, she'd be glad to give us civilian clothes, but she was only a servant. The farmer and his wife were not home, and even their son was out. She expected them any minute now. The Germans, too, would be here any minute, I said. Didn't she see the two cyclists through the window? Of course she saw them, she said. When they passed by, the Alsatian jumped up, stuck his arm through the window and shouted *"Heil Hitler!"* So long as he was in the house, nothing could be done. In that case, we'd better be going, I said. She held us back. No, she said, we could hide in the attic till the coast was clear or the farmer and his wife returned. She'd tell the Alsatian she had thrown us out. All this sounded simple, intelligent, motherly, and courageous. We followed her suggestion without thinking. We tiptoed up to the attic, and she closed a creaking door behind us.

The attic had the moldy smell of tobacco, smoked meat, and dust. A couple of hams hung in the chimney. In one corner there was an old sewing machine, a sickle, a large framed photograph and some scattered playing cards. Through an opening in the roof I could see the woods and part of the road. From time to time a German cyclist passed. The woods were quiet and peaceful, and it was impossible to think that our life had come to an end.

An old bedstead stood opposite the door. Cautiously, we placed our steel helmets on the floor and lay down. The steel springs of the worn old bed pressed into our hips, but we did not care. Our bodies were sore and our legs were dead.

"In one or two hours at most the Germans will occupy the house," said Alfred.

I looked at my watch. It was half-past nine. Night was falling.

"If they come up here and bash in the door, they'll shoot at once," Alfred went on. "Wouldn't it be better to wait downstairs?"

"No," I said. "I'll stay."

We lay side by side on our backs, with our hands crossed under our heads. We stared fixedly at the door.

"If they kill me, send word to my sister," said Alfred.

He gave me the address.

"Shall I write it down for you?"

"No. I'll remember it."

"You're sure?"

"Yes."

"And if you—"

I gave him the addresses of my wife and parents.

We remained silent for a while. I folded my hands to pray. I thought so hard of my wife and parents that suddenly I had a feeling they were in the room. The feeling was so strong that I unbuckled the belt with my revolver holster and hung it on a three-legged, broken chair. I was giving the revolver to my father.

"Shall we sleep?" said Alfred.

"Yes," I said.

We shook hands. The day before we had been almost strangers. Now we knew that this was a handshake for death or life.

"Good-by," said Alfred as though he were going away.

"Good-by," I said as though I were going away.

We did not look at one another. Our eyes were glued to the door. "Any minute now . . ." we thought. But at the same time, superstitiously: "The door cannot open so long as we watch it." The attic slowly sank into darkness. Anxiously, our eyes clung to the outline of the door. Now and then a flashlight flickered. Soon a flashlight would bite into our eyes. We waited. The night wrapped everything in a gray veil, as though the dust of the attic had been stirred up and would not settle down. I sank deeper and deeper into a fantastic grayness from which only the bedsprings protruded. I fell into a deep sleep.

A scream awakened me.

A shrill woman's voice shouted: "Down with you! *Les Allemands sont là!*"

At the same time the door was torn open. An unknown woman with a candle in her hand stood on the staircase.

"Hurry up, quick, they're waiting for you!"

We rose mechanically. We followed her downstairs and across the yard which smelled headily of jasmine and manure. The moon stood high in the sky. It was two o'clock in the morning.

As soon as we were out of the yard, two flashlights lit up our faces. Two hands felt my body.

"No arms?"

"No."

"Go join the rest!"

Only then did we realize that several hundred French soldiers were standing on the road. Three or four officers were among them. Apart from the Germans who had gone over us, there was a third with an automatic rifle who kept watch over the prisoners.

A cool wind played around my temples. Something had changed in me the moment the Germans seized me. Or had something happened to me in my sleep, something decisive, radical, final? Or was it only the realization that, after having been a wheel in a clockwork for a year—a wheel in a rotten clockwork—I was now at the helm of my own destiny? I do not know. But I was no longer afraid. I put aside all notions of suicide. A great joyous calm took hold of me. I pushed my hair back from my forehead. And when the German sergeant asked whether any of us could speak German, I stepped forward, to Sienkiewitz's horror, and declared: "I speak German."

I imitated the French accent.

"Splendid," said the non-com. "Come with me."

We went to the woods. He ordered me to untie a few horses and get a wagon ready.

"Well, for you the war's over," he said.

I said something.

"You're a good fellow!" said the sergeant jovially. As a precautionary measure, he kept his revolver pointed at me.

Yes, a good fellow, I thought. That's my fate now. All right! I'll play the game. To the end. . . . No price is too high.

And my game began.

When we were out of the woods, the sergeant took counsel with a corporal. Then I heard him give instructions to the man with the automatic rifle: "You take this gang to headquarters. We've still got some work on our hands. You won't be afraid, alone, will you?"

"No."

"They're unarmed. Besides they're glad to be out of the war. There are five hundred of them at the most."

He turned to me.

"You stay with us. Maybe we can use you."

"All right."

I added: "Can my friend stay with me?"

"For all I care!"

I made a sign to Sienkiewitz to stay. I had previously told him to pretend that he did not understand a word of German.

The four of us—the German non-com, the corporal, Alfred, and I—went back to the farm. The peasant woman stood in front of the gate and asked whether the "gentlemen" would do her the honor of accepting a glass of milk. The four of us entered the house. Under the lamp sat the old peasant with his hands folded on the table. He rose and without a word made room for us. The young servant went out and got some warm milk. As she passed by me, she said: "Courage! Everything isn't lost!"

"What did she say?" inquired the sergeant.

"She asked whether I wanted some milk," I promptly answered.

They sat at the table. I remained standing. I felt ready to fight. For the first time the enemy was tangibly near. The war was perhaps over, but my own war was only beginning. I remained standing. Stiff upper lip, I thought. Now is the time to be cautious and clever.

"Sit down, please," said the sergeant. He had grown suddenly polite.

He was quite young and wore round unframed eyeglasses. He looked like a caricature of a member of a German student corps. He had a tiny mouth, and his nose seemed to be always smelling something foul. By contrast, the corporal was a sturdy man with the curious, glassy, sadistic eyes that I was later to see so often in young German faces. They were the eyes of a drunkard who has had nothing to drink, the eyes of a morphine addict whose dosage is being reduced. The eyes of a frustrated sensualist.

"We've got to round up a couple of hundred more prisoners today," said the sergeant, spreading out a map on a velvet tablecloth embroidered with woolen flowers. It was the most recent French General Staff map. For weeks I had been vainly requesting one like it for my observation post.

"Has Charmes been occupied?" the corporal asked me.

"I am sorry, I don't know."

"Shall we occupy the town, *Herr Unteroffizier?*" he asked

his superior. There was a studied insolence in his voice that sent the blood to my head.

"Why not? But first let's get a couple of hundred Frenchies from the woods."

He drank his milk and turned to the peasant.

"Well," he said benevolently, "soon the war will be over."

The old man looked at him without understanding. Not a nerve stirred in his good, hard face.

"Translate!"

I translated. The old man did not answer. The corporal added: "Now we're going to hop over to England. In a fortnight the whole lousy swindle will be over and done with."

And then, turning to me: "Translate!"

I translated.

"Go on, say something." The peasant's wife prodded her man. But he folded his wrinkled hands and remained silent.

At that point our attention was suddenly diverted from the peasant. An animal grunt came from the door. A head—more animal than human—appeared in the crack. A voice roared: "Hitler's got to sew up my pants!"

To illustrate what he meant, the man turned around pointing at his torn seat from which naked flesh protruded.

The corporal jumped up. He had no idea what the drunk had said, he had only heard the name of his Führer and seen the obscene gesture. Swinging the butt of his revolver, he struck the man over the head with all his might. The drunk collapsed without a sound. The sergeant and his subordinate stepped over the body. Sienkiewitz and I followed at a sign.

In the street, the man with the eyeglasses said: "We want to round up a couple of hundred prisoners. But there are only two of us. We can't go into the woods. You'll go in. Your job will be to shout: 'The war is over! Come out!' Get me?"

I got him only too well. But I pretended to understand nothing at all.

"Is the war really over?"

I wanted to gain time to think.

"No," he said. "But it's over for the ones who come out of the woods. They'll stay with us."

He laughed softly.

"Go ahead! Start shouting!"

I went obediently to the edge of the woods. I thought for a while. If I shouted, *"La guerre n'est pas finie! Ne bougez pas!"* the German would understand the negation. So I chose a different wording.

"La guerre continue! Bougez pas! Bougez pas!" I cried. (The war is still going on. Don't move.)

Nothing stirred in the woods. There was a dead silence. We walked on. The moon began to pale. There was only my voice in the great silent solitude.

Suddenly the corporal stopped. His angular body bent over me. I looked into his sick eyes.

"What have you been shouting?"

"The war is over! Come out!"

"Hm!" He gulped, accepting my explanation. He couldn't believe that I would dare lie to him.

The woods all around us were full of soldiers, arms, and ammunition. You could almost hear the repressed breathing of a thousand men.

The sergeant was walking beside me. Suddenly he stopped. Ten or twelve bicycles lay at the edge of the wood.

"What's that?" he said, eyeing me distrustfully through his glasses. "There must be soldiers in the woods. Shout again!"

I shouted; not a breath stirred.

"What does '*guerre*' mean?" the sergeant inquired.

"War."

"And *'continue'?*"

"Is over."

"Good!"

But he remained standing. "And these bicycles?"

"Oh," I said. "The soldiers must have left them when they ran away. In all this disorder—"

The word "disorder," applied to the French, pleased him. The patent absurdity of fleeing men leaving their conveyances behind, seemed to escape him. We continued our rounds.

We reached the railway embankment outside of Charmes, which we had so hopefully passed a few hours before. A burning tank stood on the tracks, and even from a distance you could see the glow. The corporal climbed up, but drew back in terror. He cried down to us: "There's an officer in the driver's seat. He has shot himself."

"He probably set the tank on fire, too," the sergeant answered irritably. "Get down!"

But the corporal stared as though hypnotized into the inside of the tank. The flames rising from the steel monster nearly licked his face. I saw him bend over the driver's seat, pulling strenuously. He gritted his teeth with fury—something on the driver's seat seemed to resist him. Finally his features relaxed. He jumped down and cried, "At last!" He held a revolver, which he had torn out of the dead officer's hands.

We crossed the railway embankment. The two Germans kept their automatic rifles in readiness, holding them like babes in arms.

Suddenly a French soldier emerged from the darkness. The Germans started, drew their guns and called out: "Hands up!"

The Frenchman raised his hands. He was unarmed. I recognized the uniform of an adjutant of colonials.

"I want to ask you a favor," said the Frenchman.

I translated.

"I would like to see the general," he went on. "The general is under guard over there in the cellar."

"Then Charmes has been occupied?"

"Of course."

"Too bad," said the sergeant. "Why do you want to see the general?"

"He promised me the *Croix de Guerre*. I want him to keep his promise."

I don't know what the German answered, for at this moment a lusty *"Heil Hitler!"* resounded from the orchard where we had rested a few hours before.

The Germans turned their flashlight toward the orchard. A soldier in French uniform came forward, raising his right hand in the German salute.

"Heil Hitler!" the man repeated.

"Heil Hitler!" said the Germans.

For a moment they stood facing one another. It was a rare sight: the French soldier and the German soldier, face to face, their arms raised in the air. Behind the French soldier stood the adjutant with wide-open eyes. Sienkiewitz and I stood behind the Germans. And the whole scene was illuminated by the burning tank, tomb of a French officer who had not wanted to witness this scene.

"You must be hungry," said the Frenchman in good German, paying no attention to us. "I've prepared a meal for you."

The two Germans thanked him. I cleared my throat to attract their attention. The sergeant turned to me.

"You go back to the farm now. It's all right with us if you

sleep there. Tomorrow morning just walk out of the house and let the first German truck take you along. They'll put you in some camp."

They spoke to the man in French uniform.

"We'll stay here," said the man with the eyeglasses. "A few more generals are supposed to be hidden here."

I asked for a pass, so that we wouldn't be molested on our way back to the farm. The sergeant tore out a page of his notebook and asked for my name. At this moment I realized that I had forgotten to take the tag off my arm and to throw away my army book.

I hesitated for the fraction of a second.

"What's your name?" the sergeant repeated.

"My name is—" I said—"my name is—"

The soldier in French uniform looked at me. He had triangular eyebrows, like the devil.

"Diable," I said. "Jean Diable."

The German wrote down the name without looking up. "And you?"

I answered for Alfred.

"My comrade's name is Alfred. Alfred Polonais."

The sergeant wrote. Finally he gave me a paper with these words: "Sergeant Jean Diable and Private Alfred Polonais have been serving as my interpreters. They may sleep here. Tomorrow they must report to the nearest German post." Place, date, signature.

I thanked him and we went away. The others vanished in the opposite direction—both Germans, the man in uniform, and the adjutant. When we passed the tank, we both stopped. We did not say a word. But we knew that we were thinking the same thing.

We waited till all was still. Somewhere a car was moving away. Then Sienkiewitz climbed up on the tank. The inside was burning quietly, like the stove of a field kitchen. Sienkiewitz bent deeply into the section that had not yet caught fire. He remained in this position for about a minute. Then he straightened up, groaning.

"He is heavy," said Alfred Sienkiewitz, *alias* Polonais.

He pulled out the dead man by the arms. The lieutenant's face was calm and smooth. Only from his mouth, from his delicate, tender mouth, a line of blood ran over his chin, his neck, his uniform. The flames lent color and life to the sensitive face. But his hair, licked by the first flames, was singed.

The officer's body weighed heavily on my shoulders. In silence we carried him by turns. His arms hung down over my back. When I quickened my pace, the arms struck my back. I slowed down. The day was breaking.

We buried Second Lieutenant René Pierre Duval—born in Saint-Raphael (Alpes-Maritimes) on May 10th, 1913, and residing at Chambéry (Savoie)—at the edge of the forest of Charmes, twenty steps from the Rue de la Gare in the direction of Baccarat. His army book said to inform his mother in case of an accident. We gave the peasant woman, our hostess, his documents, his watch, and his badge. She promised to send them to the lieutenant's mother at the first opportunity. I hope she has kept her promise.

It was after four o'clock when we reached the farm. The house was dark. We went into the yard and made a noise. A window opened, and soon afterward the peasant woman appeared in a long white nightgown and a nightcap, bearing a candle. I explained to her that we had permission to sleep in her house. She took Alfred to the first floor and ordered the servant to make up a bed for me in the dining room. I asked her to let us sleep the next morning.

I remained alone in the dining room. The servant girl came in and put a candle on the table. Then she returned with such a pile of fresh, snow-white sheets and pillows and blankets that she was invisible behind their splendor. I helped her. We spread the immense, crackling sheet on the old plush sofa; she beat up the pillows. Over her white, slightly starched shirt, she wore a small gray cloak. When she bent down, her cloak opened and the outlines of her fresh small breasts were clearly visible. Beneath the starched white shirt those tender breasts stood out as beneath a coat of mail. She reminded me of the Maid of Orleans.

She did not look up till she had beaten the third pillow. She gave another tug at the blanket and then she looked up. She threw back her hair and smiled. Then she took the candle and put it back on the table. Her tiny feet protruded from her torn red slippers. The whole girl smelled of hay and youth.

I caressed the soft, full blanket. Then I felt her breath in my face. All the lost summer was in that breath, the heat of the day and the coolness of the night at sea.

The next morning she brought me, smiling, a large pot of hot, thick milk. Then I asked her her name.

It was Yvette.

We spent nearly the whole of next day trying desperately to obtain civilian clothes. In the morning we went back to our attic. The Germans had occupied the whole region, and Yvette, who came to see us as often as she could, told us that the Germans regarded the house as their kitchen. In the courtyard stood an immense goulash "cannon," and through the attic window we could see the Germans passing in and out of the house. At the moment they were searching the woods, driving stray French soldiers together, untying artillery horses, collecting arms and ammunition, and trying to put some automobiles in working order. Yvette had several times asked the peasant to give us some civilian clothes, but so far he had refused. She had also tried vainly to piece a couple of suits together from old rags. Then she relayed to us the rumor that the Germans were holding civilians of military age and treating them worse than soldiers. Despite all this, we were determined to smuggle ourselves through the lines in civilian clothes—but first we needed the clothes.

We lay on the bedstead, spoke little, and scarcely moved. Yvette said that our steps could be heard down in the kitchen and that one of the Germans—the chef—had asked who was walking around "on his head." This chef was "very angry at the English" and could scarcely wait to "go over there." He had told her that twenty men were being billeted on the house and that the attic must be cleared for the guests.

There had been a sort of incident, Yvette reported. The Anglophobe chef had poked around with a pitchfork in the hayloft and found the drunken French soldier sleeping off his liquor and rough treatment. The peasants had assured the German that they knew nothing of the hidden soldier, and the dictatorial cook had let it pass "this once." Once the peasant woman came up and assured us, pale and trembling, that we would have to go soon, for neither she nor her husband had any intention of being stood up against a wall on our account.

At two in the afternoon, Yvette brought us bread and warm milk and told us the coast was clear. The Germans were going away. We could hear their boots squeaking on the wooden stairs, and their nasal voices, so hard to distinguish from the squeaking of boots.

All was still. Alfred and I cautiously descended the stairs. The peasant woman was working in the kitchen. She was a dour, elderly woman with weary, care-worn features and tucked-up hair. She bade us wait for her husband. He and their son were very busy; a horse had fallen into the manure pit, and they were trying to pull him out. For ten whole minutes, ten times sixty precious seconds, she spoke with great animation about the horse and the manure pit, and it looked as though this episode were more important to her than the defeat and occupation of her country. And yet all her talking did me good. Inwardly I took my leave of life; there was a comforting pain in everything that signified life— a life without war, without hate, without all things of weight. There was no horror in this farewell to life, except that your nerves lay bare, and you perceived everything with double clarity. All the things you were seeing for the last time imprinted themselves on your mind with a sharpness that almost hurt; every gesture, every object seemed to be highlighted, like a close-up in a movie. On the shelf over the stove stood jars marked "Cloves," "Pepper," "Salt,"—the good old porcelain jars, in which no housewife ever keeps what is marked on them; there were flowers and dwarfs and rabbits on the jars, and they too signified life. Over the door hung a curtain of bone-lace, the sun sifted in through the half-opened door, and the little squares in the lace drew a checkerboard on the stone floor. A soft breeze swayed the curtain, and the sun and the breeze were life. From time to time Yvette came in, brown and sweating, carrying wash and laughing; and she, especially, was life.

At last the peasant came in wearing a giant straw hat. His hands were full of manure and his hard eyes full of earth; as he walked and stood, he carried with him the certainty that life would go on. The more sharply I saw my departure, the deeper I sank into the hopelessness of my own situation, the clearer it became to me that the world would not stop still because of my own downfall. And strange as it seemed to me, I gathered strength from the life that was slipping away from me. While I was held prisoner, some men would still be moving about, and that thought lent me the certainty that some day I should find a place on this earth. My heart clung to the salt-jars, the play of the sun on the floor, the straw hat, a smile, the breeze, the smell of manure. For in all things there is life. Only in dying is there death.

For minutes the peasant took no notice either of us or of the lost war. He spoke of the horse in the pit. "Your son," he said to his wife, "is still trying to pull him out. The German soldiers are helping him." Then, at last, the peasant turned to us.

I described our plan, and asked him to give us civilian clothes and either pass us off as his servants for a few days or let us go. I said that we would prefer to stay on a few days, as the armistice would be signed any minute and after that it would be easier to move about.

He listened in silence. He sat across the table from me, smoked his pipe, and said nothing. His wife leaned against his chair and looked over his shoulder.

"Hm," the man grumbled. "Maybe we can arrange something. After all, we Frenchmen have to help one another."

"Do you want to be stood up against the wall?" his wife asked.

"No. They won't do that so quick."

I tried to support this view.

"If you don't want to keep us," I said, "then we'll leave here at once. As soon as we are out of the house, no one will know who gave us the clothes."

"Yes," the peasant repeated. "No one will know . . ."

The woman sat down beside her husband. They both held their hands clasped in their laps. They were worn hands; the two pairs strangely resembled one another, like the features of married couples who grow old together. The fingers were

226

clasped lightly; they did not hold but merely touched one another; they rested in one another.

Suddenly the woman asked: "What part of France are you from?"

I hesitated. Then I said, "From the Pyrenees."

The hands made no move. But a spark of suspicion came into the woman's small, colorless eyes.

"From the Pyrenees. You wouldn't think so . . ."

I said nothing. Through the little window I saw the cyclists riding past the house. There was a constant coming and going of German soldiers. I bent over to avoid being seen.

Sienkiewitz began to exercise his own persuasive gifts. The peasant wiped the sweat from his forehead with his big red handkerchief. After some hesitation he turned to his wife: "The good Lord has commanded us to help our neighbor."

"*Monsieur* speaks such funny French," said the woman.

The peasant stood up: "Funny or not—I'll help you. Yvette! Yvette!"

He called Yvette. But instead of Yvette his son came in. He was still covered with filth, but two merry eyes shone in his face.

"Father! Father!" he cried.

"Did you get the horse out?"

"Yes," said the boy. "The soldiers helped me. But that's nothing. They gave us two horses besides. Horses they found somewhere. Come quick!"

The peasant woman rushed to the door. The old man put on his straw hat with slow dignity, but he whistled between his teeth as he followed the others. We were left alone. We exchanged glances. Never could anyone have felt more clearly that two horses were more valuable than two men.

We spoke not a word. Sienkiewitz paced back and forth. Finally I said: "Sit down. You're driving me crazy."

227

And again we fell silent.

I don't know how much time passed. At length the woman came back alone.

"Well—" she said.

We waited.

"Well—" she repeated. "You'll have to go soon. It can't be so bad to be a prisoner. The Germans are very nice. And they say the war will be over in two weeks. I'll give you some cigarettes."

She stood by the stove and turned her back to us. We knew that we were lost.

We tore each other's identification tags off our wrists and threw them into the open stove. The woman watched us in amazement, but we offered no explanation. After the tags we threw in all our papers. Our army books crackled in the flames. I tore up a few envelopes but kept the letters to which I was attached. My personal observer's notes and the drawings of German airplane models were sacrificed. At last, recalling the advice of Saint-Brice, we tore the regimental numbers off our uniforms and coats. The green thread with which my number was sewn on had run. Green was the color only of the Foreign Legion and the volunteer regiments, and the color alone would have given me away. I folded my tunic and threw it into a corner. I kept only a brown pullover, a present from my wife, and my coat, from which I was luckily able to tear the *écussons*, without leaving a green mark.

Then we turned to go. The woman offered us cigarettes, cheese, butter, chocolate.

We refused.

For over two months that was our last gesture reminiscent of human dignity.

CHAPTER EIGHT: MY NAME WAS

MAURICE NAPIER

The first passing german army truck stopped at the sight of us and "took us along." The soldiers on board had been collecting the gas-masks thrown away by the French, and we sat on a mountain of gas-masks.

At five o'clock we reached the village of Bayon. Outside the Hôtel des Deux Frères stood an endless column of prisoners. Certainly all prisoners have a heart-rending look. Man is not made to be another man's prisoner. But these prisoners, from all parts of France, had surrendered their dignity more quickly than usual. One detail, purely external, made them look particularly disconsolate. Nearly all of them had thrown off their steel helmets. Hardly any possessed caps. To protect themselves from the sun, the soldiers had ripped the leather and felt linings out of their helmets and put them on their heads. The black straps which held the linings together hung down their necks. Their faces were ghastly pale beneath the black felt rags.

Alfred and I took our places in the last row. Surrounded by our comrades, we were able to grasp the full extent of what had happened. From all the houses the swastika flag was flying. The symbol was so overwhelmingly clear that I still thought myself the dupe of a bad dream. A column of German soldiers kept marching past us. There were about a hundred men in the column, and they kept marching up and down the street, four abreast. While we stood waiting, they must have passed us twenty times, laughing as they watched the prisoners. I shall remember some of those faces years from now, though Hitler's soldiers were strangely alike. Every face expressed triumph and scorn. The soldiers had no guns, and they were all bareheaded; marching was easy for them. Even the goose-step was like a voluntary sport. Whenever the column passed us, the soldiers turned their heads to right or left and stared at us. A sharp command rang out, and they all began to sing: *"Wir marschieren nach Frankreich hinein"* (We are marching into France) or *"Jetzt geht's ins Heimatland, ins schöne Schwabenland"* (Now we are bound for home, our fair land of Swabia). Trucks kept passing, bearing more and more prisoners to an unknown destination. In one truck stood a French captain, arm raised in the German salute to the swastika flag over the hotel.

Behind me stood a group of German non-coms. One of them began talking to me, and when I answered in German, the others joined us. My feet hurt and I asked when we would be leaving.

"First we've got to catch all the hedge-shooters," said one of the non-coms, a man with the intelligent face of a typical German scholar.

"What's that?" I asked.

"You know that well enough," said another, and laughed like a man pleased with his own joke.

"Hedge-shooters," said the scholar, "are the dirty bastards that shoot from roofs and windows when we make our peaceful entry into a village. That's a specialty with you Frenchmen. Especially the black gentlemen. Those fellows!" He pointed to a number of Negroes and Arabs in our ranks. "The pillars of French culture! Here in Bayon two men of

230

our regiment were killed by snipers. You'd better pray that we find the guilty parties in a hurry. If we don't—"

The singing column passed again. Again I stared at the faces of these well-combed and well-scrubbed youths. And again the song leaped at me, as a village dog leaps at a ragged beggar.

"If we don't," the scholar concluded, "you'll all be shot."

Officers emerged from the restaurant across the street. Orderlies drove up, sprang to attention, delivered letters.

I risked a question: "Have you any news of the war?"

"Of the war?" said one of the non-coms. "There is no more war. France is suing for an armistice, and we'll finish off England in two weeks. The Führer is in Compiègne."

One of the Germans was writing a field postcard on a comrade's back.

"This time I can really write my wife: *Auf baldiges Wiedersehen!* (See you soon!)"

Someone delivered himself of the expected obscenity. Everyone laughed.

The scholar turned to me: "Have you any news of your family?"

Surprised at his interest, I answered honestly: "No, not for the last six weeks."

The non-com adjusted his pince-nez and turned to his comrades in a professorial manner: "Do you hear that, gentlemen—no mail in the last six weeks. Haven't we a right to be grateful? Didn't we have mail every day, even in the front lines?"

All agreed. A chubby-faced little non-com with the black and red ribbon of the Iron Cross, Second Class, stepped up to the group. He spoke in a muffled voice, but so that I could hear him distinctly: "Can't find the sniper. I guess we'll stand the whole gang of them against the wall."

I didn't stir.

"Snipers!" said the scholar. "What a lousy way to act! A German could never do such a thing."

The little fat one with the ribbon caught his breath and went on: "We've found out at least that they were black men. But you can't tell the difference between these fellows. They're all black."

"So much the better," said the man with the pince-nez. "Who cares if we shoot the black cut-throats a little sooner?"

In front of me and beside me stood Negroes. In their helmet linings they seemed even more wretched than the others. One handsome young giant standing beside me saw that they were talking about him. He looked at the Germans and smiled a broad smile.

"Just smile," said the scholar to the black man. "We'll soon make you a Moor's head shorter."

The joke was a hit. Everyone laughed. Even the Negro laughed.

Our column grew longer and longer. From all sides came trucks with groups of prisoners. In every group there were black men. The colonial regiments had covered the last retreat.

"These black bastards and the Jews were supposed to bring culture to Germany," said the young professor. Again his wit was well received.

"Captain Kral has given them fifteen minutes more to hand over the sniper," said the fat man.

Alfred and I looked at one another. Neither of us spoke a word. But both of us felt that there was no fear left in us.

"Fifteen minutes," a non-com repeated.

The hundred men came by, turning their heads and singing. Suddenly our column started moving. The fat man, the

scholar and the others looked after us. Soldiers with fixed
bayonets were driving us forward, three abreast.

We marched about an hour before we sighted a camp on
a grassy hillside behind the village of Villacourt. Its only resemblance to a camp lay in the triple barbed-wire barrier
which the Germans had hastily strung around it. Machine
guns had been set up at the four corners of this barrier; behind each gun two German soldiers lay in the grass. Through
a narrow cleft in the barbed wire, the prisoners were driven,
one by one, into the enclosed meadow. Despite the broad
expanse, there was barely room enough for the forty thousand prisoners in that camp to sit or lie body to body. And
there was no shelter whatsoever.

As I slipped through the barbed wire, a voice struck my
ear: "Habe!"

It was an unfamiliar voice. I didn't look around. I felt my
heart pounding in my throat. I thought in a flash: my regiment! Taken prisoner near here. My name. Someone has betrayed me. It's all over. But afterward I saw no one I knew.
To this day, I do not know who called my name.

German soldiers were shouting in all directions. They ordered members of the same regiments to sit down together.
Some regiments had fallen into German hands intact. Alfred
and I stood alone in the crowd, doubly lonely, doubly lost.
At length we decided to "pal up" with one of the regiments.
We chose the Ninety-eighth Infantry and sat down beside
them.

For supper we still had something to eat. We shared our
rations. Meager as they were, they left us with an unquench-
able thirst. Our canteens were empty. The Germans had assigned us a single water wagon, and thousands of men were
lined up around it. We joined the line. The Germans stood
idly by as the prisoners shoved, cursed, scratched, and

wrestled their way toward the wagon. Now and then a cry arose from a prisoner who had become wedged between the throng and the wagon. The Germans stood by and smiled at the spectacle of our "self-government." Alfred and I stood for what seemed hours, and in the end received only a handful of water. But even the few sips did us good. It was oppressively hot. A sultry summer's day was drawing to an end.

Alfred and I began to talk about the projected execution. It had been nothing but bluff, we decided, but a clever bluff that had pretty well convinced us. Then the rumor reached our ears that the Negroes were being segregated and the sniper of Bayon was still being sought in their midst. Before we had a chance to ask if there was any truth in the rumor, German soldiers came pushing through the camp, rounding up the "blacks"—meaning Negroes and Arabs—with kicks and shoves. Great storm clouds had drawn across the sky. All afternoon the heavens had been gray and leaden. Now the air stood still. A village and a church steeple beyond the barbed wire seemed improbably near. Somewhere in the distance a storm was rumbling.

The Negroes were assembled in one part of the meadow. Most of them dragged their feet, and there was something grotesque in their footsore gait, because they were naturally light-footed, and seemed to hop when they limped. The soldiers drove the black prisoners before them at bayonet point; if one of them slowed down, he was "tickled" with a bayonet. When all the "blacks" had been gathered in one place, a German officer came out and began to address them. The man stood too far from me, and the crowd around him was too dense for me to hear what he said. But he roared at them in German for minutes on end; and I saw his head turning red as a tomato. Of course none of the Negroes understood so much as a syllable. They looked on the white man in the gray uniform as a sick man: half in fear and half in amusement. Some of them laughed openly; they could not believe that his oratorical revelation was meant in earnest. The roarer must have known that the sons of Senegal and the Sudan could not understand him. But like most of the Germans whom I met in the coming months, he attached less importance to the sense than to the tone of his remarks.

Sienkiewitz and I stood close by the barbed wire. Outside, German soldiers were patrolling. One of them stopped still, folded his arms and asked: "What are you gaping at?"

I answered in German and he grew friendlier. I asked if there was any news.

"The armistice has been signed," he said.

"With Italy too?"

"No, not yet. You'll have to be patient until the war is over."

"Are we going to stay here long?" I asked. Of course I knew that the sentry had as little idea as ourselves what would be done with us. But I asked him just the same, and hoped for a favorable reply.

"You'll stay here until the war is over."

"When will that be?"

He shrugged his shoulders and went on patrolling. He was a little man with a death's head.

The officer had stopped shouting. The Negroes were lined up ten abreast. The officer went up and down in front of them, his hands folded behind his back. The drama was losing its interest, and one by one the spectators went away to find a place to sleep. Those who still had their ponchos made tents of them. We crowded beneath the tents, expecting the storm to start at any moment. The air grew more and more sultry. Dusk came. The village and the church sank beneath the mist. Behind the dark clouds the sun had gone down unnoticed. One darkness vanished beneath another.

The counting of the blacks had been completed. There were about four thousand of them, from several different regiments. Now they were told to form groups of a hundred. The Germans couldn't make themselves properly understood and screamed louder and louder. Alfred and I crawled under Alfred's poncho to shut out the sound. But that was impossible.

I was afraid to speak.

"Do you really think . . . ?" Alfred finally asked.

"What?"

"That they'll be stood up against the wall?"

"Nonsense!"

I couldn't carry the idea to its conclusion.

I cast a furtive glance at the place where the Negroes were waiting. From each group of a hundred one man was arbitrarily picked. When the forty had been chosen, the others were sent away. They seemed to have no idea what was wanted of them. They begged for food, for a sip of water, for a place to sleep or a poncho. My view of the forty was indistinct. But I could see the gleam of their white teeth. They seemed to enjoy the special attention paid them.

We tried to sleep, but the heat was too oppressive. We lay still for fear of losing our places beneath the poncho. There was lightning on the horizon, followed by a rumbling of thunder. Up on the hill, close by the barbed wire, the forty were standing.

Suddenly the beam of a searchlight swept over us. I lifted my head. A few hundred prisoners raised themselves on their elbows. Ten or twelve German soldiers marched past our heads. Only one at a time was visible in the light, for the beam stood still. It was directed at the forty Negroes.

Sienkiewitz gripped my arm.

The forty Negroes marched off. One after another they marched through the beam of light.

At that moment church bells began to ring. The bright, cheery sound was not from a single church. All the village churches round about rang their bells at once. A motorcycle rattled down the road behind the camp. The cyclist called to our guards: "Peace! Peace! The peace has been signed."

Throughout the camp men jumped up. Everywhere there was movement in the night. A truck climbed up the steep road and stopped behind the camp. All I could hear was: "Where is the captain?"

"In the mayor's house, next to the church. What have you got?"

"Champagne for the victory celebration."

The truck chugged on. And the church bells went on ringing. The bright festive sound grew more and more like the ringing of bells announcing fire: a burning house in a village. The unceasing bells of peace sounded like an alarm.

"La paix! La paix!" cried a Frenchman beside me, an old soldier with a beard.

On the road the motorcycles drove back and forth. The guards began to sing softly. Somewhere near me a Frenchman was singing too.

I lay still, my face close to the steaming ground.

And then the first shots rang out. The volley was repeated four times. Then all was still. The camp had turned to stone. The beam swept over a ghastly waxworks. Then it went out, and only the bells continued to ring and ring.

I do not know how this rigidity can have melted. But suddenly the rain began to fall. The storm had hung over us all day. Such was the violence of its discharge it made you feel that the heavens could no longer bear their agony.

Forty thousand men sought shelter beneath a few scraps of yellow oilcloth.

All next day the prisoners kept streaming in. A few of them were men of the region; one had fought with his battalion a hundred yards behind his own house. His wife had seen him fall into the hands of the Germans. He showed us his house, right beside the little village church. He looked sadly toward his home through the barbed wire, past the soldiers lying in the field with their machine gun. All day long they lay there, pointing their machine guns at us. We saw only their gray steel helmets. But even if we had seen their faces, we could have read nothing in them. That had struck me in the very first hours: the remarkable similarity of the faces beneath the gray steel helmets. I had known Germany and the Germans—but in the last years an inexplicable change must have occurred. It was hard to tell the soldiers apart. Their faces seemed to obey a command. They had all grown alike, expressionless, smooth, hard, and grim.

Sienkiewitz and I wandered about all day, in search of an identity. We couldn't go on forever being Diable and Polonais, Devil and Pole; some sort of papers or identification had to be found. I hoped that many soldiers had lost their tags and papers, so that we might remain unnoticed at the inexorably approaching registration. But I had underestimated the bureaucratic spirit of the French: they lost everything but their papers.

The hunt for confirmation of my existence became a mania. For hours I passed up and down the camp. But I saw no men: all I saw was identification tags. I saw black and white wrists, rough wrists and delicate wrists, bony wrists and fat wrists; some were emaciated and on some the veins stood out: but every wrist had its little oval tag with the name, number, class, and place of mobilization. More and more I felt that this tiny plaque of punched metal meant life or death. Five times I crossed the camp. I looked on the ground, among the knapsacks; I bent down whenever I saw something gleaming on the ground; several times I mistook a piece of glass for a plaque. For the first time in my life I felt that a man is not a man unless he is stamped and registered.

For hours a rumor had been going around that we would be organized by regiments and shipped off somewhere. Previously, of course, our names would be registered. At last we were actually ordered to line up according to regiments. Alfred and I were separated from the Ninety-eighth Infantry. For the *isolés*—those whose entire regiment had not been captured, but who had been taken singly or in groups of one, two, or three—the Germans reserved the worst place. Latrines had been dug at one end of the camp—by the prisoners of course—and all day long there was a steady pilgrimage in that direction. The *isolés* were ordered to form a group beside the latrines. I buckled on my belt and sauntered over. Only a few yards away there were green, sweet-smelling fields. That lovely brown potato field must have given off the smell of earth after rain. But in the potato field lay the gray steel helmets behind their machine guns. And here it smelled as though we were rotting in our own graves.

Strange are the ways of the Lord, and God's backdrops do not always consist of blue sky and white clouds. The good Lord sometimes shows himself at the edge of a latrine for forty thousand prisoners. In the midst of the stench, the good Lord sent me His angel. His name was Maurice Napier.

Tired and despairing, I sat down—and suddenly I beheld a pair of red boots. They were well made, and their color was nearly bright red. The sight was so strange that I couldn't help looking up. Beside me lay a prisoner, yawning. He was very young, twenty or twenty-one. He had light blond hair that hung down over his forehead in a riotous mop. His kindly gray eyes attracted my attention almost as much as the boots. For days, weeks perhaps, I had seen only wild, exhausted, gloomy eyes. But this young fellow looked out on the world with merry indifference. Everything seemed to amuse him.

We looked at one another and smiled.

"Where did you get the red boots?" I asked.

"Found them in a house," he said. And then he began to sing. He sang like a man who has made up his mind to keep himself amused for the rest of his days.

"Are you alone?" I asked.

"Yes," the young fellow said. "That is, there are two of us. Bedaud and I. That's about all there was left of our regiment."

As though hypnotized, I gazed at the identification tag on his slender, supple wrist. I was like an alcoholic going back to his vice.

"What regiment?"

"Three Hundred Thirty-first Infantry. We went through the assault on Sedan. Or rather, we didn't go through it. The regiment was broken up. Nothing left of it. A fine mess."

He crossed his arms beneath his head and prepared to take a sun bath. He had deftly stuck two leaves in his nostrils to serve as a nose shade.

"I lost my regiment too," I said.

"Which one?"

I named it.

He whistled through his teeth.

"You'd better not mention it," he said. "At Laon the Germans shot all the volunteers."

"I know," I said. "I threw my papers away."

240

"What will you do when they release the prisoners?" he asked. "They'll keep you."

I had no answer. He leaned on his elbows and looked at me.

We spoke of indifferent matters. He told me he was a truck driver. His last job had been driving a circus truck. His mother was a widow, living in Millau, the old city of the glove-makers. She too made gloves. He had an elder brother, but God knows where he was.

"You could be my elder brother," he said.

"Yes . . . I guess I could . . ."

He pulled out his penknife and began slowly to open the chain of his identification tag.

"What are you doing?" I asked with bated breath.

"I'm giving you my tag. Why shouldn't there be two Napiers? I still have my army book."

"Thank you, Maurice," I said. "But there can't be two Napiers with the same first name and the same number in the same camp."

That stopped him.

"No, of course there can't," he agreed. Angrily he hurled his knife into the ground. Little round beads of sweat stood over his well-formed eyebrows. "I'll have a look around," he said finally. He stood up and left me.

Ten minutes later he came back.

"*Tout va bien*," he said, laughing. He held his tag in his hand. "From here we're going to be sent to ten different camps. All we have to do is arrange to march off in two different groups."

He sat down beside me and gave me the dog license, as he called it. I seized his hand and shook it.

"Nothing to thank me for," he said simply. He was a little embarrassed. "And by the way—"

He took out his wallet. It was a torn old wallet of brown leather. He looked through the letters and picked three or four, which he held out to me.

"Here are some letters from my mother," he said. "From *our* mother, rather. Luckily I kept the envelopes. If anybody doubts your identity, you show him these letters that you received at the front."

I didn't want to take the letters, but he insisted. He kept only the last one he had received, just before the fall of Sedan.

"I had luck up there," he said. "That obligates a fellow."

I cast a look at the letters, which were now my own. The trembling hand of an old woman. She must have been a simple soul, an old peasant woman with innumerable wrinkles and a shawl around her head. Take care, my son, and don't catch cold. Wrap your muffler around your neck and God will keep you. All mothers write the same letters.

We shared our last piece of bread. Alfred brought a cookpot full of hot soup which a woman of Villacourt had passed over the wire, telling him to keep the pot. We celebrated my brotherhood with Maurice Napier. Alfred hadn't found any papers, but he seemed less concerned. He had procured all the necessary information about a disbanded regiment and planned to say he had belonged to it.

"That reminds me," said Maurice, "that there are two of us survivors of the Three Hundred Thirty-first, Bedaud and myself. Bedaud has gone to look for water. Don't tell Bedaud about all this. He worked for the post-office and he's difficult."

We understood. Bedaud returned a minute later. He was a little man with bad skin full of little red pimples. He was hard of hearing; the explosion of a Stuka bomb had burst his eardrum. He brought no water.

Alfred and I joined the line at the water-wagon. "And whosoever shall give to drink unto one of these little ones a cup of cold water only in the name of a disciple," wrote St. Matthew, "verily I say unto you, he shall in no wise lose his reward." But the Germans gave us no cup of cold water—neither in a disciple's nor the devil's name. When we reached the wagon, there wasn't a drop left. Hundreds of men were turned away thirsty. My throat burned, and my dry tongue stuck to the roof of my mouth. My mouth felt as though I had eaten paper. And yet I was saved. I no longer saw wrists. The world no longer consisted of dangling disks. I was no longer chained like Gulliver, with a thousand dwarfs' chains around my wrist.

And I had my name. My name was Maurice Napier.

We left Villacourt for Lunéville in a group of a thousand men. Maurice Napier I and Maurice Napier II had parted. I joined the first group, Maurice the last. In this way we were certain to be sent to two different camps.

The villages and towns through which we marched had all been occupied by the Germans. It was high summer and the day was particularly hot. The sun beat straight down at us. We marched in our long heavy coats, bathed in sweat. The entire landscape was yellow as an egg-yolk in the sun. A summery buzzing filled the stillness, like the buzzing of bees. The dust swirled up and turned into millions of glittering grains. In the villages the Germans sat half naked in the sun and drank beer. The whole thing was like a bad dream. In nightmares you find yourself naked in the midst of a fully-clothed crowd. This was the opposite, and it was no less ghastly. We were ashamed of the clothes and the weight we were carrying.

The Germans sat in front of the houses in provocative nakedness. I do not know whether the German conquerors in Paris, Oslo, Prague or any of the cities they have occupied, ever proclaimed their contempt for the natives as openly as here; or whether there is any more brutal way of flaunting your power than nakedness. By their nakedness the Germans "made themselves at home"; they showed their disrespect for the defenseless women of the conquered; they enjoyed the summer in plain sight of all those for whom there were no more seasons. In this nakedness there lay an unchivalrous and unmanly exhibition of physical superiority, a bragging self-assurance, and not least, a sadistic desire to intensify the prisoners' sufferings from the heat. Most of the Germans wore nothing but tiny swimming trunks on their bodies, and forage caps on their smooth-shorn heads. Naked, they pastured their horses; naked, they sat drinking beer in front of the inns; naked, they bowled in the middle of the street; naked, they played cards outside the houses of the peasants. But the chief amusement of this army of flesh lay in taking our pictures. In every village our pictures were taken ten, twenty, fifty times; and if the Negroes or Arabs marched apart, they were driven in with us, to give the pictures a "black-and-white" effect. They especially liked to photograph those prisoners who wore the up-turned lining of their steel helmets and looked like the participants in a hunger march.

Outwardly at least, the French villages had been transformed into German villages with lightning speed. The visible aspects of the organization were complete. (Later I was to see that there were actually great gaps in this organization.) There were printed German signs all over the walls: an arrow showed the way to the horse trough; the local command was clearly indicated; decrees were pasted up on all the stable doors. In every small town an anti-aircraft post was set up. Everything was clear, visual, almost strident, and I couldn't help thinking of the French army, forever hiding and slinking along walls.

Hundreds of cars, trucks, troop transports drove by us. Soldiers driving to work had neat, spotlessly clean white work clothes instead of the warmer uniforms; of course none of them wore a coat. The coats of our guards were carried after them in trucks. Everything we saw in this very first day showed us that discipline in the German army was a fighting discipline. Germany had no desire to turn its soldiers into pacifists.

Our thirst became more and more unbearable as we marched. The villagers had set chairs and tables in front of their houses, and enormous pails full of fresh clear water stood upon them. We had our cups in our hands, and in passing we could have dipped them into the pails. But the soldiers escorting us with fixed bayonets were opposed to this contact with the civilian population. Thousands of us passed the wells with parched throats, stretching out our cups like blind beggars seeking alms. The soldiers were not numerous enough to prevent a few of us from getting a cup of water from time to time. Women and girls ran after us with their pails, brought us glasses filled with water, sprinkled cooling water on our burning foreheads. This was France at its best; these merciful women cooling our misery, despising death. For not only were they challenging our guards, who rushed at them with lowered bayonets, but, what was worse, they remained behind in the villages with German soldiers who witnessed the entire scene as they took the air, pouring cold beer down their throats.

A German drill sergeant—to judge by his cap, which was all he had on aside from his tiny swimming trunks—was standing with a beer mug in hand before one of the peasant houses as we passed by. He was a gigantic fellow; his belly hung down in folds over his trunks. A young woman had set several pails full of water on a table by the roadside. When he saw her running after us, he flew into a rage and kicked the whole table over. The pails fell on the road, tumbling in all directions, and the blessed wetness was soaked up by the dusty white highway. The soldiers around him clapped their hands in approval.

We had been prisoners for three days and had received nothing to eat. There were no more "provisions" lying along the roads. Except for the dead horses, poisoning the air for miles around with their sugary smell, the conquerors had picked up everything and carried it away with magic swiftness. The villagers themselves had nothing to eat, not even bread. Besides, hundreds of thousands of us had all taken the same route to Germany, by way of Lunéville, Dieuze, Sarrebourg, Sarre Union, and Sarreguemines. To the first contingents the women had apparently given all they had. Our torment was enhanced by the sight of innumerable loaves of bread piled high on German trucks moving in both directions. From time to time the white-clad German soldiers tossed a loaf among the marchers; in amusement they looked on as the prisoners flung themselves on the bread. After two hours marching, we rested five minutes. A bread truck drove by, a soldier threw a loaf in our midst, and a frightful scramble ensued. Our guards were not tired. They carried nothing but their rifles, and many even had bicycles. They thoroughly enjoyed the battle for a morsel of bread, and they interfered only when a black took part in the mêlée. The gymnastics teacher—for that is what he must have been in civil life—who drove my column along, tore a piece of bread from the hands of an Arab, and magnanimously extended it to a white prisoner. Never was surprise at human baseness more eloquently expressed than in the features of the "black."

Alfred, who hobbled along by my side—his feet bloody and swollen—was horrified at my imprudence in speaking German. But I couldn't resist the temptation to sound out my guards: I had not yet begun to decide what sort of fairy tale I should dish up later. The gymnastics teacher said: "You must be an Alsatian. I saw that at once. The Alsatians look much more intelligent."

Good manners prevented me from protesting at the man's flattery. Besides, it netted me a little white wine and a loaf of bread. In one of the villages a group of non-coms was sitting on the terrace of a café drinking wine. Perhaps there was a German Alsatian among them, or perhaps the purpose was merely to reward the conduct of most of the Alsatians in the French army: in any case, they asked in genial tones whether there were any Alsatians in our midst. When my gymnastics teacher amiably prodded me in the back with his bayonet point and described me as an Alsatian, I was rewarded with a word of friendly encouragement, a bottle of white wine, and a loaf of bread. These I divided with Alfred and the Arab while the gymnastics teacher wasn't looking.

In nearly all the villages the women ran after us. Their eyes were full of pity and horror in that strange combination created only by self-pity. And indeed nearly all the women asked after some regiment or other, some company, some name. We would have had to know all France, the entire French army to answer the thousands of questions: Is he among you? Where can he be? Searching eyes, hopeless amid hope, followed the defeated army. No, we knew none of the names. All we could have said was that "he" was just as wretched as we were.

More and more of our number fell by the wayside. They fell down and they couldn't go on. Had there really been so many old men in the army, or had so many of the soldiers become old men? We had a feeling that only old men lay by the roadside. Men with red, gray, black beards lay still, until a German soldier rushed at them with his gun.

"Get up out of there!" roared the German soldiers.

It sounded like the barking of dogs.

If a man couldn't get up, a few kicks helped him.

"Get up! Get up!"

You heard it all along the road leading to the city of Lunéville, where the once famous Peace of Lunéville had been signed.

It was late at night when we reached the camp at Lunéville —the city sports stadium. There was nothing either to eat or drink. Alfred and I threw ourselves on the black dirty sand of the race track and fell asleep.

When I woke up, Maurice Napier stood before me.

During the next few days we were dragged from one camp to another. We made two vain attempts to separate Maurice Napier I from Maurice Napier II. On the third night we reached a city whose name they told us was Dieuze. The real Maurice Napier had vanished. He had apparently been taken to another camp.

The rain was coming down in buckets when we reached Dieuze. On the way Alfred and I had fallen in with three other *isolés:* Jean, a dry-goods clerk; Paul, a driver for the Renault works; and Denis, an insurance agent—all three from Paris. We passed through Dieuze without getting a good look at the place. The town was wrapped in darkness; from the numerous inns you could hear the singing of drinking German soldiers. Here and there a door opened and spewed forth a group of singing soldiers.

During our whole journey I had been certain that we were marching directly toward the German border; Dieuze itself was forty kilometers north of Nancy; according to my calculations, the German border could be no more than fifty kilometers further on. I had every reason to suppose that the next stage would take us to the border. But from the very first moment I had resolved to escape sooner or later. And I knew that flight would only be conceivable while we were still near the French cities, where I could count on the help of the French civilian population. I decided to remain in Dieuze at all costs.

The camp itself was none too inviting. In the midst of a cloudburst we marched through the broad gate and suddenly found ourselves behind high red walls. At that point it seemed impossible that we should ever escape from the German dungeon. There were about twenty thousand of us lined up in the enormous courtyard.

Before 1914, when Dieuze had been German, the Prussians had built a barracks here. The enormous square courtyard, bordered on three sides by a wall and on the fourth by a riding academy, was the typical German barracks yard, dusty and desolate. The riding academy and the barracks, built of red brick with a black, slightly inclined slate roof, also recalled the age of the Wilhelms. Later, in a pacifist age, under the French Republic, the barracks had been transformed into auto repair shops. During the war, a new transformation took place. The repair shops were turned into military garages; the administration building became the Hôpital Buttini.

From nine that night till four in the morning we remained in the courtyard. The rain had lost its violent character; first there was one of nature's silences, then it began to rain again, just as hard, but more quietly. The water ran down our faces and necks, collected in our shoes. You could no longer distinguish between one face and another. Again I thought of

Saint-Brice and felt that none of these twenty thousand had known what they were fighting for; how else explain this great cold strangeness? A mild yellow light sifted through the windows of the administration building, the Hôpital Buttini. From time to time a German soldier stepped out of the riding academy, in a raincoat with a yellow, green, and black pattern. Now and then there was a cry of "Get up!" Some prisoner had fallen down and lay in the water. All of us had looked death in the eye countless times in the past month. But never had we felt it so distinctly as at the sight of these unwounded men who fell down beside us and lay insensible with their faces in the mounting puddles. To live is to defend yourself. To die is to cease defending yourself against water with all the filth of the courtyard in it.

Alfred, Jean, Paul, Denis, and I clung together, afraid to lose one another. We held each other by our sleeves, belts, coats, loose buttons. To us it seemed terribly important to stay together, to form an island in this lifeless sea, on which heads floated like little black dirty waves. Here and there the number of a regiment was called out. A dark group plucked itself out of the dark mass and moved off toward one of the houses. Only the *isolés* were never called. About four in the morning, when our fatigue was intolerable and we had a feeling that the rain was not only falling from the slowly graying sky but also rising from below, I suggested that we try to find a place to sleep.

We wandered about through dark courtyards, stumbling over sleepers, stubbing our toes on rocks. We bumped into walls, fell headlong over soldiers, grasped at the darkness. Innumerable ruins of cars stood about. Cars without wheels, trucks without motors, smashed army trucks. We climbed into every car that seemed to have a halfway intact top. But each had its load of sleepers. There were soldiers even in open cars, sleeping with their faces in the rain, glad not to be standing. And so we wandered from car to car.

At length we found one. As far as we could tell in the faint dawn, it was a French ambulance with four "beds" inside. It must have been out of commission for some time, for it had neither tires nor rims, but stood on its spokes: it was like the war cripples who had so terrified me as a child, crawling along on their amputated leg-stumps.

We greeted our sleeping car with cries of joy. For each of us there was a separate bed; Paul, the red-blond driver with the sly eyes, who looked like the fox in the Disney pictures, slept on the sheltered driver's seat. We closed the back door of the ambulance, determined to sleep no matter what happened.

Next morning I awoke to the sound of somebody roaring *"Raus! Raus!"* in Prussian. I looked around our ambulance. And I saw that I had been sleeping on a sheet covered with blood.

I wondered who had died there.

We found four berths on the stone floor of Workshop No. 3, and then I decided to have a look around the camp. I wanted to explore the possibilities of escape and find out how the guards were organized.

As I walked out of my barracks, assembly was just being blown. I had to postpone my exploration and join the ranks. The rumor spread quickly that we were to be searched. Four or five German soldiers stood before each column and ordered us, through interpreters, to hand over all cameras, knives, razor blades, maps, fountain pens and flashlights, which they gathered into a large bag. The "detachment" was headed by a little blond sergeant who looked like an Aryan tadpole. He went from one man to another weighing the objects in his hand like a pawnbroker. Everything happened quickly, efficiently and—above all—with remarkable impudence. If a French sergeant had ever appropriated a prisoner's camera for his own personal use, he would have been sent to jail. But I think that France was wrong. War is an immoral business, and it is absurd to set up moral principles within the framework of its immorality. One of the main reasons for the warlike spirit of the Germans was assuredly the fact that they looked on war as an occasion for unrestricted plunder. Victory belonged not only to the army as a whole, but to each individual soldier: victory meant booty and pillage. The uniformed tadpole stuck a camera, a flashlight, a fountain pen and a hunting knife into his belt. But whenever this Hans in Luck discovered something "better," he tossed the previously acquired fountain pen or camera into the bag. The value of his holdings increased from minute to minute. He went on taking everything that happened to please him, and in the end looked like a cowboy with a complete drugstore in his belt, instead of cartridges.

When we had all been "searched" and the soldiers, bowed beneath the weight of their bags, had gone away, I set out to explore the camp. I found out that it was divided into two parts. The front part consisted of the dilapidated riding school, three or four garages, and the administration building where the commandant had his office. The whole was surrounded by high walls. In the middle was the immense Prussian drill ground into which we had been herded the day before. This front part of the camp bordered on a road that came from the village of Dieuze; at the time I did not know where it led to. The road was barred. There were sentries outside the high red walls. The rear part of the camp was somewhat less forbidding. Its yard bordered on the large drill ground in front and a broad open gate led from one section of the camp to the other. This second part of the camp included the junk yard, twenty to thirty garages, and a four-story building of the German period, used as an infirmary for the prisoners of war. This house, I was told, was once a barracks for the *Gardes Mobiles,* and had served as an infirmary in the first World War. For the present, of course, the sick and the wounded lay on the strawless floor of one of the abandoned garages, exactly like the rest of us. A cloud of black dust hovered over the whole camp. This junk-yard dust was no common dust; it was a black powder, a sea of silvery-black metallic sawdust.

But at the very rear of the camp, there were three or four trees, a small green patch of grass and, best of all, a free vista into the open. Here no wall barred the view, only a wooden fence no taller than a man, and a barbed-wire barrier separated us from the outside world. Here too there were German sentries, of course; but if you climbed up on a sand hill or an old cart, you could see far into the countryside, beyond the fence and the barbed wire. You could see the railway tracks passing close behind the camp, the road twisting down to Dieuze, a few lovely red roofs, the church tower, a forest, another church tower, a field, a horse; you could see another narrow road, right behind the camp. From time to time a girl in white would bicycle by, holding her skirt down over her knees with one hand. The only disadvantage of this blissful spot was that the Germans had chosen it for the latrines. All along the fence there were squatting soldiers. If you wanted to look out into the country, you had to climb the mound of earth thrown up in digging the latrines, and that destroyed some of the enchantment of the green, summery meadows.

As I stood there watching the fields and the numerous soldiers—they looked like frogs ready to leap—I decided that at night it would not be too hard to jump over the fence and the barbed wire: one could either avoid the guards or spring at their necks. But then I felt that I was being watched. I turned around and saw that field-gray sentries were posted on the roofs of two garages. They had climbed up on ladders, and could easily survey the whole terrain; they even had portable telephones beside them. You couldn't move a step without being seen by the spies on the roofs. Wherever you went, their eyes were glued to your back. I would have to think up something else.

When I returned to our garage, I heard that we were getting warm food and straw for our berths that same day. An hour later, two large trucks actually rolled into the yard, both piled high with straw. We stood in groups at a respectful distance, assuming that the straw would be distributed. But nothing of the sort occurred. After some time, the soldiers in the straw trucks motioned us to "come and get it." A wild mêlée ensued. Hundreds of prisoners rushed at the loaded trucks. Men vanished beneath the straw. Each one tried to seize as much as possible. All crowded around the trucks with open arms. Some grasped a human head or two along with their straw, pulling both straw and hair with equal vigor. When a man actually came off with an armful of straw, ten, twelve, twenty others ran after him, tugging in all directions. The hard-won "bed" slipped through the poor fellow's fingers. After a mighty struggle, scarcely anyone was left with more than a few miserable wisps of straw. Only a few of the strongest managed to save a whole bundle and dash across the yard with it. Paul, our fox-faced mechanic, was one of these, but a few others caught up with him: one seized him by the legs and tripped him, and the lovely yellow straw dropped into the black dust of the yard. A little lawyer from Marseille, whom I had met the night before, was wiping his broken eyeglasses. He had tears in his eyes, and anxiously clasped ten or twelve wisps of straw under one arm, like a briefcase. My nose, my eyes, my neck were full of straw. A few minutes passed before I could see anything. Then I noticed the two Germans in the truck. They did not resemble one another. One of them wore unframed spectacles, and the only noteworthy thing in his face was his mouth, which was so small that it seemed incapable of taking in food. This man, I thought, must have drunk lemonade instead of milk as a child. In civilian life he must have been some sort of lesser court official. The other was more like a peasant, with clipped hair, clipped eyebrows, clipped eyes. A quadrangular man. Yet as they stood up there, in the straw truck, with legs widespread and arms folded, they seemed strangely alike. Both were laughing, and it was this identical laughter that created the resemblance in their features. They laughed loudly, with open mouths, shaking yet motionless. The whole yard resounded with their laughter as an army of prisoners groveled in black dust.

The expected warm food was "postponed" till the following day. But the kitchen was beginning to function, and I set out to explore around it. I was frightfully hungry and I heard that it might be possible to get a piece of bread.

The kitchen occupied a one-story building in the second yard facing the infirmary. A barbed-wire barrier as tall as a man surrounded it. Inside the barrier stood a number of field kitchens and enticing warm vapors rose from two or three kettles. Guards paced up and down outside: but their power was limited. They were unable to chase away the prisoners who clung to the wire as grapes cling to a vine and sucked in the aroma of the kettles. They clung to one another, they pushed one another aside, and all they were waiting for was a smell. Greedy, hungry eyes seemed to jump over heads and fences. Now and then one of the prisoners would let go the wire, fall down, get up and slip away—like a man tired and disgusted with himself, coming out of a brothel. Another would immediately take his place; other fingers would clutch the wire.

A soldier appeared on the stairs leading down from the kitchen. He stood there for a moment, then turned around and disappeared inside. He was a middle-aged man, with a swollen, rather friendly beer-drinker's face and thick, red ear lobes. A white apron over his army coat made him look almost human. Once again he came back and cried out something that could be interpreted as a promise that we would soon get something to eat. With redoubled determination each man strained and pushed to defend his place at the barrier. Then, lo and behold, the fat man actually did come back with a loaf of army bread under each arm. There were at least five hundred of us at the barrier. The fat man in the apron pondered for a moment, called two additional comrades from the kitchen, and then again paused.

The tension was unbearable. Each man felt the taste of bread in his mouth. My mouth was full of sand and my stomach was empty. But I had bread in my teeth.

The fat man was still waiting.

Then, like an ancient discus-thrower, he hurled one loaf in our midst, and a few seconds later the second loaf followed. Hundreds of hands were outstretched. And before I had even time to take part in the wild struggle for the two army loaves, I saw the three men from the kitchen bending, shaking, coughing, and bellowing with laughter. I saw the round one, the friendly one. I looked into his face and saw that he resembled the assistant judge with the lemon mouth; that he resembled the quadrangular man in the straw truck, as well. I had a vision of a zoo, with a barrier between men and beasts. But this time it was the beasts who were feeding the men.

The bread was gone. Only crumbs remained.

That very first day in the camp of Dieuze I realized what was behind all this. Twenty-two thousand men were to be broken like the loaves of bread, shredded like the straw. Twenty-two thousand here, two million altogether.

I decided then and there not to be one of them.

For the moment there was no chance of carrying out any of the various plans I was turning over in my mind.

At five o'clock in the morning—four o'clock French time— we were awakened by the trumpet. The German barracks commander, Corporal Josef Berger of Nuremberg, was waiting at the door. A second later he shouted: "Out with you!" and at one past five, the thousand men sleeping in Workshop No. 3 had to be dressed and standing at attention beside their bunks. This was not so difficult. We slept fully clad. We had to: though it was high summer, the stone floor of the garage was ice cold. Only a handful of us had blankets; we had to choose between lying on our coats or covering ourselves with them. Corporal Berger, a giant with a heavy tread, then proceeded to "inspect" the room. From time to time he had the idea of putting on a foot parade: we all had to lie on our backs, take off our shoes and hold out our feet. Those whose feet were not clean were deprived of all food for twenty-four hours. When Berger had finished his inspection, he again shouted "Out with you!" and in the space of one minute the barracks had to be empty. It was high time. All of us had dysentery in a more or less violent form, and it was most active in the morning. As soon as we were out of the garages, we rushed to the latrines. Of course they were occupied. We had to stand in line. We offered the moon in the sky for a comrade's place in line. But such kindly souls were rare. As a rule you stood there with your pants down, cramped, tortured, certain that the world was coming to an end. Lovers of nature, like Alfred and me, hurried to the hindmost latrines; there at least we could see horses, cows, sheep, and other animals that did not have dysentery, as we waited. The inevitable question of paper is a chapter in itself. Every night a paper bourse was held: no gilt-edged stock has every sky-rocketed like those scraps of old newspaper in the camp at Dieuze. We had become accustomed to begging, and so we begged for paper. For one page out of a newspaper, you could get half a cup of soup and a share in the use of a razor blade.

But we were in a hurry to get back to our barracks. Breakfast was waiting. It consisted of tea, or what they called tea, without sugar or anything else. It was a greenish concoction rather like thinned spinach soup. But the greenish water was warm and it did you good to feel the hot wetness gurgle down your throat. By six in the morning this ceremony was over. We were allowed to lie down for an hour, after we had meticulously cleaned our bunks. This was often a painful process. We tried to keep together the few straws we possessed, like a bald man trying to cover his head with his few sparse hairs. We laid out our poor wisps of straw, smoothed them, arranged them, put them up in ranks like tin soldiers, trying to create an illusion for our weary backs.

At seven o'clock, after another inspection by the barracks commander—during which he uttered nothing but commands and commands—we were driven to the large drill ground. There we remained standing from seven to nine, until we were so exhausted that we believed our legs had been drilled into our bodies and would pop out of our shoulders at any moment. Then Captain Brühl, the camp commandant, or his substitute, Lieutenant Dr. Schmidt, would appear. Sometimes Captain Kohlrusch, in charge of the Gestapo, or young Lieutenant Brandt, would also come. Captain Brühl, commanding officer of the *Wachbataillon Hauptmann Brühl* of the Fourth Fortress Infantry, was a man of about fifty with an enormous nose, two sharp lines running from the sides of his nose to the corners of his lips, a mouth without an upper lip and a chiseled underlip—a real German Reichswehr officer of the Prussian era. It was said that Captain Brühl felt slighted, that he should have been made a major long ago and that we would remain in this camp until he was promoted to the rank of major. Of course this might take some time. We also heard that the captain's promotion had been delayed because he belonged to the "old school" and treated his subordinates with too much friendliness. That was to be changed. In civil life, Lieutenant Dr. Schmidt had been the director of a high school for girls. Two student scars crossed the whole breadth of his face. His hair was clipped short over his ears; only a thorny tuft graced the spot above his forehead. Dr. Schmidt wore a pince-nez which clung to his small, pointed nose like an uncertain rider clinging to his saddle. He always smoked a gigantic cigar. He did not seem a fundamentally evil man; but I had a feeling that he was always defending himself against something. In the school he had probably been afraid of the girls; now that he had finally escaped the school, he was afraid of the soldiers. That must have been why he was as severe with the soldiers as he had been with the girls—or vice versa. The worst moment was when Captain Kohlrusch, commander of the Fourth Company of the *Wachbataillon*, read the order of the day. This Captain Kohlrusch was a "party man"; he was in charge of the Gestapo for the whole district. A scraggy man with hollow features, he breathed gastric acidity. Looking at him was enough to give you a pain in the stomach.

Though there wasn't a horse in the camp, Captain Kohlrusch always walked with a riding crop in hand; he kept striking his boots as though to whip them to a run. His legs were so thin that they surely would have refused to run without being struck. Finally there was Lieutenant Brandt, but he was so thoroughly German that the only thing that can be said of him is that nothing can be said of him.

These gentlemen were accompanied by their interpreter— a French Second Lieutenant and Alsatian notary—Dr. Schneider. He spoke French with a German accent and German with a French accent, and he tried particularly hard to translate abuse in a literary style. He always stood at attention as he listened to a German officer, and shouted at us just as the Germans did, in an improbable feminine treble. I think that such exaggerated tonal devotion displeased the German officers; they felt that a parrot was imitating them. Sometimes they reluctantly ordered Dr. Schneider to be silent.

We had to stand at attention while the order of the day was read. Two or three times a week it explained why we received no mail, and why we ourselves were not permitted to write letters; equally often it told us that the Germans themselves had no soap; it promised us straw, though we never received any; finally it informed us that fugitives were shot, that for disobedience you went to the "cellars" and didn't always come back. These pointers on daily life were followed by a discussion of current events. The Germans were winning always and everywhere; the English people were not responsible for its plutocratic leaders; France had been brought to disaster by the democrats. The Führer—Dr. Schneider translated: *notre Führer*—would soon reconstruct Europe and return the French prisoners to their families. At about ten o'clock the German officers abandoned the field, and we were treated to an hour of radio broadcasts which were not exactly anti-German in tendency. Shortly before eleven we had ten minutes of midday music. After the music the French daily newspaper for prisoners, *The Echo,* was distributed. At about eleven we were permitted to return to our barracks and stand in line for lunch. The sun beat heavily upon the camp; the latrines poisoned the air, and even the springlike breeze from beyond the wooden fence smelled of urine.

From eleven to two we were "free." Lunch never took much time. It consisted of half a pint of soup; sometimes you managed to get half a cup more. The soup was a murky, but not distasteful, warm liquid, mostly made of pea or bean substitute. The substitute had a definitely good taste; I don't know anything about its food value. The soup was distributed not by Germans, but by the French monitor. A German soldier only supervised the distribution. That is, he watched the scuffle that was repeated daily with absolute regularity.

One would have liked best to sleep from eleven to two. But for "hygienic and moral reasons" it was strictly forbidden to enter the garage, and the open spots in the camp were rare. The "park" by the latrines was usually so overcrowded that the men sprawled over one another—and that was no fun. Consequently we went to the Casino. The Casino consisted of a series of "roulette tables" set up in the midst of the junk yard. Many prisoners had constructed roulette wheels out of old automobile parts; you could bet from twenty-five centimes to two francs. The bets were placed on playing cards spread out on the tables, also made by the prisoners. The Germans expressly permitted these games of chance; only Jews were not allowed to play or to hold bank. Apparently the Germans regarded roulette as an occupation so eminently moral that Jews were unworthy to play at it. The bank-holders enriched themselves in the shortest possible time. A "turnover" of a thousand francs a day was nothing extraordinary with these vest-pocket Zaharoffs. It was a pity that the first suicide in camp killed himself not over grief at the fall of France, but over gaming losses. . . .

At two o'clock we were again summoned to assembly. Before then, you had to study *The Echo*. *The Echo* was published on two, or—more often—on four pages; a certain Herr Schwerdfeger was listed as responsible editor. Of course it was not Herr Schwerdfeger who wrote the newspaper, for *The Echo* was written in flawless French. The newspaper was destined exclusively for prisoners and had a circulation of two million. The first page contained the German and Italian war communiqués and a series of reports from France. The second page celebrated the greatness of the German Reich and of the National Socialist system. We learned that the workers were nowhere paid so highly as in Germany, that housewives were nowhere so happy as in Germany, that children were nowhere so well cared for as in Germany, and that nowhere did men die so blissfully for their fatherland as the Germans. The following two pages were devoted to "stories." These stories all told about France "as she used to be," that is, before she had the great good fortune to lose the war. One series of articles, entitled "They All Were Involved in the Stavisky Scandal," showed that all French parliamentarians had been corrupt; "Visitors at the House of Rothschild" revealed the name of everyone who had ever taken coffee at the Rothschilds; another series enumerated all the cabinet changes during the last decades, and a serial entitled "France Was Ruined by the Rule of Mistresses" gave spicy details about the lives of French statesmen. There was even a cross-word puzzle—and it was a distinctly humorous cross-word puzzle. Six letters across, defined as "A Jewish Pig Who Robbed France," was Mandel, former Minister of

Interior, while "American Warmonger" in nine letters was, of course, Roosevelt. The "Country That Began the War" (seven letters down) was Poland. There was a riddle. "What do the prisoners lack?" and the whimsical answer was "soap." Those who neatly wrote in the correct solutions and delivered them, with signature, to their barracks commanders, were allowed to take part in a daily lottery with a whole loaf as a prize. I am glad to say that the majority of the prisoners resisted this enticement for weeks. But though it was not compulsory to solve the cross-word puzzle, you did have to study *The Echo* from eleven to two. Almost every day, from ten to twenty French prisoners were questioned about the contents of the newspaper. They had to know everything—from the excessive number of French ministers to the names of the political *cocottes.* Dr. Schmidt especially loved to examine the prisoners about the articles in *The Echo.* He had it in his blood, from the girls' school, no doubt. . . .

In the afternoon we stood from two to five: partly waiting—mostly waiting!—partly listening to speeches, lectures, broadcasts, and orders. At five supper was distributed. It consisted of a quarter loaf of bread and a small portion of artificial honey or margarine. The bread was intended not only for the evening meal, but for the whole next day. But hardly anyone had the moral strength to save any bread. We devoured it in a few minutes, except perhaps for a crust to be eaten during the night.

After supper there were interminable discussions, all hinging about a single question: When are we going home? The question had many aspects: When will we be released? What are the Germans saying about us? When will the peace treaty be signed? Do the Germans need us in Germany? When will the war with England be over? We looked on all world events only as they seemed to affect the possibility of our freedom. If a Laval government is most likely to get us out of here, then let Laval rule France. If necessary, let the English be defeated: France is lost anyway.

Elaborate deductions were drawn from the slightest sign. And strange to say, the prevailing mood was optimism. Among the twenty-two thousand prisoners in the camp at Dieuze, I found not a single pessimist. There was not a one who in the bottom of his heart had given up hope, or was even willing to admit things as they were. They had a ready explanation for every misfortune. If we had no soap—and such was the case—the explanation was that "it was an oversight." If we were forbidden to write, the explanation was that we "would be home before the mail gets there." If Captain Brühl had a warlike day and said that his battalion wouldn't go on guarding us forever—meaning that he wanted to leave for the English front—the explanation was that we were being sent home next day. If the radio said France would have to pay reparations until she was blue in the face, even that was good news: in order to pay France would have to produce, to produce she would have to work, and to work she would need our young muscles. The most extreme optimists refused to set their watches by German time. At five o'clock in the morning, it was only four by their time-pieces —but what did that matter? Tomorrow they would be home in France, living by French time. One day the Germans would lend support to this optimism, the next they would paint the gloomiest picture. Every corporal was a god or at least a demi-god, who had his information direct from the Führer; but no one believed him unless he had something pleasant to report. Just for the fun of it, one of them might say, "Well, soon you'll all be sent home," and the word would spread through the camp like wildfire. By the time it had gone the rounds, it was a concrete promise for a definite

day. There was always a date. One day a rumor arose that
the Stuttgart radio had promised the 14th of July: "Mothers
of France, rejoice, your sons will be home soon." Another
time, Dr. Schmidt had let fall something about August 1st.
And no one doubted that we should all be released before
September 1st: "Why should they waste food and fuel on
us?" Every night we went to sleep with new hopes, and each
morning awoke disillusioned.

Each man had to be in his bunk at the stroke of nine. It
was absolutely forbidden to go outside during the night. If
you absolutely had to leave the barracks, it was at the risk of
your life. The guards on the roofs shot at you without so
much as a challenge. Every night there were shots. But we no
longer heard them. We slept and dreamed. And what sweet
dreams! That is the strange and wonderful thing about nature, that it restores at night what you have lost during the
day. Every night I was at home with my mother, or with my
wife, in our lovely bright home in Geneva. Sleep compensated for all hardships: never was I bothered by nightmares.
The good angels came down and hovered over my resting
place. Even the dreams of hunger—repeated regularly every
night—had nothing terrible about them. I did not eat raven-
ously. No, I nibbled at delicacies. Ham with *pâté* at Gerst-
ner's pastry shop in Vienna. Eggs with mayonnaise, fresh
lobster. After such a night you felt empty and gray, like a
wooden mousetrap . . . but you had your dreams. A merciful divine hand had been stretched forth by night to atone
for man's crimes by day.

Alfred and I spent our free time in the most strenuous efforts to appease our hunger. At the edge of the camp, right in
front of the administration building, stood a few cherry trees
of the peculiar Lorraine variety: old and tall as an oak. The

cherries grew only in the highest branches of these patrician, gloomy trees. In all the "free" hours, there were prisoners down below, throwing stones at the cherries. Once in a blue moon a pathetic shade-grown cherry fell into the dust of the courtyard. But we never gave up. Even those wintry Lorraine cherries were harbingers of spring.

Double soup rations were served in the infirmary. For the present, the infirmary was a garage like all the others, except that there was a little more straw on the floor. The sick and wounded—120 of the Frenchmen had been more or less severely wounded when taken prisoner—lay side by side on the floor. In the middle of the garage stood a long table and a chest containing meager medicaments and even less bandage. For days the dispensary was entirely out of bismuth, the only halfway effective remedy for dysentery. Of course the sick men could not dress or undress. They lay in their uniforms—though without shoes. Instead of medicine, they received volumes of the *L'Illustration*, years 1902 to 1912. Now and then one of them died; but that happens elsewhere too. The French doctors—twenty-eight in number—were helpless in the face of death.

In this "hospital" I found an old friend, a Russian count, René Dmitri Korzakoff, who had fought as a volunteer in my regiment. He had been our *agent de liaison* and had fallen into the hands of the Germans on his way to divisional headquarters. At first we pretended not to recognize each other. Then, when no one was looking, we shook hands. From Count Korzakoff I had nothing to fear. He had read all my books and even liked one or two of them. He too was hiding under an assumed name, having registered as René Mage. The sick prisoners were not questioned as closely as the rest of us. René Korzakoff's main profession was photography. He had been born in Paris, whither his parents had emigrated. He

266

was a man of refinement, with the hands of a woman. He had
the restrained hardness and pleasantly tempered melancholy
of many Russians. He was an oasis in this world of optimists
whose world collapsed every morning.

He had an appetite that stood in ludicrous contrast to his
looks. He was always hungry. With his shadowy refinement,
his nobly chiseled lips, you would have expected him to live
on air and nectar. But hunger had given him the ingenuity of
a madman. Ever since our arrival in camp he had been simu-
lating all possible and impossible ailments, partly to avoid the
stricter registration outside the infirmary, but also to get a
double ration of soup. His consumptive appearance came in
very handy.

René told me that the soup was brought in at eleven-thirty.
But I had my scruples.

"I can't take away food from the sick," I said.

René shrugged his shoulders. "You can have scruples in
love, literature, and cards," he said, "but not in soup."

Alfred and I went to see him every day at the soup hour.
The pot was brought in, and pleasant warm vapors arose
from it. The soup smelled pleasantly of soap and washing,
and you would have thought you were in a laundry. The
sick men arose from their bunks and hobbled over to the pot
with their tin bowls. They emptied them and then they stood
in line again.

Once a month each invalid received a card. When you got
your soup, a hole was punched in a box marked with the date.
Every day we went to see René in the unexpressed hope of
obtaining an unused card. The senseless optimism of the
stomach cannot believe that it will remain empty forever.

Beside René lay a Lorrainer named Bolomey, a merchant
from the birthplace of Jeanne d'Arc. My regiment had passed
through Domrémy and on the first day we exchanged mem-

ories. But after that Bolomey went into a rapid decline. He had a long red beard, and for days that was all there was to his face. He lay unconscious nearly all the time. When he did come to, he asked for paper to write his family. René had no paper, but he cut the margins off an old number of *L'Illustration,* and on these white strips Bolomey wrote his letters of farewell. He kept promising us that he would die without any noise, and would try to die in the daytime, so as not to wake anyone up. We tried to give him some words of encouragement, but we knew that he would keep his promise: you could see that the mask behind the red beard had no strength to die noisily.

One day when we came into the infirmary, our first glance fell on Bolomey. It was never easy to tell whether the grocer from Domrémy was dead or alive. But today one of the doctors had told René that Bolomey had only a few hours to live. That morning he had come to for a while, and René had cut out some paper for him. He had scribbled all sorts of confused nonsense to his wife and insisted on ordering candles, soap, and noodles from his wholesaler. For the last three hours he had been râling.

We sat down beside him and waited. It was a few minutes past eleven. If Bolomey were to die before half-past, we could have his soup. The orange-yellow ticket stuck out of the pocket of his army coat. We sat beside him with crossed legs, and from time to time cast a furtive glance at the door. You could see that Bolomey's eyes were beginning to look into the beyond. I have seen death often, and when a man has that look, it has been given to him to see into the other world. No more can he return among men. He has been entrusted with a secret, and his mouth is forever sealed. It had never struck me before that Bolomey had lovely blue eyes, and I do not think he had. It was the blue of heaven that I now saw in his eyes. And the soup would be there at any moment. Bolomey seemed to sense it. His breathing was feeble; his râle came faster and faster. Bolomey was in a hurry to die.

And then the door opened. The infirmary began to smell like the attic of a country house on wash day. The sick men arose from their beds and went on their pilgrimage to the soup-pot as cripples go to the sacred spring at Lourdes. Bolomey breathed deeply. The three of us exchanged glances, the Russian count, the Polish Jew, and I. None of us said a word. In silence Korzakoff took his tin bowl. Now the line extended the whole length of the garage. The orange-yellow card glittered. Alfred's eyes were red with hunger. The invalids screamed and shouted as the soup was dished out. The soup diminished, the smoke grew thicker and thicker. I had averted my eyes from Bolomey. Suddenly a loud râle issued from his throat. He was still a moment, and then he opened his eyes wide—not with horror, but in happy surprise. Then a sigh came from his lips.

For the first time I felt what it means for a man to breathe out his soul. I could see the soul of Francisque Bolomey, grocer from Domrémy, rising out of his mouth and floating through the room. All the heaviness had gone from him. And I know that Francisque Bolomey had a beautiful soul which hastened to depart before the soup was all gone.

Alfred and I each received a bowlful of soup on Bolomey's card. After that we had to give it up, for the Germans said dead men needed no nourishment.

It wasn't every day that a Bolomey died. But necessity is the mother of invention. At night when the bread was handed out, each barracks received one loaf of bread more than its ration. The monitor in charge of the distribution usually kept this *rabiot*—as the French soldiers called it—for himself and his friends. We decided to muscle in. Four of us volunteered for the *corvée*—the task of bringing the food from the kitchen. Alfred, Jean, Paul, and I carried the loaves in a blanket, and Denis trailed behind us. The bread was frightfully heavy, but we didn't mind, for *en route* we managed to drop the extra loaf. Denis picked it up and vanished. An extra loaf of bread for four men was nothing to be sneezed at—even if you had to make it last for four or five days.

Another way of augmenting the rations was to cook your own. You could volunteer for peeling potatoes, and carry a few away in your pockets. Unfortunately everyone else volunteered, and you had to wait outside the fence for days before the chef admitted you to his kitchen paradise. Besides, the potato stocks were rapidly dwindling. For a time it was easier to cook yourself a little salad. Salad of course was a poetic exaggeration—but is it any more unreasonable to call grass salad than to call a piece of beef Chateaubriand? Unfortunately the grass couldn't last forever. But in the first few days, you simply went into the vegetable garden—the little lawn among the gray trees behind the auto-graveyard—and picked a handful of grass. You found three or four bricks or slates from the roof and made a fireplace near the rear walls of the repair shops, where you were sheltered from the wind. Then you lighted a fire and cooked the grass in your tin pot. Grass tastes like nothing. But this is a gastronomic deception or a prejudice. For nothing does not fill the stomach. And cooked grass does fill the stomach.

The disadvantage of this kitchen was its situation. It was the only spot sheltered from the wind, but it was also right next to the latrines. Our stoves were in the latrines, so to speak. And from time to time German soldiers came by and kicked them over—this of course in our own interest and for hygienic reasons.

Werner Pape was a plump little German sergeant, a student of philosophy from Dortmund. He knew I spoke German and sometimes addressed me. Together we walked along the garage wall between two lines of crouching men. To the right they were crouched over the latrines; to the left they crouched over their fires and pots full of grass. All had the same frightened look, from head to toe, when Pape passed. The student of philosophy never shoved anyone into the latrine or upset anyone's stove. He only turned up his nose and said to me with an indescribable contempt in his voice: "*La grande nation!* That's what you Frenchmen used to call yourselves."

I did not answer. All I could have said was that no nation is great that is hungry.

CHAPTER NINE: HAIR TONIC, PEPPER,

AND WOMEN

EVERY DAY, ALFRED, RENE, AND I WEIGHED PLANS OF ESCAPE, most of which had to be discarded at once. Often they were wild and hopeless, but we were determined that no day should pass without a project. I believe that these plans for escape kept us alive. But however vague the rest of our plans may have been, one thing was certain: some day we had to find our way to the town of Dieuze and establish contact with the civil population. And this seemed impossible. The only prisoner permitted to leave camp, even under guard, was Dr. Schneider, the Alsatian interpreter. Yet we refused to believe that this obstacle was insuperable when all that separated us from freedom was a high red wall or a barbed-wire barrier. We could stand for hours behind the wall or behind the wire—five yards from the fence, as provided in the camp regulations—and almost physically feel the proximity of freedom. But we saw so many roads of escape that no real road remained.

I was obsessed by the fear that my true identity would be discovered, and this fear mounted from day to day. I had been registered without incident. Our names were listed by barracks, and no details were asked. But if Napier, the true one, was in another camp, Bedaud, his comrade, proved an embarrassing inheritance. To this day I do not know whether Bedaud, hard of hearing and pock-marked, was malicious or only stupid—whether he had learned of the assistance given me by Napier and disapproved of it, or whether he was merely so half-witted as to think that I knew something that had been withheld from him. The fact remains that every time he saw me in the yard, he called:

"Hello. Have you had news of Napier?"

And Napier was my own name.

One day I was walking across the yard with the commander of my barracks, Corporal Josef Berger, when I heard the shrill, familiar voice from the wall separating the two yards: "Hello. Have you had any news of Napier?"

I turned my head away. The corporal was amazed: "But your own name is Napier?"

"Yes."

"What is he shouting then?"

"Oh, leave him alone. He is a deaf idiot."

This time the corporal accepted the explanation. But Bedaud was like an indiscreet parrot in the boudoir of a pretty woman, obstinately repeating the name of her old lover in the presence of the new one. Like all deaf men, the last survivor of the Three Hundred Thirty-first Infantry roared for fear that he wouldn't be understood. He was a dangerous parrot and I would gladly have strangled him with my own hands. But that too was impossible.

There were numerous indications of our imminent transfer from Dieuze to a camp deep within Germany. Some German soldiers spoke of the Silesian coal mines. Others said we would be taken to German industrial regions to see the effect of the bombings by our "dear English allies." Several camps had already been transferred from occupied France to bombed German regions. In our morning talk the Dieuze camp was repeatedly described as a *Dulag* (*Durchzugslager*) or Transit Camp; later, they said, we would be interned in

a *Stalag* (Soldiers' Camp) or an *Offlag* (Officers' Camp).
(A fourth kind of camp obviously did not concern me.
This was the *Gelag* or Generals' Camp, where the Germans had interned over two hundred French generals and
admirals.) And it was true that every week two to three
thousand prisoners arrived at the camp of Dieuze, and as
many were sent on to Germany. A batch of more than ten
thousand was taken to Kassel in Thuringia. And one morning special lists were drawn up, classifying us by occupations. All these were bad signs, calling for quick action.

Alfred and I often lay awake at night, speaking of all the
dangers and possibilities. It was bad to be awake when everyone was asleep, for at night my optimistic fellow-prisoners
were far from optimistic. At night, they sighed and
screamed. One cried out in his sleep; another would whimper like a sick child; many uttered the names of women;
and even the silence was full of repressed calls. As you lay
awake, you could sense the dreams of the sleepers; you could
see gray ghosts rising from a hundred dreams. A hundred
nightmares tormented the non-dreamer. You waited tensely
for the next sound, the next sob, the next call.

Each day we grew more determined to attempt something. Then the unexpected happened.

One morning in July, Lieutenant Dr. Schmidt came to assembly without Lieutenant Dr. Schneider, his interpreter.
The day before, our captors had begun to release "persons
of German blood"—that is, Aryan Alsatians. Dr. Schmidt
came into the drill ground with long, artificially military
steps. He had just doused his cigar; during the whole assembly he held it behind his back. With his pointed nose and
pince-nez, his small compressed mouth, his képi on an almost bald skull, the high school principal and assistant camp
commander was every inch a motorized unit. The prisoners

stood motionless, lined up by barracks; the German barracks commander stood at the head of each group. Only the Polish prisoners stood apart; while the Arabs and Negroes were excluded from assembly.

The barracks commander on duty reported to the commander that all were present. Dr. Schmidt thanked him.

"Eyes forward!"

We all stood at attention.

"At ease!"

We put our left feet forward.

Dr. Schmidt looked around him.

"Where is the interpreter?"

The sergeant on duty reported: "Released as Alsatian."

When speaking to the officer, he stood at attention, his hands on the seams of his trousers.

"Ah! Right. I forgot."

Dr. Schmidt looked around. Our eyes met once. Dr. Schmidt noticed nothing. Then he asked: "Does anyone here know German? Can anyone replace the interpreter?"

I thought fast. I knew that the moment had come to play a dangerous game. At least fifteen thousand prisoners were standing in the horseshoe-shaped yard. Not a one of them would take me for a Frenchman when I spoke publicly before them. At least one of them would give me away. Thirty or forty German soldiers stood in the yard. Not a one of them would take me for a foreigner when I spoke German. At least one would be struck by my flawless accent. But this was my only chance of getting out of the camp. Alfred held me by my sleeve. He knew what I was thinking. I tore loose from him. I came forward, clicked my heels and reported: "I speak German, *Herr Oberleutnant.*"

"Good! Stand beside me."

I obeyed. Fifteen thousand pairs of eyes were directed at

me. I felt that it was impossible to defend myself against so many eyes. It was like facing machine-gun fire, with bullets whistling to right and left of me. You can go on fighting against one pair of eyes, but not against fifteen thousand. I found one pair of eyes. They were the round, dull eyes of a little French adjutant standing in the front rank. I fixed my gaze on his eyes. I clung to them and refused to see the others.

Lieutenant Dr. Schmidt began. He said only three words, and asked me to translate them. I summoned up all my energy to conceal my foreign accent in speaking French. I tried to speak good French and bad German. The high school principal saw that translating caused me no difficulty. The next time he said six or seven words. I translated. My eyes clung more and more desperately to the cowlike eyes of the adjutant. To the right and left the other glances shot past me.

"German officers returning from imprisonment . . ." said Dr. Schmidt, beginning a new item. I translated and waited. In some confusion, the lieutenant went on: ". . . have reported the scandalous treatment . . ." He stopped, made a sort of encouraging gesture with his free hand, noticed that I had already translated, and continued, this time in whole sentences: ". . . have reported the scandalous treatment to which they had been subjected by the French. They were locked up with syphilitic Negroes."

Like a drowning man I clung to the poor adjutant's protruding eyes. I translated: ". . . locked up with syphilitic Negroes . . ."

Dr. Schmidt strode up and down the yard. When he shouted, his student scars swelled and reddened. The scars were like bloody stripes in his cold, gray face.

"All Negroes are syphilitic!"

I echoed: "All Negroes are syphilitic."

Dr. Schmidt stood still.

"And, in general, all Frenchmen are syphilitic."

Cow-eyed adjutant, help me, I thought. But not a sound crossed my lips. Dr. Schmidt stood in front of me. He folded his arms across his chest and looked at me. I felt Alfred's anxious gaze. You're staking his head too, I thought. My tongue was glued to my palate. Dr. Schmidt walked up and down in front of me with quick, short steps. Fifteen thousand pairs of eyes blankly watched the silent struggle. The sun hung heavy over the barracks yard. Then Dr. Schmidt said: "It goes without saying that such treatment of German officers cannot go unpunished."

He looked at me. I translated. Then I knew that I had won the game.

"The camp will receive no food for twenty-four hours."

I translated. Dr. Schmidt paused for a minute and then went on: "We Germans are always too kind-hearted. You have probably noticed it yourselves. After the reports submitted by returning German officers all that will change. A prison camp is no rest cure."

"No rest cure . . ." I said. Had my French been correct?

"Those guilty of the slightest breech of discipline will learn that every German soldier has at his disposal three means of punishing the prisoners: the gun-butt, the bayonet, the bullet."

I hesitated. Gun-butt in French is *crosse*. But was it *"le" crosse* or *"la" crosse?* Fifteen thousand pairs of eyes threatened to shoot me if I used the wrong article.

Dr. Schmidt repeated: "The gun-butt. The bayonet. And the bullet."

"La crosse. La baionnette. Le fusil," I translated. I waited. The eyes were not shooting. It was *"la" crosse* all right.

The assembly lasted another fifteen minutes. Then the lieutenant ordered the prisoners to scatter. I saluted, meaning to go back to Alfred. Dr. Schmidt re-lighted his half-burned cigar and made a sign to me with the hand that held the match.

He approached me.

"What's your name?"

"Sergeant Maurice Napier, Three Hundred Thirty-first Infantry," I reported, in the Prussian-military style.

"What was your occupation as a civilian?"

I had not expected the question. I thought for a moment and quickly lied: "Secretary in an embassy."

"Aha!" said the high school teacher. "That explains your knowledge of languages."

"Yes, sir."

I tried to imitate a foreign accent. I knew at once that I would be unable to imitate the French way of speaking German. But I had spent the six years before the war in Switzerland. The best I could do was try to imitate the curious German pronunciation of the Swiss.

"Where were you last?"

"I have been living in Switzerland for twenty years, *Herr Oberleutnant.*"

"How is that?"

"My father was ambassador in Berne. I grew up in Berne."

"Aha! I see."

A self-satisfied smirk passed over his features. His pince-nez smirked, too.

"I knew the accent right off," said Dr. Schmidt. He was quite satisfied with his philological erudition.

He eyed me. His cigar filled his entire small mouth.

"I like you," he said at last. "From now on you'll be our official interpreter. Understand?"

Hair Tonic, Pepper, and Women

"Yes, *Herr Oberleutnant*."

I saluted like a drill sergeant from Potsdam. Then I turned on my heels and went back to Alfred Sienkiewitz. White as chalk, he was waiting for me in front of the garage.

In the meantime Dr. Schmidt marched out of the yard, probably wondering whether all Frenchmen weren't syphilitic after all.

Lies, deception, cunning, violence: no means is too evil when the purpose is to combat evil.

My rise was phenomenal.

It began when Dr. Frank, the chief physician, required my services.

One or two days after I had taken over the functions of official interpreter, Dr. Schmidt wished to give me certain instructions, and I accompanied him to his house. The officers' dwellings were on the other side of the road. We went out of the camp, crossed the road and found ourselves in a large yard surrounded by the German officers' "villas." Never had I felt the meaning of freedom as keenly as in the twenty seconds required to pass from one yard to the other. These were my first five steps outside the camp walls.

Dr. Frank, the chief physician, and a few other officers were calling on Dr. Schmidt. Dr. Frank was a tall man with a face like a death mask. To look at him, you couldn't help thinking that if he didn't carry a sickle, it was only because such an instrument was too obsolete for modern death. Instead of a sickle, Dr. Frank always carried a revolver, a tiny, almost jewel-like weapon, a Belgian officer's gun that he must have secured somewhere in Flanders. This miniature gun sat on Dr. Frank's enormous posterior like a little wart on the nose of a drunkard. Dr. Frank was haranguing the officers. I could only hear him through the door of the antechamber, but I could make out that Dr. Frank was railing indiscriminately against Jews, Elite Guards, silk merchants, women, and Lorrainers.

Later I heard the story. Dr. Frank's wife lived in some provincial town in Saxony and had written her husband a letter asking him to send her four yards of silk for a dress (hence the condemnation of extravagant women). Dr. Frank had shopped all over Dieuze and Nancy for the silk—an order that could not have been filled in all Germany. But the shopkeepers had lied to him, saying they had no silk (hence his rage at silk merchants). Finally he was told that unlimited amounts of silk could be found in the *Paradis de Soie* at Nancy. But the Lorrainers charged the Germans double prices (hence his rage at Lorrainers). Nevertheless he treated himself to four yards of silk. But the Elite Guards, who for some time had been in charge of the frontier service between Nancy and Dieuze, confiscated his silk (hence his "negative" attitude toward the Elite Guards). As for the Jews, they were responsible for everything anyway, and no particular reasons were required to abuse them. While I waited, I heard Dr. Schmidt praise my qualities and suggest that I might be sent on various errands in Nancy. My pulse quickened. I felt that my future hung by a hair. At length the door was pushed open and Dr. Schmidt ordered me to come in.

It was a petty-bourgeois dining and sitting room, formerly belonging to a non-commissioned officer of the *Gardes Mobiles*. A wine-red velvet cloth covered the table; a light brown radio and a terra-cotta bust of a shepherdess stood on a cupboard. Thick clouds of smoke hovered in the air. Captain Kohlrusch, the Gestapo man, Dr. Frank, and two other officers unknown to me sat around the table drinking beer. Sergeant Werner Pape, the plump philosophy student from Dortmund, was doing something in the background.

"Would you like to take a little trip to Nancy?" asked Dr. Schmidt.

"Yes, *Herr Oberleutnant*."

"Could you take care of purchases, too?"

"Certainly."

There was a short pause. Then Captain Kohlrusch asked: "Do you know that there is a frontier between Nancy and Dieuze?"

"I did not know, *Herr Hauptmann*."

I spoke my painstakingly manufactured Swiss German.

Dr. Frank explained: "Yes, you see, a few days ago, a forbidden zone was established. We are in it. Nancy is regarded as occupied territory, but still as a French town. But Dieuze is definitely German. Understand?"

"I understand."

Dr. Frank rose from his chair and paced up and down the room.

"The border runs twenty-four kilometers north of Nancy and sixteen kilometers south of Dieuze. There is a border control station at Arracourt—the frontier post was there before the World War. Once you pass Arracourt on your way from Nancy, you are in Germany. Beyond Dieuze there is no control. But here we are in the forbidden zone. No one is allowed in from any side. Excepting soldiers, of course."

I pricked up my ears but made a stupid face.

"You don't seem to understand," said Dr. Frank nervously, and stopped his pacing.

"I understand, *Herr Oberarzt*."

"Splendid!" said Dr. Schmidt. "Be ready to go to Nancy. We'll draw up a list for you."

I clicked my heels.

Captain Kohlrusch scrutinized me with his cold fish eyes, lashing his boots with his crop, as usual.

"Hm . . ." he said finally. "You know what will happen to you if you get caught at the border?"

"No."

"You'll be shot."

His long nails drummed on his beer glass.

"And do you know what will happen to you if you say whom you are bringing the goods for?"

"No, *Herr Hauptmann*."

"I personally will have you shot if the Elite Guards release you."

He laughed hoarsely. They all laughed. The gigantic Dr. Frank put a chocolate in his mouth with his pointed fingers.

Dr. Schmidt wiped his pince-nez.

"How do you plan to go there?" he asked pensively.

"Perhaps in an ambulance—" I ventured.

"Excellent idea," said Dr. Frank. "I'll give you a Red Cross arm-band. Our evacuation hospital is in Nancy anyway. Severe cases must be sent there. Find a reliable man in the infirmary and have him put in the ambulance. You'll go along as his nurse." And then, turning to Pape: "Would you like to be chaperon?"

"Certainly, *Herr Oberarzt*."

"Fine. Get your gun and be ready."

I went to the infirmary and told Count Korzakoff that he was gravely wounded and we were taking him to Nancy. Meanwhile, Dr. Frank had sent me a German Red Cross arm-band. It was a white band with a large red cross and a black swastika stamp. I fastened it around my left sleeve with a safety pin. I wondered which would prove stronger, the Red Cross or the swastika on my arm. But the answer was a foregone conclusion.

Meanwhile Pape came over with the list. It was the handi-

work of the five officers, aided most likely by a few others.
The German officers' letter to Santa Claus ran as follows:

8 yards red silk
4 yards blue silk (sky blue if possible)
2 lbs. pepper
Soap (as much as possible)
Chocolate (as much as possible)
14 bottles of *Eau de Cologne*
6 bottles of perfume (only the genuine French article!)
5 bottles of hair tonic
5 wrist watches (gold or silver) for ladies.

Pape also gave me one thousand marks on account. They
were, of course, occupation marks, current only in occupied
territory. I asked him how we were expected to transport
all these goods. He shrugged his shoulders.

"That's your headache!"

I went back to the infirmary and had Korzakoff's head
bandaged. "Shot in the head!" I said. René was wrapped into
blankets and laid in the ambulance bed. He was pale as death.
I sat by his side. Jeannot, the chauffeur, a good fellow from
Lyon who had been taken prisoner while driving an ambulance, took the wheel. Pape, gun in hand, sat beside him. I
remained inside the car with the patient. Dr. Frank handed
us a stamped pass: "Ambulance No. WH 567112 *Wachbataillon Hauptmann Brühl,* evacuation of a casualty to
Nancy, traveling time both ways, four hours." At last the
French ambulance rolled out of the German barracks yard.

How inconceivably happy and free I felt, locked up in
that cramped compartment. The window of the former
French ambulance was small and barred. I pressed my nose
against the pane. Outside there was summer—and it had nothing in common with the sickly, brooding summer of my
dusty camp. The meadows were infinitely green, the crowns

of the trees were as full and fragrant as a woman's hair. From time to time an old peasant would walk across a field. So friendly and soft were the hills of Lorraine, it seemed as though you had only to walk across them to be rid of all cares. The road was beautiful and endless. The very idea that we were prisoners seemed inconceivable, unreal.

I tried to study the terrain through the small window. I realized that to get to Nancy you had to go through Dieuze. In Dieuze itself every house was occupied by Germans. Any plan of escape had to take Nancy as a starting point. If we made a good job of our smuggling, we would be sent frequently to Nancy. To be sure, the capital of old Lorraine was still 250 kilometers from the border between occupied and unoccupied France. But south of Nancy the road could not be excessively guarded, for even between Dieuze and Nancy, the heart of the "forbidden zone," the highways seemed rather deserted.

A short distance before Arracourt our car halted. Arracourt itself, a little town with winding streets, had the aspect of a frontier fortress. A swastika flag flew from nearly every roof, sentries stood at the gates, patrols moved along the streets, and immense signs showed that every second house sheltered some military authority.

I jumped out of the car and surveyed the scene. On the road stood a small, jerry-built sentry-box. Railway tracks ran off to the left. To the right there was a graveyard for French soldiers killed in the first World War; across the tracks to the left there was a smaller graveyard for German soldiers. On both sides the hills sloped gently down to the road. Young forests extended behind the French graveyard; to get from one town to the other without using the road it would be necessary to force a path through them.

We passed the border post without inspection. No one

supposed that any goods would be taken from Germany to France. But I saw the frontier guards make a thorough search of a German officer's car passing in the opposite direction. Two black-clad Elite Guards opened the hood and examined the engine, while a green-clad frontier guard dismounted the spare tire. It made me hot all over to think that in two or three hours we would have to take the same road back.

It goes without saying that we carefully avoided the Nancy hospital. Our car with the patient in it cruised slowly along Nancy's main street, the Rue St. Jean, while Pape and I made the rounds of the stores. They were mostly empty. By order of the *Kommandantur* they were not permitted to close, but it was as though a master magician had passed his wand over the show-cases: all foodstuffs, wines, shirts, shoes, gloves, had vanished. The stores looked as if they had been plundered. The one or two miserable objects that remained only stressed the desolation. Several stores insisted on preserving the old magnificence of their windows. The show-case of a perfume store contained all sorts of green, yellow, and lavender bottles, but when we asked for some perfume, we were told with a smile that for weeks the bottles had contained nothing but water. Certain objects were simply unobtainable. No amount of money could purchase a cake of soap or a razor blade, not to mention chocolate, straight razors, or leather goods. The Germans had bought up everything with their fictitious marks. Hair tonic, perfumes, champagne, silk underwear, silk stockings, and leather gloves: these six symbols of luxury had been the first articles acquired by the Germans. It was useless for the *Kommandantur* to insist on inventories and organize raids; all you could find in the stores were polite shopkeepers and empty shelves.

After a vain round of the stores, I set out to execute my plan. I asked Pape to wait for me outside and went into the

shops by myself. My aim, of course, was to make contact
with the shopkeepers with a view to preparing my flight.
Pape wanted to buy some hair tonic and a wrist watch; he
agreed to my suggestion.

Alone, I obtained excellent results. Soaps wrapped in flow-
ered paper, all sorts of hair tonic came up from hidden cellars; a watchmaker brought Omegas, Eternas and Zeniths
from his summerhouse, and I even unearthed a few pounds
of pepper. Everything was loaded into our ambulance. Of
course the good people knew that the Germans and not the
French prisoners would get all these things, but they also
knew that through me one or more prisoners would be
helped. These men and women of Nancy were full of courage and hope for the future. Every single merchant who refused his wares to Pape and myself—only to hand them out
two minutes later when I came back alone—was risking his
neck. But for them no stake was too high.

Soon our car was fully loaded. Our wounded soldier lay
half smothered beneath quart bottles of *Eau de Cologne*,
cases of soap and chocolate. We now turned our attention
to the *Paradis de Soie*.

The largest silk shop in Nancy lay in a side street off the
Rue St. Jean, not far from the famous gold gates and portals
of the Place Stanislas. The owners had not been able to conceal their plentiful stocks. Followed by my armed guard, I
mounted the stairs to the shop, situated in the second story
of an old house.

The store, consisting of two immense rooms, was literally
besieged by German soldiers. Privates were tugging at bundles of silk, officers armed with great shears were shoving
their way toward a counter, orderlies were wrapping crêpe-
de-chine in newspaper, non-coms were ripping crêpe-satin
off a roll with their bare hands. A stout captain lay face

down on one of the counters, embracing "his" bundles in both arms. The gaudy silks had destroyed all trace of the famous German comradeship. A lieutenant and a captain tugged like two dogs at a remnant of dark green material, decorated with light green flowers. Both claimed to have sighted it first. The captain was a scrawny fellow with a monocle. His face was so convulsed from the struggle that his monocle seemed in danger of digging into his cheek and getting stuck in the cleft. The lieutenant, obviously a reservist, was a fat man with audible asthma—he panted with the exertion and his sweating nose looked like a soaked roll. An unwritten code forbids an officer off-duty to exploit his rank. But in the end the captain threw all fair play to the winds. "I order you to let go," said the man with the monocle, and the lieutenant dropped his green treasure.

This struggle in the *Paradis de Soie* could only have been likened to an orgy: only sexual desire can so deprive men of their humanity. In the Paradise of Silk, you could feel how far man has descended from paradise.

In the midst of this tumult, there were two or three other prisoners—from the camp at Nancy. A guard with his gun over his shoulder shoved his way through the delicate stuffs. Bayonet points drilled into the feathery silk, dirty hands grasped dreams of georgette, boots trampled fluffy samples, rifles were set down on melodies of color. No one cared what he bought. The wildest colors would do, imitations were accepted as the genuine article, silk prices were paid for rayon. What mattered was that you left the store with a giant package under your arm. A major with the head of a shaved bird wrapped his form in light yellow silk, to see how many yards he would need for his wife who was the "same size," a handsome young lieutenant, for want of better, seized a whole bundle of black mourning crepe. I was jostled in all directions; whenever I picked up a piece of goods, some officer took it out of my hand. I had a package all ready. A drill sergeant confiscated it. At length one of the salesgirls, herself hard-pressed, took me aside. I escaped with eight yards of red silk and four yards of silk as "sky-blue as possible."

Not dissatisfied with our visit, we left Nancy. At the edge of a forest a few kilometers from the city, I told the driver to stop. We stowed our bottles under René Korzakoff's blanket. I removed my own clothes and wrapped the red and sky-blue materials around my body. After inspecting me from all sides, my guard declared that I had grown a good deal stouter in Nancy but otherwise looked all right. We hid the chocolate bars in the bandage box and the watches in the bandage around Korzakoff's head. We fixed it again to comfort him and drove off.

We knew that the guard had been changed in Arracourt an hour before, so we could say that the sick man whom we had "evacuated" to Nancy was being brought home from the Nancy hospital.

It was late afternoon when the soldiers' cemeteries came in sight. The summer sky was violet and green like an unripe plum, bathing the entire scene in a gentle late light. Several cars had halted at the border post. Ahead of us there was a beer truck, a hay truck, and an officer's car. Two Elite Guards in black uniform, with high boots and faces full of élite brutality, were taking the cushions out of the officer's car. The officer, a gray-haired lieutenant, stood leaning against his car, nervously biting his icy gray mustache and his thin upper lip. Two customs guards in green were prodding the hay in the truck with their bayonets. Two others rolled down the beer barrels, to see if anything was hidden beneath them.

Pape and I stood beside our ambulance. I kept myself in the background. Swollen as I was, with twelve yards of silk around me, I felt ill at ease. I adjusted my arm-band with the two-fold symbol: the symbol of the murderer and the symbol of the Samaritan.

The Elite Guards put the cushions back in the officer's car and saluted. The lieutenant got in, hissing maliciously through his teeth: "I hope you gentlemen are as attentive to the other cars."

I felt as though someone had struck me in the solar plexus. My heart jumped into my throat and cut off my wind.

The two black-clad guards stepped up to us. One was short, particularly ignoble in build. Everything about him was plebeian: his square head, his protruding teeth, his flat forehead, his broad hips. He wore an exact replica of his Führer's mustache. The second was larger, reddish blond, with a pair of spectacles which may have been intended to extenuate the natural brutality of his features, but only enhanced it.

Pape held out our pass.

The little Elite Guard opened the ambulance door.

"What's that?" he asked, pointing to our wounded man.

"A prisoner," said Pape. "We're bringing him from the hospital."

"Can't he walk?"

Meanwhile the big one was tinkering with the hood.

"No," said my guard. "Shot in the head."

"And what about this guy?" The little man with his prophet's mustache pointed to me.

"He's our orderly!"

The little man stepped up to me, and looked me over from top to toe. Then he yelled at me: "Take the sick man out."

I didn't stir. I knew that we were lost if we lifted Korzakoff out of the car. Pape stood, pale as a ghost, behind the Elite Guard. The green customs guards had finished their work on the hay truck. They too approached us.

"Won't you please help me?" I asked. "I can't hold up the bed by myself."

I spoke flawless German. The little man was taken aback. "Where are you from?"

"I lived in Berne for twenty years."

The man with the magic mustache entered the ambulance and stood at the lower end of the stretcher. All I could do was make a gesture of despair.

"You are from Munich?" I asked.

He bent down over the bed, but stood up again.

"How did you know that?"

"By your pronunciation. I know Munich. I used to work in the French consulate there. Wonderful city, Munich. The beer . . . and the Maximilianeum. . . ." Everything I knew about Munich burbled out of me.

The little man climbed out of the ambulance and graciously offered me a cigarette. Then they let me get in with René and slammed the door.

"Drive on!" the Elite Guard commanded.

The motor started. And I drove back to my prison as happily as though it were freedom itself.

My life changed completely. Within a week I had brought all possible and impossible objects from Nancy to Dieuze. It goes without saying that I could not take the road going through Arracourt every time. Often I rode in the ambulance to a place near the border post, got out there and passed through the woods. Twice I had to hide in the cemetery because of patrols. But I was always aware of the grotesqueness of the situation: there I went guarded by an armed soldier, while at the same time the two of us were hiding from other German soldiers. The French prisoner and his German guard lay flat on their bellies behind a soldier's grave from the first World War, until the steps of the black-clad frontier guard had died away. We rose smiling with embarrassment. But a few yards of silk, a bottle of champagne, or a lady's shirt were always more important than national solidarity.

The closed shops of Nancy and Sarrebourg, which no force of arms could compel to deliver up their treasures, opened themselves to me. Every day I was able to garner food enough for ten or twenty of my comrades. As leader of a growing smugglers' ring, I was able to make contact with the civilian population. Dr. Schmidt asked me to collaborate on his new school textbook disproving the war guilt lie. Captain Brühl discussed politics with me. He was delighted with my frank admission that as a Frenchman of the extreme right I had no sympathy for Germany, but did prefer Hitler to Léon Blum. Captain Kohlrusch intimated that he would have "interesting work" for me after my release—and perhaps before. A week after I had replaced Dr. Schneider, it was announced at assembly that Sergeant Maurice Napier of the Three Hundred Thirty-first Infantry had been chosen "responsible French camp commandant."

I was transferred from my sleeping quarters in Workshop No. 3. By this time the infirmary had somehow been organized. It was the only real building in the prisoners' section. Here the twenty-eight French doctors—the only officers in Dieuze—were lodged three or four to a room. As for me, I had a light room to myself. I obtained permission for the doctors to cook in their own kitchen, and wangled special rations for the sick. An office was opened for me, adjacent to my bedroom. The incomplete lists of prisoners were brought to my office, and it was my job to have them arranged and copied. A French doctor who had two uniforms gave me one of them in exchange for a bottle of pernod. I had the insignia changed and sported a brand-new uniform. The French chief doctor, Captain Felix Mauvoisin, a Parisian of Basque origin, who, incidentally, had been Maurice Chevalier's physician, invited me to eat at the officers' table.

Alfred was delighted and at the same time worried sick. His situation, of course, improved with mine, for under some absurd pretext I had him taken into the infirmary. Like myself, he now slept in a bed. To be sure, he had neither mattress, pillow, nor sheets, but he did have a straw pallet, a blanket, and a roof over his head. However, Alfred felt sure that since I had become the most conspicuous among twenty-two thousand prisoners, my true identity would soon be discovered.

"The way you have swindled the Germans and misused their confidence," he said, "they'll send not only you, but Captain Brühl himself, to Dachau if the truth comes out."

I shrugged my shoulders. It was too late to turn back.

The inevitable epidemic broke out among the Negroes.

The black soldiers—Negroes and Arabs—were segregated on the very first day. They were assigned a single large garage, the worst in the camp. Into that garage, nearly a thousand blacks were herded on reduced rations and no straw. The holes in the roof were left unrepaired. When it rained, the blacks slept in puddles of water. If the French were treated as "subhuman" the Negroes were treated as subhumans among subhumans.

But the worst was not the garage, not the sleeping, not the food. The worst was the fence. For around Workshop No. 8-A, the Negroes' barracks, a fence the height of a man was erected with barbed wire on top. Between the garage and the fence there was a space four yards wide, and this was the only place where the Negroes were allowed to walk. This monkey cage had a single gate with a padlock on it. The guard had the key. Negroes were not allowed in the yard: no Negro was allowed among the whites. Also the latrines were situated in the four-yard space around the garage. Three times a day food was handed in through the gate. It was like feeding animals. Of course the Negroes never received any soap. In their case, this was "justified." "The black cutthroats," said Captain Kohlrusch at assembly, "need no soap. They are black to begin with." This was the captain's opinion. And when he uttered it, he expected laughter and applause.

There was a constant hustle and bustle around the "Negro village," as the Germans wittily called it. All day long the Negroes were photographed. The German soldiers came out with cameras, most of which the prisoners sadly recognized as their former property, and photographed the blacks in all possible postures. "Negroes on the Latrines" was, of course, the favorite subject of this neo-German art. The best pictures were sent to German newspapers. Corporal Ciarnelly from Fürth, a facetious fellow who looked like an unwashed fish, proudly showed me a highly realistic photo of a few black bottoms. "And that," he said, "is what they wanted to save world culture from the Germans with."

But it was not just the Germans who kept looking across the fence. The French prisoners spent a good part of their free time in the same way. They stood at the gate like children in a zoo. What they thought I do not know. Most likely they were consoling themselves with the thought that misery still had its gradations.

From time to time a Negro was taken out of the village and brought to the administration building. Then I was obliged to go along, as interpreter. Courses on the black race and its inferiority were given in the dining salon. The professor—Captain Kohlrusch—maintained that the liberation of the slaves and the emancipation of the Jews were the cultural disgrace of the last centuries. "Yes," said the captain, lashing his spindle legs to a trot with his riding crop, "the German must and will have his slaves." The soldiers applauded. The black man stood on the platform. Sometimes he smiled, thinking that the applause was meant for him. The captain explained the racial characteristics of the Negro. He took the "subject's" head in his hand and turned it round, so that it could be seen from all sides like a globe. He said something about the Negro's ears and led the black man through the hall by the ear. After the course I escorted the subject back to Workshop No. 8-A.

Scabies broke out among the Negroes—caused, no doubt, by dirt. The first symptom was that the skin between the fingers began to peel. Then the whole body became covered with an itching rash. Scabies is highly contagious, and the itch it induces is well-nigh intolerable. The Negroes roared all night. You could hear them all over the camp. Off and on the sentries on the roof fired a few shots, and there was a moment's silence. But immediately afterward the screaming and whimpering resumed.

Two or three days passed. Then I was awakened one night. Sergeant Paul Daxer of Stuttgart, responsible for our infirmary, stood at my bedside.

"Come!" he said. "We've got a fine mess out there."

I dressed in haste and followed him. In the tiny flower garden between the infirmary and the camp wall, ten or twelve persons had gathered. The beams of three or four flashlights flitted across the grass. In the middle of the garden lay a man with a crushed head. A Negro.

For some minutes we stood helpless, viewing the "fine mess." The flashlights shone into the wide-open eyes of the Negro. In the harsh gleam, he looked white. A newly planted rose bush had been crushed. Two broken fingers hung limp from the Negro's hand. From the wall you could hear the monotonous steps of the guard.

The tragedy was not hard to reconstruct. During the night the black soldier had somehow crept out of the fenced inclosure. He probably dashed across the yard as fast as he could, zigzagging to avoid the beam of the reflectors. He ran as though fighting for his life, though actually he was fighting for his death. He ran to the infirmary, the only four-story building in the camp. The door was open. He climbed the stairs, softly and stealthily, so as to awaken no one. He opened one of the windows in the corridor, or else the window was already open. He stood on the sill and leaped. And he was lucky; he fell on a sharp stone. He had not suffered.

We brought the dead man to Dr. Mauvoisin's room. There was nothing more for us to do. We covered his crushed skull with newspaper. Then we went back to bed. It was three in the morning. The camp lay asleep. In the branches of the old cherry trees the first birds were twittering.

The next day was fraught with impending storm. Everything seemed more and more incomprehensible. At first Dr. Schmidt declared at assembly that only black subhumans could run away from life's duties so ignominiously. But the very next day we were told that the white prisoners had driven the poor Negro to his death, that we would be deprived of our midday soup ration, and that our ration would be given to "the poor comrades of the unfortunate victim."

But the first morning of the three lean days the most surprising thing of all occurred. Captain Brühl appeared in my office. Without further explanation he instructed me to appoint twenty or thirty men to take away the fence around the "Negro village," and to tell the Negroes that those not afflicted with the scabies might appear at assembly. The sick would soon be sent to a hospital, Brühl informed me. In the afternoon two hundred shirts would be distributed. "You will be responsible to me personally," the captain concluded, "that they are distributed fairly, and above all, that none of the shirts falls into the hands of a white prisoner." With this the captain and his creaking boots left the room.

Scarcely an hour later he sent for me.

"The black soldier," he said, sitting in his old-fashioned plush armchair, "will be buried tonight in the cemetery at Dieuze. Do you think he should be accompanied by his white or his black comrades?"

I stood speechless, thinking it over.

"Maybe the black comrades would get more fun out of it," the commandant decided. He looked out of the window, and said with the concern of a man worried about his brother's skiing trip: "A pity that the weather is so bad." Then he added: "All right. Appoint twenty black comrades to escort him. Speak kindly to them. You will come along as representative of the French. I will send a guard of honor, of course."

Things were getting more and more mysterious.

Late that afternoon four black soldiers laid the dead man in a rough-hewn coffin. It was made of light-colored wood, and the dead soldier looked like a black doll in a wash trough. The coffin lid was nailed shut. The four black soldiers took the coffin on their shoulders. None of them spoke a word.

Outside it had been raining all day. Suddenly it had grown cold. Only in northern Lorraine can it grow so cold in midsummer. The sky was a hopeless gray. A mist descended, thin but opaque.

296

Four Negroes carried the coffin at the head of the procession. They were followed by the twenty black comrades, marching four abreast. Lieutenant Brandt, Assistant-Interpreter Beer—a Saarlander of the Second Engineering Corps—Sergeant Werner Pape, and I brought up the rear. Beside us—serving as guards and escort of honor—marched ten German soldiers, led by a sergeant. Whenever we passed a German sentry, he presented arms. The Negroes looked around in terror.

The charming little cemetery was surrounded by a low wall. A grave for Ali ben Alib had been dug beneath the wall, beside the family plot of a Dieuze burgher. Two photographs in oval gold frames were affixed to the white marble: one showed a man in a wing collar and bristling mustache, the other a woman with hair combed high and silk ribbons around her neck. Ali ben Alib would have no white marble tombstone. I remembered that I would have to write to his wife.

The coffin was lowered into the earth. The twenty blacks threw themselves on the ground. Lieutenant Brandt, with the blond mass-production face, stood at the head of the grave. The Germans grouped themselves on either side of their superior.

Then the lieutenant spoke. But he was no great orator and frequently interrupted himself:

"Ali ben Alib is dead," he said. "He is dead, and we have come here to escort him on his last journey. (Pause) Ali ben Alib was a soldier. We too are soldiers. One soldier cannot fail to honor another. The German soldier . . . (pause) the German soldier will not begrudge this dead soldier his due honor. No . . . and that is why we have come here. (Pause) We have come to bury the soldier Ali ben Alib in honor. He fought against us German soldiers as a soldier. And as soldiers we respect him for it. That is why . . . (pause) why we do not begrudge him his last honor. Ali ben Alib is dead."

He paused again, pondering whether to go on speaking. Perhaps he wanted to assure us once more that Ali ben Alib was dead, and that the German soldier did not begrudge him the honor. But then he impatiently broke off, like a bad orator running away from himself. "Fire!" he commanded so suddenly that the sergeant forgot to pass on the command. Finally the soldiers fired a salute.

The black men had heard none of the lieutenant's speech. They lay on the wet clay and prayed. They had turned their faces to the west, toward the setting sun. But in the western plain, behind the church tower, the sun had gone down long before. There was only a feeble yellow light behind the gray rain clouds. The chants of the black soldiers sounded like a monotonous murmur. Only here and there, one of them cried aloud the name of Allah the Almighty. But their prayer did not seem to be directed toward heaven. Kneeling, lying on the ground, they muttered their prayers, they whispered them to the earth. The wet, foreign French soil received them. The dead man beneath the ground may have heard them. But heaven was too far away.

I stood beside Werner Pape. The little man with the wide hips of a stout girl and the innocent face of a child, regarded the praying Negroes with the interest of a schoolboy listening to Indian stories. I stood motionless. While the earth was being shoveled into the grave, I looked out across the cemetery wall into the cold summer twilight. The church-bell rang, the blacks were still praying.

Returning to the camp, I learned—with mounting amazement—that the camp commandant had set aside twenty portions of *ersatz* cheese and ten loaves of army bread for the twenty friends of the dead man. I was instructed to pick a *corvée* to bear the gift from the kitchen. With Pape I passed across the empty courtyard. At length I could no longer control my curiosity.

"Tell me, sergeant . . . what has happened? This transformation is more than anyone can understand."

Pape laughed contentedly.

"Look," he said with the boastful satisfaction of a gambler whose cards are so good that he can't help winning, even if he shows them. "Germany wants no dissatisfied slaves. Germany wants slaves who love their masters. Yesterday an order came through from the High Command: Germany is developing a colonial policy."

Now I understood why a salute had been fired over the grave of the dead Ali ben Alib.

In my new position I saw far more than I wanted to. One hot afternoon, Dr. Schmidt invited me to "tea"—ersatz-lemonade. We discussed political questions. I tried to find out something about the German offensive against England.

"You know," said Dr. Schmidt, "that the Nuremberg Party Congress has been set for September 9th." He pulled out a newspaper and gave it to me. Giant headlines proclaimed that the "Party Congress of Peace" would be held on September 9th. "That means that we shall have defeated England by September 9th," said Dr. Schmidt.

He noted my hesitation and continued: "If the Führer says the Party Congress of Peace will take place on September 9th, then it will take place on September 9th. And even if we don't launch our offensive until the 7th, you can be sure that the Führer will settle England's hash in two days."

As usual, the conversation gradually turned into a monologue on the part of the German.

"That is the wonderful thing about the Führer," Dr.

Schmidt went on. "He never asks anyone's advice and never notifies anyone of his decisions until the proper moment. Not even the general staff knows when the offensive will be launched. Only the Führer knows."

"And what if something should happen to your Führer?" I ventured to ask.

Dr. Schmidt gazed at me over the rimless lenses of his pince-nez. Suddenly his round expressionless eyes were wide with amazement. I sensed that the man could not understand my question. Something happen to the Führer? Doesn't this foreigner know that the Führer is immortal?

A corporal had come in as we were speaking.

"Beg to report," said the corporal. "The chief drill sergeant would like you to come to the lock-up. One of the prisoners keeps talking French; we don't know what he's saying."

"We'll have a look," said Dr. Schmidt. He arose, put his tunic in order, and straightened his collar with the gesture of a Prussian officer, slipping his index finger between the collar and his neck and holding his chin aloft. "Come with me, Napier."

"*Jawohl, Herr Oberleutnant.*"

We crossed the courtyard. The soldiers we passed sprang to a salute. Some of them were playing football in front of their houses. It was Sunday, I remembered. I had forgotten all about it—here there was nothing to distinguish a Sunday from a week-day. And yet it was a summer Sunday: with church in the morning, the small-town silence, visits in the afternoon, excursionists from the neighboring villages. The football players went rigid as the officer passed. One of them ran over and reported the number of players. Dr. Schmidt's gait grew more and more military.

I had vaguely heard about the lock-up, but never any details. Dr. Schmidt seemed to know the way. We entered the three-storied red administration building, the former Hô-pital Buttini, and descended the stairs to the cellar. The corporal ran along ahead of us. Down below, he knocked on a heavy iron door. A muffled voice was heard from within: "Password?"

"Brabant!"

The door opened. The soldier behind it said: "Corporal Kessler of the First Company. Seventeen prisoners." Dr. Schmidt raised his hand to his cap: "Thank you."

Even his "thank you" sounded like a command.

It took my eyes some time to get used to the light. The air was thick enough to cut. I vaguely discerned the round face of Corporal Kessler, the oil lamp on the wall, an indefinable mass on the floor. It seemed to me that the place would be lighter if there were no lamp at all, for the wretched light seemed an opaque vapor of smoke, dampness, and cold sweat. It hovered like a cloud over the men who lay huddled on the floor.

"He just stopped yelling," said Kessler apologetically. He stepped over two or three bodies and kicked a gray heap that must have been a man. Then he roared at him: "Why don't you yell now, you dog? You've been at it all day."

The prisoner looked up. So disfigured was his face that only his eyes reminded me of anything human. He held up both arms as though to protect his head. His face was covered with bloody welts, and there was black dried blood in his sparse hair.

"Speak up, you lousy dog!" cried the corporal, again kicking the motionless heap. I was struck by Corporal Kessler's shining black boots.

"*Je veux mourir,*" said the prisoner.

That quieted the corporal.

"What is he saying?" Lieutenant Dr. Schmidt asked me.

"He wants to die," I said.

The lieutenant was at a loss. He didn't know why they had sent for him. And perhaps he regretted having brought me along. I wondered if he would introduce the same methods in his young ladies' high school.

"What is the prisoner here for?" Dr. Schmidt asked finally.

The corporal went to the little wooden table beneath the oil lamp by the wall, opened a squeaky drawer and took out a chain. It was a long metal chain, made of round single links.

"This was found on the prisoner."

Dr. Schmidt took the chain, weighed it in his palm, and turned to me: "Do you know what this is?"

"No."

"It's from the motor of a German plane."

I looked into his eyes. They were bloodshot. I was almost frightened by the transformation in his face. The veins on his forehead stood out. The clouds of smoke that hung between us seemed to turn red in the flames darting from his eyes. The professor began to look just like the jailer.

Dr. Schmidt turned toward the prisoner.

"Did you kill a German?" he roared. "Did you kill a German?"

In a monotone the prisoner answered: "*Je veux mourir.*"

"Ask the fellow if he robbed a German corpse?" said Dr. Schmidt.

I asked in French: "Where did you find the chain?"

The man's eyes turned to me. He tried to raise himself but sank back again.

"*Je veux mourir,*" he said, and looked up at me as though I had life and death to give away.

I bent down over him, nearly sitting on another prisoner.

"Say something," I said to the man.

"They beat me all day," he said softly, and clung convulsively to my arm. His head lay on my breast. No flowing blood could have been so terrible as the dried black blood in his thin gray hair. "Today they made me lick the German soldiers' boots," he said even more softly. He was shaken with sobs. Were you ashamed, poor comrade? I thought. *You* have nothing to be ashamed of.

They stood over us with folded arms: Lieutenant Dr. Schmidt, Corporal Kessler, and the corporal who had brought us.

"What does he say?" asked Dr. Schmidt impatiently.

"He says a comrade gave him the chain as a souvenir. He didn't even know what it was."

"He didn't know what it was," echoed the round-faced corporal. "As a souvenir. Well, here's a souvenir for you!" And he kicked the prisoner in the stomach. It is a terrible thing when another man gets the kick that belongs to you.

Dr. Schmidt said not a word. He drew a fresh cigar. The two corporals eagerly held out matches, and nearly knocked their heads together.

"Thank you," Dr. Schmidt smiled. He had the refined smile of a marquis.

He looked around, visibly bored.

"How long has the man been here?" he asked absently.

"Ten days, *Herr Oberleutnant*."

"What food?"

"Normal rations every fourth day. Bread and water the rest of the time."

"Good."

The acting camp commandant turned around, nearly stepping on the head of one of the prisoners.

"What did that one do?"

"Went to the latrines at night," replied the omniscient Kessler.

"To the latrines. I see. No self-control."

He puffed at his cigar. The room was so narrow that it didn't seem possible, but the prisoners—without blankets on the cold stone floor—drew closer together as we passed through.

"And what about that one?"

"Tried to smuggle out a letter."

"And that one?"

"Failed to salute Drill-Sergeant Havlick."

"No discipline! See here, Napier, it really isn't hard to salute."

A look of recognition passed over Dr. Schmidt's features. He looked down at a bald-headed old man.

"Oh, there is my client."

"Right, *Herr Oberleutnant*," said the corporal. "Your client. Had his hands in his trouser pockets at assembly."

"See here, Napier," said the officer in the tone of a benevolent professor. "If you fellows had stopped that kind of thing in time—" And to Kessler: "Take good care of my client for me, will you?"

The client received a well-aimed kick with the shining boots—a token of special attention.

"And that one?" Dr. Schmidt went on.

Kessler bent closer to his superior's ear.

"Very interesting! Very interesting!" Dr. Schmidt muttered from time to time. And then in a confidential tone to me: "Captain Kohlrusch discovered this one. A naturalized German. That is, he was a German subject. A Jew. Fine rabble you chose to naturalize." And in his most professorial, girls' high school tone: "With that sort of thing, my dear Napier, you were bound to lose the war."

How glad I was that the Germans never expect an answer!

Dr. Schmidt had reached the iron door. He turned back and asked: "What about this one?"

"Stole bread from a fellow-prisoner."

"From a comrade?"

"Right, *Herr Oberleutnant!*"

"How long is he in for?"

"He's getting out tomorrow."

Dr. Schmidt took a deep drag at his cigar.

"No," he said. "Give him a week more. I can stand almost anything, but not uncomradely behavior."

The corporals clicked their heels. Dr. Schmidt left the room with a maximum of theatrical effect.

"Yes," he said on the stairs, "comradeship is what counts, my dear Napier. Your comrades should be thankful to us for teaching them to be human beings."

We came out into the sunlit yard. There was so much light that I had to close my eyes. A few prisoners were working in the garden in front of the administration building. Suddenly a great Sunday silence lay over the camp. It was like coming out into the street after an afternoon at a horror movie. A bee was humming in the clear air.

"Yes, education," said Dr. Schmidt, lieutenant and school principal. "That's what counts, my dear Napier. When the Führer took power, not all the Germans were National Socialists. We had plenty of democrats, Bolsheviks, and all sorts of misfits. We locked them up in concentration camps for a year or two, and by God, when they came back they were all good National Socialists. A pedagogical miracle, my dear Napier! I am convinced that after one or two years of education, the French will know what's good for them. Believe me, no man is born perfect. Everyone needs to be educated.

We ourselves needed to be educated by the Führer before we could become what we are now. The same will happen to you. Don't worry, my dear Napier!"

No, I didn't worry. I was confident in their educational efforts.

Next morning at the assembly, Captain Brühl announced that at noon the prisoners would be offered an extraordinary treat: a broadcast from London. Germany, he added, had no interest in concealing certain British broadcasts; quite to the contrary, these broadcasts clearly exposed the true nature of the British people.

I must admit that I myself was curious to hear London. Because of my various activities, I was excused from all assemblies that did not require my services as interpreter, but that day I appeared in the drill-ground at twelve sharp to listen to the British broadcast which the Germans regarded as useful to their own propaganda. I wondered if I would really hear the voice of Britain. My doubts were dispelled when the most British of all voices issued from the loudspeaker.

"The Jews, persecuted by Germany and expelled from virtually every other European country, have turned to Britain for assistance," said this extraordinarily British voice. "After long negotiations with the 'Jewish World Congress' and the 'Jewish Agency,' King George has agreed to take world Jewry under his wing. On this eighteenth day of July, 1940, King George VI of England will be crowned King of the Jews. In attendance will be leading Jewish personalities, delegates from the churches and Churchill's cabinet, Queen Wilhelmina of Holland, King Haakon of Norway, the Grand Duchess of Luxembourg, the Secretary General of the League of Nations, and H.M. Haile Selassie, Emperor of

Ethiopia. George VI will henceforth be known as King of all Britons and Jews."

All this was announced by the London station; the most important passages were translated into French by one of the prisoners.

It was only by accident that I learned the true origin of the broadcast. Having listened for about ten minutes, I decided to make better use of my time. Sergeant Webke, the German chef for whom I had once purchased eight yards of cloth, had promised to let me take a bath that afternoon, alone and undisturbed, in the German soldiers' shower room, situated in an annex to the kitchen building. He had the water heated, and I left the yard and the Jewish coronation ceremonies to cleanse my body of the day's dirt. I passed through the empty kitchen, found the key that Webke had left on the kitchen table, and unlocked the shower room. I was alone to enjoy the solitude and the foretaste of a warm bath. As I undressed, I hummed a French marching song. Occupied by these ritualistic preparations, I paid no attention to the fact that the voice of the B.B.C. was still pursuing me. Yet the kitchen was in the second yard, a good distance away from the loudspeakers which had been set up in the large drill-ground; actually it was impossible that the words of the British announcer should carry so far. Not until I was actually standing beneath the swishing hot spray did I grow aware of the implausible voice. I abruptly let go of the chain governing the flow of water, and listened. The voice sounded hoarse but distinct. That voice did not sound "canned." Someone was speaking in the adjoining room.

I moved cautiously, clinging to the wet walls of the shower room. Adjoining it, I knew, there were two or three rooms where all sorts of rubbish was usually kept. In one of the rooms, imprisoned mechanics worked at various repair jobs.

Now I recalled that the mechanics had just been transferred to another barracks. At one spot on the wall the voice was especially distinct. I pressed my ear close to it. Someone was speaking near by. Speaking English.

I crept back to my shower. And as the hot jets of water streamed over my body, I saw before me the twenty thousand men who stood outside in the bare drill-ground, naïvely imagining that they were listening to the voice of London. The pedagogical miracle was on the march!

I learned no further details of this curious broadcast. Much later I heard that the camps of Nancy, Lunéville and Château-Salins had been favored with the same program—on different days, of course. To avoid an English disavowal, possibly out of consideration for American ears, the London "pick-ups" were not broadcast by the German radio; instead, the "Englishman" was sent on a lecture tour through the German prison camps. The "London" station traveled from camp to camp, from store room to store room.

That night I paid a visit to Workshop No. 3, my former barracks, to learn my comrades' reaction to the "London" broadcast.

Jean, Denis, Paul and Alfred were eating supper when I came in. I brought them a loaf of bread and was received with jubilation. Five or six other prisoners joined us. I quickly steered the conversation toward the broadcast.

What I heard depressed me. Excepting Alfred, no one doubted the authenticity of the broadcast, and even Alfred's doubts were feeble. That night I began to realize that German propaganda was not so clumsy as it seemed, and that in the end its effects on the two million prisoners captured by the Germans would be devastating.

I asked Alfred to take a walk with me in the yard. When we were alone, I told him of my discovery; I knew that it was too dangerous to speak of it in front of the others. Alfred pretended that he had seen through the trick at once.

"No," I said. "They manage it all too cleverly. We've got to recognize the fact and learn our lesson. It's true that our jailers have it easy. Look at the crowd they have to deal with."

We were in the yard where the gambling went on. Hundreds of men crowded around the tables. The roulette wheels were made of wire and tin, the *tapis* of dirty playing cards. The croupiers were yelling, the balls were rolling. Corporations had been formed. A man on top of a dismantled car was trying to attract new customers.

"Never was a sacred cause in worse hands," I said to Alfred. "This nation never knew what the fight was about and why it was fighting. It doesn't know why it lost the war. These men came here with the great silent question: Why? They were betrayed by their leaders, sold out by those they trusted. They were completely in the dark. And then the Germans came and gave them an answer. It doesn't matter a bit whether the answer is true or false."

I saw that I was speaking to myself. Alfred was fascinated by the tables and the game. *"Faites vos jeux, messieurs!"* the croupiers cried. *"Les jeux sont faits—rien ne va plus!"*

"Yes," I said to Alfred, or perhaps to myself, "the game goes on. It is no accident that the Germans stand for it. They know that such games have corrupted France. They know more. They know that not hunger but weariness produces rebellion. First they undermine our physical powers of resistance. Then, instead of food, they give us a ready-baked philosophy. Who will preserve the inner force necessary to resist it?"

Alfred objected absently: "Do you think the French will love the Germans for starving them?"

"No, my friend. But you don't know how people are. Brutality, in any form, provokes their envy, not their disgust. It's quite clear how the Germans have figured it. This is how they expect the French to feel: If I had won the war, I could have been brutal now. I could have eaten while the others were starving. I could have breathed the air of freedom, while the others were stifling. I could have slept with girls, while the others tossed on their lonely camp cots. But why did I lose the war, why did the others win it? I lost it because I had no Führer. They won it because they had a Führer. I want to be like them . . . and cry 'Heil!' when a scarecrow passes by in an automobile. Then I'll be a jailer and not a prisoner. In this world which thinks only in terms of jailers and prisoners, the jailers make propaganda for the chains they have bound us with."

Alfred had ceased listening. On the table near the dismantled Citroën, number nine came out for the third time.

My position in the camp took a turn for the worse.

Every afternoon—except for the days when I was sent to Nancy with a "patient"—I went to Dieuze. The purpose of these daily trips was to collect gifts for the sick prisoners. The Red Cross representative in Dieuze was an old spinster who lived in the Rue Clemenceau. Every afternoon I was sent to her to collect. The *Sana* department store had let me have a small black hand-car with a lock, to carry the precious gifts to our patients. Every day, between three and four, people came out of their one-story houses bringing something for the imprisoned French. Windows opened; girls and women handed out baskets full of fruit, vegetables, flowers, wine—everything they possessed. Here, in Lorraine, the heart of France was alive. Old peasant women brought their carefully hidden eggs; Frau Klein, a gentle old lady with a velvet ribbon around her neck who owned the stationery store on the main square, provided us with cigarettes, and would gladly have given her entire store; Frau Jaeger, the pastry shop owner, used her last precious bit of flour to bake pastry for the sick prisoners; one little old woman surprised me every day with another pot of jam—she had kept it for her son's return, but he had fallen in Flanders. Every afternoon I pushed a heavily laden cart up the gently sloping road to the camp; every night, Captain Mauvoisin, our chief physician, distributed the gifts among the 150 patients.

Among the women of Dieuze who daily loaded us with gifts was the druggist's wife. Her husband was a prisoner—she did not know where. She was a handsome blonde, this druggist's wife, and it was a pleasure to look at her. When I came by with my little cart, she waited for me on the steps of the pharmacy and each time she gave me what Dr. Mauvoisin or his assistant, Dr. Laffont, most urgently needed.

My excursions to Dieuze, authorized by the camp commander, made me popular among the German soldiers. I had a special pass saying I was permitted to "make purchases in the town of Dieuze," but only if "accompanied by German soldiers." Whenever I went to Dieuze I had to ask one of my guards to come with me. To the German soldiers, these excursions were a most welcome diversion. Many of them begged me to choose them for my companion, and each day I picked a new guard. We strolled down to Dieuze, chatting all the way. In the beginning, these chats wearied me because of my constant efforts to speak Swiss-German; but soon I grew accustomed to them.

All our excursions followed the same pattern. We passed by the church, we crossed the silent church square, we came to the shoemaker's shop. The old man stood before his store smoking his pipe; he had long ceased accepting shoes for repair. From time to time he gave us a few nails, which were always useful in mending our miserable army shoes when they began to fall apart. In the second house to the right, over the closed dairy shop, two girls stood at a window full of flowers. The two girls, one blonde and one brunette, pulled aside the white lace curtain and smiled. They never came downstairs; I do not know who they were. All they ever gave me was a smile.

The baker's wife sat in front of the bakery rocking her child. The baby carriage was light blue and the child looked like a freshly baked pound-cake. Bread was sold only for bread cards. But when we came by, she stopped rocking her child; she went into the store and brought us a loaf of white bread. In the afternoons, the butcher shop was closed; meat cards had been introduced some time before. We entered the shop from the rear, and I was given meat for the patients' soup and my guard a piece of sausage. Then we went to Frau Jaeger's.

Her shop had been closed ever since the occupation of Dieuze by the Germans, and the windows were boarded up. Men can be made to carry stones and sell trousers, but no one can be forced to bake delicious little tarts. Frau Jaeger's nut-tarts were famous all over Lorraine. She was a woman with an imposing double chin, a pneumatic bosom, and a voice like a man. Beside her, the husky German soldiers looked frail and small. She never paid the slightest attention to them. In her back kitchen she baked for the sick prisoners in the infirmary. When we came for our package, she usually gave one or two of her cakes to my German guard. There is nothing the Germans like better than sweets. They can live on chocolate and beer. Frau Jaeger gave her little tarts to the Germans with an admirable look of dignified contempt.

312

Hair Tonic, Pepper, and Women

By six o'clock our rounds were completed. The heat was less intolerable. The church tower shone like gold in the sun. Our steps resounded on the great cobblestones. A dog would yawn in some doorway. If you could forget the Prussian military signs on every second house, the steel-helmeted, armed patrols pacing up and down the streets, you could imagine yourself in a peaceful little town in lovely Lorraine.

At six we went to the Café des Voyageurs in the Rue Bernard du Fort, behind the Main Square. It was a small café, owned by a widow who ran it with the help of her daughter Stella. The mother was small and graceful; Stella was tall and strong. But they were alike in one thing—their admirable aloofness from the Germans. All day long they resisted the advances of the German soldiers without hostility, but also without fear. What these smiling heroines went through is indescribable. They suffered—because the Germans regarded Dieuze as German territory "once and for all." But never did these silent heroines utter a complaint. Without any theatrical displays of virtue or injured innocence, they repulsed threats, proposals, abuse, and flattery. Once a German corporal who had drunk too much beer asked the little widow whether her daughter was still a virgin. I shall never forget his helpless blush when the widow answered quietly and sadly: "You see, I am only a widow who tried to educate her children honorably. I always used to take good care of my daughter. But now I don't have to worry. I know that she would rather die than let a German touch her."

So saying, she arose and went to get the soldier's beer.

Every evening at six we repaired to this Café des Voyageurs for half an hour. Leaving the "delivery wagon" outside, my guard and I would sit down at one of the rear tables. The widow would turn on the radio, and Stella would come in and ask: "How is your guard today? Does he behave?"

When I answered that he was very friendly, she would give him a glass of schnapps or a free beer.

One afternoon there were several German soldiers sitting at the bar. One of them was Sergeant Peter Weitlingen. He was a student of literature at the University of Düsseldorf, a Catholic from the Rhineland. Weitlingen was nineteen years old, a tall, slender youth with light blond hair and light blue eyes. I became friendly with him one day when he brought the prisoners some letters from their wives. These were Lorraine women who, having learned that their husbands were in the camp at Dieuze, had come to the little town to establish some sort of "contact" with "their" prisoners. The nineteen-year-old boy had smuggled the women's letters—and occasional packages—into the camp. Since I lived in the infirmary, he often came to see me in the evening. In my dark room, at the open window, we discussed German and French literature, men and women, God and His enemies. Peter Weitlingen was in love with a girl from Dieuze, but had never declared his love. He said with touching naïveté: "I am unworthy of her, because I wear the German uniform." The population of Dieuze called him *le sergeant gentil*.

Weitlingen came up and held out his hand to me as I followed Corporal Berger into the café.

"Good evening, Napier!"

Unthinkingly, I shook hands with him.

"Good evening, *Herr Unteroffizier*."

Only then did I see the pair of eyes turned toward me. Sergeant-Major Engel was sitting on one of the high stools at the bar. This Engel, one of the most important men in camp, if not the most important, was chief of the guards. He was a small blond man from Nuremberg with two pro-

truding teeth that dug into his lower lip, and enormous ears
with lobes like two thick pink sausages. Some people remind
you of the zoo at the very first glance, and Engel was one
of them.

Only after his eyes met mine did I realize what had happened. Weitlingen had shaken hands with me! German
soldiers were forbidden under the severest penalties to shake
hands with French prisoners. I should have disregarded
Weitlingen's gesture. But what on earth had given him the
idea of shaking hands with me in public!

Engel said nothing. He kept staring at me with red-rimmed
drunken eyes. I did not know whether he had seen me. He
rocked his high stool. His boots creaked as he pressed them
against the bar. Every moment he was in danger of falling.

Josef Berger, a huge, bearlike fellow, and I sat down at a
table. Stella brought a small glass of beer for each of us. We
kept silent.

But this afternoon everything conspired against me. We
had been sitting no more than a few minutes when the druggist's wife appeared on the scene. For the last few days she
had come to the Café des Voyageurs nearly every time I was
there. She was very blonde, with soft gray eyes, a small nose,
and a delicate white skin over her high cheekbones. She
laughed when I told her that it was her cheekbones that I
liked best about her. Most of the time she only shook hands
with me and went quickly to the kitchen. She was a friend
of the widow's, and often came to sit with her or iron in the
kitchen.

She came straight up to me holding out a package. I
opened it. It contained a new French soldier's cap. She had
noticed that my own *calot* was in rags and was presenting
me with a new one. I thanked her in embarrassment. She said
loudly: "Don't mention it. But—what have you got there?"

There was a loose button on my coat. Before I had time to think, she brought a needle and thread from the kitchen and began sewing. Her loose blonde hair grazed my neck.

The sergeant-major's eyes had not left me for an instant. Only now did I notice, above the woman's blond head, that the sergeant-major was not alone. Corporal Kessler of the resplendent boots stood behind him. The corporal's round childish face was now dominated by two enormous black nostrils—a childish face with the hollow nasal cavities of a death's head.

For a short eternity we looked into each other's eyes. Corporal Berger at my side did not know what to say. It was a sultry summer evening outside. The sky hung low over Dieuze.

The widow noticed that something was wrong. She set down a jug with fresh, foaming beer near Engel. He pushed the beer aside violently without so much as looking at it. He saw only us. There was such a mixture of lust and hatred in those protruding, glassy eyes that a cold shiver ran down my back. It was as though, instead of a woman sewing, the men were viewing an utterly obscene spectacle.

I attempted to concentrate the sergeant's look on myself. The druggist's wife—I never even knew her name—had her back turned to the bar; she saw nothing. She went on with her sewing. After a while she started looking for her scissors. She had forgotten to bring them. She bent down and bit off the thread with her teeth. Her head touched my chest.

Then a voice resounded from the bar: "Come here!"

I stepped forward.

"No, not you!" said Engel with a gesture of dismissal. "You!" He pointed his finger at the woman. "You!"

She didn't understand a word of German.

"Come here!" croaked the sergeant.

We all stood petrified. Only the sergeant-major sat leaning and rocking on his stool, clinging with one hand to the rail. Instinctively the druggist's wife came close to me.

Engel turned to Kessler.

"Tell the bitch to come here!"

Up till then Weitlingen had not budged. Suddenly he stepped between Engel and me.

"Prisoner Napier," he said sharply, "it's high time for you to go home!"

My guard jumped up. The atmosphere grew less tense. Weitlingen bent toward me as though about to scold me.

"Don't be afraid!" he whispered. "I'll take the lady home."

I paid and we went out. The last I saw was the short body of the sergeant-major bent forward ready to jump.

Later that night I found a note under my pillow.

"Look out! Danger! I took Mrs. G. safely home. Be careful. E. has doubts about your identity. Tear up this note. P. W."

I tore the paper into a thousand pieces. God had ordained that even among the Nazis there should be one human being. . . .

CHAPTER TEN: TOMORROW IS ANOTHER DAY

EVERY DAY ALFRED WARNED ME OF NEW DANGERS. MY privileged position in the camp aroused the envy of numerous other prisoners, and they began to see certain things that had previously passed unnoticed. More and more prisoners noted that my French pronunciation permitted doubts as to my French origin. Alfred assured me that dozens of my comrades were constantly on the lookout for a slip when I translated the order of the day. Others openly suggested that it mightn't be quite fair for a "non-Frenchman" to be their camp commander. How much of all this had come to the ears of the Germans I could not ascertain.

But clearly something was brewing. One night Weitlingen came to my room and said: "I've come just for a minute. My bicycle mustn't be seen in front of the infirmary. So far everything has been all right, though Engel is in love with the druggist's wife. But for God's sake be careful. Somebody must have put a flea in Engel's ear, and told him you were a naturalized Frenchman, possibly of German origin. The other day, after you left the Café des Voyageurs, Engel said that he wouldn't rest till he had you investigated. So far I've succeeded in keeping him quiet. But watch out!"

He gave me a pack of good German cigarettes and left me. In the moonlight I saw him riding off to Dieuze on his bicycle.

318

And there were other disturbing developments. More and more prisoners were sent north to Germany, particularly to regions bombed by the R.A.F. About a thousand left every week, and only three hundred to four hundred new ones arrived. Our original twenty-two thousand prisoners had dwindled to twelve thousand. And every incoming transport set my nerves on edge—the real Maurice Napier might be among them. Usually Alfred went to see if Napier had arrived. Luckily for me, there had been no sign of him, but every day might bring a surprise. To make matters worse, I was instructed to draw up the lists of prisoners to be transported to Germany.

I had to take many things into account. Above all, I had to take care that the protégés of German officers and non-coms should not leave the camp. In this respect, I noticed one curious phenomenon. In so far as there is any racial instinct, the Germans certainly have it: but it is an instinct which has nothing to do with their theories. Jewish prisoners were chosen by the Germans for all the "good jobs." I trembled to think of the day when the officers would get hold of the "racial lists" we were drawing up. They would see that all their favorites were Jews. I also had to take care that the camp should not be deprived of all qualified workers in the same category. Every day this unwanted power brought me into the most unpleasant situations.

In the end, two incidents forced my hand. (I am convinced that they occurred because a superior power meant to save me.)

One morning, toward the end of July, Captain Kohlrusch came into my office on the top floor of the infirmary building. This was his first visit. I was at work with three secretaries, preparing a list of prisoners to be transported.

The captain motioned me to send the three prisoners away. I remained alone with the Gestapo officer.

"Listen to me carefully, Napier," said the captain as he sat down on my desk. "This is a confidential matter. I trust you."

I made a slight bow.

"I have received instructions to find out how many of our prisoners are naturalized Frenchmen. Of course, it is former German subjects in whom we are particularly interested. They fought against their own country. You understand me?"

"Perfectly, *Herr Hauptmann.*"

"Good. Do you know any such prisoners?"

His question sounded casual. Captain Kohlrusch was not looking at me. He absent-mindedly grazed my desk with his riding crop.

"I cannot think of any, *Herr Hauptmann.* But surely there must be some."

Still casual, Captain Kohlrusch drew a small note out of his pocket.

"Wolff! Wolff! Do you know a prisoner named Wolff?"

"There is no such prisoner in this camp, *Herr Hauptmann.*"

"Would you mind looking him up in your lists? Louis Wolff."

I went to my files.

"One or two F's?"

"What? Oh, yes. Two F's."

I thought quickly: how could I warn him if he is really here? I was relieved when I was able to announce: "No. No Wolff here. Neither with one nor with two F's."

"Hm. Strange, very strange. But after all he may be here under an assumed name. Don't you think it is possible?"

"Of course, everything is possible, *Herr Hauptmann*. But after all everyone here has his identification tag."

I pointed at my wrist.

"That's true," said Captain Kohlrusch. "But there is no photograph or fingerprint on the tags."

I remained silent. A pause ensued. From the drill-ground came the songs of marching soldiers. They sang all day long. This time it was: "We Are Sailing Against England."

"You can do me a favor, Napier," Captain Kohlrusch said suddenly. "Try to find this Louis Wolff. I am sure he is in this camp."

I did not answer. Captain Kohlrusch began drumming on my desk with his long finger nails.

"You are hesitating," he said at last. "I can understand that. But I assure you that he is no Frenchman. The man we are looking for was born in Berlin. Moreover he is a Jew."

"I see," I said.

Suddenly the captain asked me, "You have relatives in Paris, haven't you?"

"Yes."

"Your wife?"

"Yes." (This was a lie: my wife was actually in Geneva.)

"You'd like to see her again, wouldn't you? We'd all like a chance to embrace our wives."

He meant to be friendly, but he sounded cold and obscene.

"Of course, *Herr Hauptmann*."

"Good. I'll try to do something for you. How would you like a little furlough from camp? Suppose you give a few lectures in Paris. To your French friends. About the life of the French prisoners in German camps. Hm? Not a bad idea, what? You have nothing to complain of, have you?"

"Nothing at all, *Herr Hauptmann*."

When will he get out of here? I wondered. There was

something that remained unsaid—an uneasy feeling in the air. The captain held a ruler in his right hand, his riding crop in his left. He crossed them like two swords.

"So try to find this Wolff! And then—"

He drew a second crumpled piece of paper out of his pocket. But he did not finish his sentence. He said, "The aliens and Jews have ruined France. If you had had the strength to throw them out in time, as we did, it wouldn't have come to this."

"That is my own opinion," I said. "I and my family were always for a Franco-German rapprochement. All the Napiers were known as Munichmen. But we preached to deaf ears. The Popular Front—"

I employed the gesture Frenchmen used to make when speaking of the Popular Front. The duel had begun. There was no turning back.

The captain crossed his "swords."

"Quite so," he acquiesced. And then again, with the same cheap, artificial indifference he must have learned from a provincial actor: "Here is a little list of suspects. They are guilty of high treason. They fought against Germany in one or another of the volunteer hordes. The names will show you that there's not a Frenchman among them. You'll be rendering a service to your country if you can bring them to justice. It goes without saying that all these fellows have assumed false names. I can't put them in the roll-call. But perhaps you . . . quietly . . . among your comrades . . ."

He handed me the list, and added, by way of clinching the matter: "Of course I have a copy."

Abruptly he began to speak of other things. For the thousandth time he treated me to the same old refrains. All these men, officers or plain privates, spoke as though the same gramophone record were revolving in their mouths.

The paper was burning in my hand. I did not dare open it for fear of arousing suspicion. At last the captain arose. But only to go to the window. Marching German troops were singing: *"Jetzt geht's ins Heimatland, ins schöne Schwabenland."*

"Those men are going home. You'd like to go home yourself some day, wouldn't you, Napier?" And with a kindness that distorted his sour face: "To kiss the little wife? We'll see what we can do for you."

My blood rose to my head. I was only pretending to be Maurice Napier. But no decent man can constantly cheat another without losing his self-respect. Not even when the cheating is for a good cause. But Captain Kohlrusch noticed nothing. His mind was taken up with the soldiers returning home.

I noticed that the paper was crumpled in my hand, and tried to control my fingers.

It was noon before the captain was ready to leave. In the doorway he said, "Today is Monday. By Wednesday I'd like to have your report on Wolff."

When he was gone, I sat down at my desk and smoothed out the crumpled note. Down below the soldiers were still marching and singing.

The letters dissolved before my eyes. I saw the shape of the writing but was unable to grasp its meaning. I had to turn my eyes away and then bring them back to the note before I was able to read it.

There were twelve names. All twelve were from my regiment.

My own name was the fourth on the list . . .

The next day, Tuesday, another decisive event took place. Accompanied by Sergeant Paul Daxer from Stuttgart, I was on my way back to Dieuze from Nancy. As usual, we had a load of champagne, ladies' underwear, leather brief-cases and celluloid soap dishes. This time we were rather uneasy about the border control, thinking that our frequent trips must have aroused suspicion. It was pouring rain. Shortly after leaving Nancy, a German officer and his orderly stopped us and asked us for a lift. They had been dining at Nancy. I sat on the stretcher, and both our guests installed themselves inside the car.

As the lieutenant, a Hamburg merchant, engaged me in conversation, I saw his orderly eyeing me from the side. The officer was a sturdy little fellow, obviously well disposed after his abundant meal and delighted to have found pleasant traveling companions. His servant was a handsome, huge boy whose pronunciation immediately betrayed an Austrian. From the moment he saw me, he kept grinning—a mysterious, defiant grin.

I felt ill at ease. The lieutenant took my Red Cross armband seriously and inquired about the condition of the sick man. I stuttered an explanation, sitting as gingerly as I could on the stretcher, that is, on the bottles of champagne beneath the blanket. The orderly kept grinning.

We passed Arracourt without incident. The lieutenant, whose face was red from beer, dozed off and began to snore. But his orderly kept grinning, as though the grin were chiseled into his face. Finally I ventured to ask: "What are you laughing at?"

He winked to me, but gave no explanation.

"Just so."

I vainly tried to recall if I had seen his face before.

The car bumped over a hastily repaired bridge. The bottles in the body of our gravely wounded patient clattered. The

324

sound of clanking glass—a happy memory—awakened the lieutenant.

"What's up?" he said, rubbing his eyes.

"Nothing, *Herr Leutnant*," said his orderly, still smiling.

I must have seen the fellow somewhere, I thought. But my wits were as dull as wood.

Now the lieutenant also noticed the strange behavior of his orderly.

"What are you staring at, Leopold?"

Leopold, Leopold, I repeated to myself. But the name meant nothing to me.

"Nothing, *Herr Leutnant.*"

At Dieuze we stopped before headquarters to unload our Hamburg merchant. The filling station was next door and we proceeded to take on some gas. The lieutenant got out, and Sergeant Daxer began to negotiate for fuel. The officer's servant and I remained alone in the car.

Then he said quietly: "Good evening, Herr Habe."

My blood froze in my veins. I had no idea what to do. I stared into the void. I pretended not to know whom he was speaking to.

"Good evening, Herr Habe."

I still did not budge.

The man bent down to my ear and said in real Viennese: "I know, I know. You mustn't be afraid of me. I know you. I won't tell anyone."

It would have been useless to contradict him. I looked into the man's face. The grin was gone. He said softly: "Don't you remember? I waited on you many times! You and Mrs. Habe. You always gave me good tips."

I was somewhat relieved.

"Where was it?" I asked, still trembling.

"Well, just try to remember," he said cheerily.

325

"Must have been in Vienna."

"Of course." He came to my assistance. "Of course in Vienna. In the Grand Hotel."

He furtively held out his hand, looking around to make sure that no one was looking.

"Don't worry," he said magnanimously. "I won't give you away."

Then he vanished into the headquarters building.

I looked after him. I was still trembling all over. This time the god of tips had taken me under his protection. But that did not alter the fact that a German knew my secret, in the German camp of Dieuze.

I decided to flee within a week. From that moment there was room in my mind for nothing else.

The very next day—after an almost sleepless night troubled by the wildest dreams—I at last found an opportunity to prepare my flight.

I spent the night planning and dreaming. The plans were clear, the dreams confused. By morning I had decided on a course of action. What I needed was a place at Nancy where I might hide for three or four days. I would elude my guards by slipping out of some store through a rear exit, hurry to my hiding place and stay there during the period of intensive search when all the roads would be barred. The rest would take care of itself.

These were my plans. My dreams were not so clear. That night I dreamed that a waiter in the large, old-fashioned, artificially illumined dining room of the Grand Hotel in Vienna brought me hors d'œuvres on a wheel-table. But the table turned out to be an ambulance. The waiter put in his hand and drew out hors d'œuvres, champagne, and silk shirts. I refused to take anything, but the waiter insisted. I looked up and saw that the waiter was Captain Kohlrusch. He bowed ceremoniously and said: "Good evening, Herr Habe!" I felt that everyone in the dining room was looking at me. I tried to eat, but something choked me. Suddenly the waiter took me by my ear, just as Captain Kohlrusch had taken the Negroes by their ears in his lectures on colonial policy. Everyone in the dining room laughed as the soldiers in the lecture hall had laughed when the captain spoke to them about Negroes. "Good evening, Herr Habe," said the waiter-captain, very politely pulling my ear. "Have you any news of Herr Wolff?"

I woke up in a sweat, more than ever determined to carry out my plans.

The next day I went to Nancy with the chauffeur, Dr. Frank, the chief physician, Sergeant Daxer, and Dr. L'Ardennois, a French surgeon from Nancy. We had no imaginary patient this time; our trip was almost legitimate. We were to bring rolls of bandage from the Nancy hospital. That was why Lieutenant Dr. L'Ardennois was going with us. Dr. Frank meant to seize the opportunity to buy chocolate and bring it to Dieuze in the bandage boxes. He and several other officers were going on leave the following week and they needed the chocolate for gifts. Apparently I was expected to play a prominent part in the pillage, for Dr. Frank was all sugar and honey, and offered me a home-made cigarette.

It took us only a few minutes to load on our bandages. We left the fine, modern hospital and crossed the bridge over the Rhine-Marne Canal. On the Boulevard Lobau, Dr. Frank directed the chauffeur to the Rue Emile Zola. We stopped twenty yards from the chocolate factory, a long, two-story, gray building.

"Now you get out," said Dr. Frank, "and do your work.

There's a lot of chocolate stored here. The *Kommandantur* forbade us to get chocolate from the factory. They probably want it to go direct to Germany. But after all we're German soldiers, too."

He paused for a while, to give us time to take in his logic, and possibly to prepare the attack. Then he added quickly: "You go into the factory. See the manager. Tell him that you need five hundred pounds of chocolate for your patients. For the French, of course. Tell him that chocolate is indispensable for the prisoners, on account of the dysentery." And after a short silence during which I remained impassive: "Do you understand?"

"Yes, *Herr Oberarzt.*"

I climbed out of the ambulance, walked down the street, and rang the bell at the factory entrance. An old woman with dirty gray-black hair opened the gate. Her wrinkled face brightened when she saw my French uniform.

"Are you alone?" she asked.

"Yes. I'll talk to you later. Let me in first."

She quickly locked the gate behind me.

I inquired for the factory manager, and she took me to him. We crossed a deserted yard. The gray walls echoed the sound of our steps. A few windows were boarded. Everything was dead except the smell, the heavy, fat smell of chocolate, the smell of our childhood cocoa in the morning before school. The moldy, sweetish smell hung over the ruined factory.

The manager was a tiny man with a goatee. He sat in front of a map of occupied and unoccupied France. The shutters were down, a gray curtain was drawn. The telephone seemed like a dead piece of furniture. The deep old leather chairs smelled of chocolate and pastry.

I explained the situation to the manager. I told him that of course our patients would get none of the chocolate. He shrugged his shoulders. He was hunchbacked and his head sank into his chest.

"What does it matter?" he said. "Tomorrow all our reserves have to be handed over to the Germans. We have put very little aside. It all happened too quickly, *mon ami*. Whether the chocolate goes to them or to the others—"

Again he concentrated on his map. I came closer and bent over him.

"Monsieur . . ."

"Yes?"

"May I have your map?"

He looked at me. His eyes were small, intelligent, yet full of kindness. Without a word he folded the map. I stuck it in my coat.

"Well," he said. "Now let them come in. Of course I can't give them five hundred pounds. Two hundred and fifty will do."

He took a large key from the board. At the door he turned back and went to his desk. He opened a drawer and took out three bars of chocolate.

"Hide them quickly," he said.

Before I had time to thank him he walked out. I followed him across the yard. The old woman opened the iron gate for us. I made a sign to the Germans waiting in the ambulance, and a few minutes later the car rolled into the yard of the *Chocolaterie Lorraine*. The chauffeur and Dr. L'Ardennois remained outside under the guard of Dr. Frank while Sergeant Daxer and I followed the manager into the factory. We passed one or two offices and finally entered a store room. A young girl sat at a desk reading *Marie Claire*, a pre-war fashion magazine. Even the girl looked dusty and smelled of chocolate.

We brought the first half of our booty to the car and then went back for the rest. But when we returned to the yard we saw that something had happened during our absence. Dr. Frank, his hands on the seams of his trousers, stood facing a German officer. An officer's car stood beside the ambulance. The old woman was wringing her hands. She shouted something that I could not hear. Before I had realized what was going on, one of the three German soldiers with the officer struck the chocolate bars out of my hands. They fell on the sidewalk and broke. Two soldiers bent down, picked up the chocolate, and loaded it in their car. Behind me, Sergeant Daxer stood helpless with both hands full of chocolate.

The two officers were engaged in a violent quarrel. All I could make out was an uninterrupted stream of *"Herr Oberarzt"* and *"Herr Oberleutnant"* with a menacing intonation on the *"Herr."* They faced one another eye to eye, or rather eye to belly, for the lieutenant, though quite fat, was so short that he seemed to be pushing his nose into the gigantic Dr. Frank's paunch. Two of the officer's escort were about to take the first twenty pounds of chocolate from the ambulance. "Stop!" cried Dr. Frank, purple with rage. The scar on his right cheek, which extended into his upper lip, became so red that it looked like a little river of blood. "Stop that!" cried Dr. Frank, seizing his tiny Belgian revolver. The soldiers halted before the ambulance and stood motionless. The situation became more and more like a fight between two groups of gangsters.

I do not know what would have been the end of this noble dispute over 250 pounds of chocolate; and I never found out how it had begun. All I know is that I saw the little hunchbacked manager suddenly step between the two officers. The bearded dwarf's desperate efforts to push his pointed gray-

haired head between Dr. Frank's belly and the round lieutenant were both grotesque and touching. Finally he managed
with his two small hands to push the two giants apart. He
explained something in French; they did not understand, but
calmed down when he brought out another fifty pounds of
chocolate. The two officers, each with 150 pounds of chocolate, separated. They walked across the deserted factory
yard, the six-foot chief physician and the butter-ball lieutenant, each carrying a few bars of chocolate, each trying to
force a smile and look as though nothing had happened. The
two representatives of the German army returned to their
cars, and the factory manager, somewhat exhausted by his
effort, looked on. A little smile brightened his intelligent yet
kindly eyes.

We packed the chocolate under our bandages. Then we
left Dr. Frank at a restaurant. He ordered us to come for
him an hour later.

Sergeant Daxer returned to the car. Jeannot, the chauffeur,
was awaiting further orders. Daxer hesitated and suddenly
turned to me: "Listen, Napier . . ."

He gulped.

"Yes, *Herr Unteroffizier?*"

"Man does not live by bread alone."

"That's right, *Herr Unteroffizier.*"

"Nor on drink alone."

"That's right, *Herr Unteroffizier.*"

There was a pause.

Sergeant Daxer was the chief of our infirmary. No doubt
he was regarded as qualified for this job because in civil life
he was a printer. Blond, with hard features and hard eyes, he
was from Stuttgart where he owned a party printing shop.
He had a wife and two children. Now he was silent. He
waited for help.

"Man—" said Paul Daxer, the printer and family father.

"Man—" I repeated, sure of hearing another aphorism about man in general.

"Man—" the sergeant finally jumped the hurdle—"man has his needs."

"Yes, yes," I said. "That's true. Man has his needs."

Daxer waited. His steel-blue eyes drilled me with hostility. Suddenly he said: "Where is there a whorehouse in this town?"

I was unable to give him the information.

"Ask Dr. L'Ardennois. He is from Nancy. That's why I took him with us. But be discreet!"

Very discreetly I asked Dr. L'Ardennois where there was a brothel.

"There's a whole street of them," explained the lieutenant.

"Then let's go," said Daxer. You could see by his expression that he had no time to lose.

We passed by the cathedral and turned into the second side street behind it. Through my small barred window I saw at once that Dr. L'Ardennois had given the correct address. German soldiers were lined up outside every house. Their sex life was organized according to military rank. Officers with shining boots and broad caps stood in line outside a two-story house on the right side of the street. The next house was besieged by top sergeants, recognizable by the narrow silver stripes on their collars. The drill sergeants, with stars on their epaulets, stood at the foot of the stairs leading to an old, half-dilapidated house. Privates and corporals waited outside the other houses—patient and stubborn, with a look of vice, brutality, and false shame. Now and then one of the closed windows on the first or second floor opened and a half-dressed beauty leaned out in a pink, red, or canary yellow wrapper. A prostitute with disheveled hair and an

332

overbrimming bosom yelled some obscenity in the street. From time to time, in one of the old gray houses with the unwashed window-panes and the moldy walls, a window was torn open and a chamber pot was emptied into the street among the soldiers who would jump aside spitting, cursing, and laughing.

Sergeant Daxer did not know what to do with us. But the flesh was stronger. He decided to trust us this time and leave us unguarded. The risk was not very great, of course, for the street was full of German soldiers. He ordered us to wait in the car till he came back—he would return soon, but "man has his needs." Then he took his place in line outside the house with the stairs and the iron banister. We waited outside the brothel, sitting on bandages and chocolate, in our French ambulance. Twenty paces behind us the spire of the Gothic cathedral of Nancy rose high in the summer sky.

The heat was unbearable in the car. I got out and stood leaning against the radiator—a sentry for the human needs of Paul Daxer, master printer and father of a family. Suddenly I felt someone touch my sleeve; at the same time an object slid into the pocket of my coat. I turned around.

Two girls stood beside me. One was small and delicate; she wore a lace blouse and an enormous brooch. A tiny black straw hat sat on a tiny head, dominated by two big blue eyes. Her face was so small and her eyes so big that I had a feeling that they would jump out of her cheeks. The other girl was round and sturdy. She wore a blue ready-made suit and a hat with a whole botanical garden on it. Her round red cheeks radiated the health of a peasant girl who keeps her country color even long after she has been lost in the city slums.

I stuck my hand into my pocket and realized that these two girls had given me a pack of *Gauloises Bleues*, the favorite cigarettes of the French. I thanked them. But as I was thanking them, I suddenly became aware that these two girls would help me—these two heavily rouged young girls, the little one with the brooch and the stout one with the flower bed, who had given me cigarettes in front of a hundred waiting German males.

Around us was the bustling street where love could be bought, love for officers, non-coms, and privates, love for one, two, or three occupation marks. Sweating, hurrying men, reeking with beer, passed us. In a window level with the ground a gramophone with an old-fashioned horn played hurdy-gurdy tunes.

I said suddenly: "Do you want to help me?"

"Yes," said both girls at once.

"Do you know a place where I could hide for two or three days if I can get through?"

The two girls looked at one another for a short while. Then the little thin one, with the big eyes, said: "Hôtel St. Martin, Rue des Quatre Eglises."

That was all. I repeated to myself: Hôtel St. Martin, Rue des Quatre Eglises.

Meanwhile Sergeant Daxer came back, his eyes feverish with hastily consummated love. In his hands he held his leather gloves, the symbol of dignity for all German soldiers from non-coms upwards. He adjusted his bayonet in his belt and looked himself over with the uncertainty of a man expecting to find a flaw in his attire. Ill-tempered like all animals after the enjoyment of pleasure, he turned to the two girls: "What are you doing here?"

The little one measured him with her eyes. He blushed; his ears were large and glowing.

"My name is Jeannine," said the little one. "My friend's name is Irène. We're waitresses"—she whispered the name—

"in the Restaurant Stanislas, on Stanislas Square. You can leave word for us any time."

"Get on! Get on!" said Sergeant Daxer.

We drove off. The two girls remained at the curb looking after us. I saw them shoved and pushed aside by the soldiers. Their names were Jeannine and Irène. And they knew a place, the Hôtel St. Martin, in the Rue des Quatre Eglises . . .

I was still in camp, but I began to see everything as through a veil. I felt that it was my duty to take in everything around me, to imprint it on my mind, so as to communicate it some day—somewhere, somehow.

That day an inexplicable nervousness pervaded the camp. I could clearly feel that it came from the German soldiers; they all went about their occupations with expressive, discontented, silent faces. Even Sergeant Webke, the chef, was ill-tempered and bitter, though I had brought him a pork chop—the Germans had gone without meat for days. But I couldn't find out from Webke what had happened, because Inspector Kindt, a Saxon officer, who supervised our commissary and was regarded as a meddler, broke in and interrupted our conversation.

I was calling on Alfred in his ward when I heard that they were looking for me all over the camp. Lieutenant L'Ardennois wanted me in the operating room.

The operating room was a narrow space on the ground floor, next to the wash room and toilet. It was miserably equipped and suitable only for very minor operations. I went in and saw at once that something unusual was afoot. The room smelled of carbolic acid and ether, and four or five nurses stood around the operating table. Beside it stood a pail full of blood and water. Dr. L'Ardennois, wearing a white physician's tunic over his uniform, was bent over the table;

someone was trying to connect a rubber hose to the faucet
so as to bring water directly to the table; a nurse was looking
desperately for catgut—and amidst all this precise excitement
a dog was howling. The dog belonged to a German soldier—
a corporal, I think—and he was whining, howling, and tugging at his leash. The soldier was saying something in German
amid the ether vapors. L'Ardennois was answering him in
French while trying desperately to finish his work with his
primitive instruments.

"What is the trouble, *mon lieutenant?*" I asked, approaching the table.

The man on the table was more dead than alive. His head
had drooped; all blood had gone from his narrow, lipless face.
Blood was streaming from the lower part of his body;
L'Ardennois seemed to be washing his hands in blood.

"Please, Napier," L'Ardennois shouted through the vapor,
"tell this man that I cannot attend to his dog now. He should
have some consideration. My patient has had a hemorrhage;
he is dying on my hands."

The dog kept whining and raised one paw; the corporal
was shoving toward the operating table. I could see his face
but indistinctly through the mist; with his drooping cheeks
and pointed forehead he resembled a pear.

I touched the pear on the shoulder: "What do you wish?"

"I want the doctor to have a look at my dog," the corporal
said rudely. "I think he was run over."

"Just a minute," I said. "As soon as the doctor is ready.
You can see for yourself that he is operating right now."

"That makes no difference to me," replied the pear. "I
won't have time later."

I thought for a moment.

"Why don't you go to the German infirmary?" I said in
my best Swiss German. "You belong there anyway."

"I certainly do," said the man. "But not my dog."

"The lieutenant is not a veterinary," I replied. "He'd only make a mess of it."

The pear eyed me askance. He did not know whether I was telling the truth or making fun of him. The dog kept tugging at his leash, lifting his leg and raising his mouth in the air with a howl. Only at night, when the moon is shining, in solitary village graveyards, do dogs howl like that.

"Take his pulse," said the surgeon to one of the nurses. The blood was dripping to the floor with the regularity of raindrops falling from a gutter.

The pear insisted: "I want the doctor to have a look at my dog!"

I wondered what to do with this fellow. I would have loved to take him by his shoulders and shake his stinking soul out of his rotten skin. But I controlled myself.

"Don't you see," I asked him, "that the man on the table is dying?"

"He's dead anyway," said the corporal.

"Well . . ." I said. I had to gain time. "Well, in that case . . . in that case I'll have a look at your dog."

"Are you a physician?" the pear asked with distrust.

Almost indignantly I pointed at my arm-band with the red cross and the swastika. In this way I succeeded in gaining time till Dr. L'Ardennois had finished operating.

From the infirmary I went to the administration building where some of the guards lived. Here, too, I met with discontented faces. I went to the room occupied by Corporals Josef Berger and Franz Holm. The huge, kindly Berger was a bookkeeper in a canned goods factory in Fürth; Holm was an industrial designer in Nuremberg. Both collected badges of French regiments. I was bringing them a badge I had

337

bought from a prisoner. But even this failed to cheer the two men.

"What's wrong?" I asked.

Berger was eating lunch, sitting half-naked over a rind of salt pork. Silently he handed me the *N.Z.*, the daily paper read by the Germans in camp. He pointed to a little notice on the third page.

I read: "No Party Day in 1940. The Reichführer's office announces that the Nuremberg Party Day will not be held this year."

That was all. Berger and Holm silently went on eating. I myself was at a loss what to say.

"September 9th," Berger said finally, "was supposed to be the Party Day of Peace."

"We'll never get home," said Holm.

They offered me a glass of beer. They drank some themselves. The beer loosened their tongues.

"Some of us," said little Holm, who liked to speak of himself as an artist, "haven't been home in three years. First Austria, then the Sudetenland, then Prague, Poland, the Westwall, France, and now England."

He spoke of Germany's conquests as of so many stations of the Cross.

I tried a different approach.

"How can you stand it?" I said. "We would have gone home long ago."

The German awakened in Holm.

"Yes," he said. "That's different. Your life was different from ours."

"How so?"

I listened attentively. Nothing could have been more instructive than the lecture that followed.

"In the first place—" said Holm, stretching out on the old

338

sofa—"in the first place there's the pay. Your soldiers got sixty-five centimes a day. Ours get a mark and at the front as much as two marks. That means twenty to forty francs a day."

"But not in purchasing power?"

"Oh, yes."

"And what else?"

"There's no comparison," Holm went on. "During our advance we saw the French barracks. A real disgrace."

"Do you have better ones in Germany?"

He laughed and turned to his comrade.

"Listen to that, Berger! Don't make me laugh. You fellows were herded together by the dozens. You slept on the floor like prisoners. Or on wooden planks. In our new barracks there are only two or three soldiers to a room. There's running water in every room. Our barracks look like a sanatorium. Each building has a reading room, a game room, a gymnasium. With us it's no calamity to be a soldier." He sighed. "Still, a man would like to go home once in a while."

I kept asking, "And what else?"

"What else? Well, just have a look at our uniforms. Am I right, Berger?"

"Sure!" said Berger. "You've been wearing rags. But we had two of everything, and everything first class. Just look!"

He pointed at the wall. By the door, beside the little iron stove, hung Corporal Berger's reserve uniform. His second uniform. His steel helmet lay on the stove. His gun, his polished boots stood near by.

"And what else?" I went on, just for the sake of asking.

"And then—and then," Holm laughed. "Your soldiers were herded together for soup like animals. You call that democracy. No, thank you. In our barracks, everyone gets his meal and eats it comfortably in his room. And then—and then—Oh, thousands of things!"

He offered me a cigarette.

"Now look here, Napier. The cigarettes. These cigarettes are *Ecksteins*. Six for three and a half pfennigs. First class! We get eight of them a day. Perhaps you had more. But your *Troupe*, that was the devil's weed. Our army gets the very best cigarettes. Your soldiers got dirt."

I nodded agreement.

"Not to mention the matter of arms," he went on. "The ones you got must have made you think the idea was to kill you."

Holm was in full swing.

"And then . . . our women. What did your women get when you were sent to the front? Practically nothing from the state, and certainly nothing near your earnings. Our women get money from the state, and our employers are obliged to pay our full wages to our wives. My wife has put aside three thousand marks since I left home."

"Mine too," declared Berger. "Three thousand five hundred."

I ventured an objection.

"But can your women buy anything with their money?"

The two Germans exchanged a glance that I was not supposed to notice. Then Berger said, somewhat dejectedly, with a wave of his plump hand: "Maybe they can't get the things that you could. But—but everything is different with us."

"What do you mean?"

"For instance," said Berger, "formerly when I went to the theater with my wife, there was always trouble. We got a seat in the twentieth row. But chief accountant Huber and his wife were in the tenth row. All through the show my wife squirmed in her seat. And afterwards, hell broke loose.

Why can the Hubers afford the tenth row and not ourselves?
You know, Herr Napier, how women are. Your own wife
wouldn't act differently."

"No, Herr Berger, my wife is just like that. I know."

He took a deep swallow of beer.

"In that case you'll understand. Nowadays, six nights a
week, all the seats in the theater cost the same. First come,
first serve. Sometimes the Hubers sit in the tenth row and we
in the twentieth. But my wife knows that that's because the
Hubers live nearer the theater. You see, Herr Napier, the
Stadttheater—"

Berger described at length the situation of the Stadttheater,
of Huber's apartment, of Berger's apartment; the public conveyances, the plays performed in the Stadttheater.

I steered the conversation to the matter of food.

"Of course there's too little of everything," conceded
Holm.

"But you're willing to suffer for the sake of Germany's
future," I suggested.

Again both men exchanged a glance.

"Of course," said Holm. "But that's not all. The main thing
is that no one gets more than anyone else. That makes it
easier to suffer privations."

He thought for a while.

"And in the army you're not worse off than at home. I've
heard that you had worse food in the army than at home."

A pause.

"Everything would have been fine," he said finally, not
without bitterness. "But a man has to go home some time. I
was sure it would all be over by September 9th. Weren't
you, Berger?"

"Me, too. And then the women . . ." Turning to me:

"You know how women are. They write impatient letters all the time. . . ."

"As if we could do anything about it," murmured Holm.

I borrowed the *N.Z.* to show it to Dr. Mauvoisin, Alfred, and René.

I found Alfred and René at the door of the hospital and reported my conversation to them.

"Of course," said René. "That's what it is. I always knew it. Probably that was Hitler's only stroke of genius. He understood that envy is the strongest human motive. He eliminated envy by doing away with happiness. He gave a philistine bolshevism to a notion of petty bourgeois. Equality in misery—*la belle affaire!* But that's what Germany wanted."

We had no chance to continue our discussion, for Pape came to take me to Captain Brühl. That day the whole gloomy camp seemed to pass before me in review.

A few hundred yellow and orange post cards lay piled up on the table in front of Captain Brühl. He handed me one. One side of the post cards bore the inscription: *Kriegsgefangenenpost* (war prisoners' correspondence). On the other side seven sentences were printed:

1. I am a prisoner and in good health.
2. I am a prisoner and slightly wounded.
3. I am a prisoner and seriously wounded, but my life is not in danger.
4. I am a prisoner and sick.
5. I am a prisoner and very sick, but my life is not in danger.
6. I am a prisoner and in the hospital.
7. I will be able to write in about four weeks.

"You see," said the captain, "now you're even permitted to send news to your family." And after a brief reflection: "These post cards will be distributed today. No one must add a single word to the printed text. No kisses and embraces and all that stuff. Just the first name, second name, and address. Each prisoner will receive only one post card. Five out of the six first sentences must be crossed out. The seventh remains. Understand?"

"I understand, *Herr Hauptmann.*"

I took a squint at a half-covered document lying on the table. It contained instructions from the High Command about prisoners' mail. I saw that our field post office number was 17572A (266).

"May the prisoners indicate where they are, *Herr Hauptmann?*"

"Of course not."

"Are they allowed to give a field post number, so as to be able to receive news from their families?"

"No!"

The captain saw that his answer did not satisfy me. He stretched out his legs and looked at me. He knew probably that Captain Kohlrusch had ordained me for higher missions.

"You see, my dear Napier," he said patronizingly, "Germany is humane. More humane than your rotten democracies. That's why we allow the prisoners to write to their families, though you've been with us less than two months. In four or five weeks these post cards will reach their destinations. But you have no right to receive any mail—during the months spent in the Transit Camp, I mean. It's for your own good. Just think of all the nonsense your wives would write you! They'd turn your heads with their stupid lying chatter. You should know, Napier, that we don't regard you as criminals, but only as poor misled human beings. You must be given a new skin, Napier! Of course you Frenchmen can never become like us. But that isn't necessary. At least we can make men out of you—by education. But to achieve this you must first of all be isolated from your old rotten surroundings. From France."

"Our families—" I tried to object, though I knew that it was futile.

"Families, families!" exclaimed Captain Brühl as he rose and began striding up and down the room. "The families, too, are France. Everything is rotten. You must be cured of all that."

I stood at attention.

"Besides," he said, "Frenchwomen are a pain in the neck. Do you know, Napier, what is going on in Dieuze?"

"No, *Herr Hauptmann.*"

He stood still, looked at me, then resumed his pacing.

"Do you know what has been happening in Lorraine? The women have tried to hide the crops. In Marainville they even robbed our stores, just to get our goat. In Gerbevillers the furies plundered a confiscation center. They gave their gardens to the Red Cross rather than let us use them. And in Dieuze—well, that thieves' nest is being cleaned out now. In Dieuze the women hid whole stores of provisions. Bakeries were closed to prevent the German soldiers from getting any bread. I guess you hadn't heard about all that, my dear Napier. Your Frenchwomen have distinguished themselves! But now their mischief is at an end. We've deported fifteen thousand women from Lorraine at one stroke. You know that the German is patient. But God help the man or woman who abuses his patience. This time we've had enough. We called the Elite Guards to take care of the ladies."

And in a hoarse voice, again stopping before me, he added: "Do you know what that means, Napier? The Elite Guards?"

"No, *Herr Hauptmann.*"

He answered: "It means that beginning tomorrow no Frenchwoman will laugh in Dieuze."

And then suddenly, as though nothing had happened: "Well, Napier, have these post cards distributed." He gave me five. "If you need more than one for yourself—"

"Thanks, *Herr Hauptmann.*"

I saluted. As I reached the door, he called me back.

"Oh, yes, Napier! There's something else! Do you think you can get me an accordion?"

"An accordion?" I asked. But my plan of attack was ready now. I had to smuggle a letter to Jeannine and Irène. I had to get to Nancy the next day at the latest. "An accordion? Of course, *Herr Hauptmann.*"

"You see we're going to have a little private party, and we have no accordion. You understand?"

"Of course, *Herr Hauptmann.* I know of a first-class accordion in Nancy."

"Good. Evacuate a patient, then."

"At your orders, *Herr Hauptmann.*"

I clicked my heels in the Prussian manner and went out. I had a full day before me.

But my torments seemed to have no end. In my office, constantly peering at the door, I wrote a letter for one of my guardian angels in the Restaurant Stanislas. I wrote it on pink letter paper which I had received as a gift from the old stationery owner in Dieuze. It was a clear, matter-of-fact letter in which I sketched the details of my plan for escape. I particularly dwelt on my need for civilian clothes, and gave my measurements. I had scarcely finished it when little round Pape came in for me.

"A first-class scandal!" he said. "Didn't you hear the shooting?"

"No. I was working."

"One of our sentries was forced to shoot a woman."

"What happened?"

"Another of these Dieuze women. She brought some white bread for the prisoners. Of course we didn't let her in. She managed to get close to the fence, in the rear, you know, near the latrines, and threw the bread in. The sentry called out to her—once, twice. Instead of answering, she ran away. Then the sentry shot her. In the back. Straight through her heart, unfortunately. Dead. It'll be a good lesson. What do you want—after all, the sentry couldn't know. The woman might have thrown in dynamite!"

"Yes," I said. "Dynamite in white bread."

But the sergeant took no notice.

It was a hot summer evening. We went to the latrines. A few officers and soldiers with shouldered guns stood outside the fence. In this compact group it was hard to distinguish the two ambulance orderlies bearing a stretcher, and Dr. Frank's gigantic shape. By the roadside, near the camp, the jasmine was in bloom. You could feel its fragrance: strong and heady. Somewhere in the world people were lying on a beach and the waves were playing with pebbles. Somewhere in the world people were waiting for night to fall—with the scent of acacias, with music from the hotel terrace, with the red light from a lighthouse, with a last glance from a balcony. Somewhere in the world a man was putting a shawl around a woman's shoulders. Somewhere in the world you, too, were awaited.

And somewhere in the world dogs were not more important than human beings, somewhere there were no forced cures and no "adult education," no accordions for hangmen, no dynamite in white bread.

Somewhere in the world, perhaps, men had the right to be men.

The group broke up. Inside the fence stood a few hundred intimidated, confused, bewildered people. They were staring across the latrines, the fence, and the road toward the place where the group was beginning to move. In front, two soldiers carried the stretcher. The woman's face was covered. No one saw her.

It was August 5th.

Captain Brühl passed by the fence. When he saw me he said: "Don't forget my accordion!"

Then I knew that that was my next to last night in Dieuze.

The next morning I applied at the captain's office for two passes to Nancy—explaining that I might have to make two trips for the accordion. The two passes were granted, sealed, and signed.

Before noon, with Berger as my guard, I went to Dieuze to get provisions for the infirmary. It was a sultry summer day and the sky was full of storm clouds. As we passed the local commandant's office behind the church, we saw a car bearing the letters "WH"—the army letters. The sentries presented arms and two officers in black Elite Guard uniforms disappeared into the beautiful, oblong building, formerly the town hall. There were no other visible signs of Elite Guards, but there was something menacing and heavy in the air.

I stopped with my cart in front of the drugstore. The druggist's wife was not on the stairs. I looked into the window, but she was not at the cashier's desk either. I pretended that I had to buy something, and leaving Berger outside, went into the store. The clerk pointed silently to the rear, where a door led to the druggist's apartment. I knocked. There was no answer. Hesitantly I pressed the doorknob.

She was alone. The room was full of dresses, shoes, papers, hats. A half-packed suitcase stood on the floor. Amidst this picturesque disarray, the woman sat on the old plush sofa holding her chin in her hands.

347

I stood in the doorway and cleared my throat.

She looked up, rose slowly, and came toward me.

"Ah, it's you," she said rather absently. "I thought it was—" She broke off.

"What did you think?"

"That they were coming for me."

I took her hand.

"That's not true!"

"It is true," she said, trying to smile. "They're coming for me. In an hour or two. I am going to be deported."

"But aren't you from Dieuze?"

"Yes," she answered. "I was born here. But that doesn't matter."

She looked around her room. She tried to smile.

I did not know what to say.

"Don't look around," she went on, still smiling. "There's so much useless stuff. It is hard to pack when you've never done it before. It is hard to know what to take when you don't know if you will ever return." She paused. "Twenty-five pounds—I am allowed to take twenty-five pounds of baggage. And four hundred francs."

I was still unable to find a word. There is a sort of baseness committed by your enemy that makes you feel as ashamed as if you had committed it yourself.

"And your husband?" I asked at last.

"When he comes home, he won't find me," she said. "He will look for me somewhere in France. We are homeless in our own home."

I pressed her hand, but she seemed to take no notice. She was taking leave of her plush sofa, a charming pink hat, a plaster statue, her husband's framed diploma, a bottle of fragrant old perfume.

348

"And do they give a reason?" I asked, to break the unbearable silence.

For the first time she gave up trying to smile. She looked at me with her large, earnest eyes.

"Reason? No reason," she said.

"Is it on account of me?"

My conscience was not easy.

She smiled again: "No. There are at least a hundred of us in Dieuze."

"Do you know where you are going?"

"Of course not. They are letting us spend three days in Nancy. That is all."

"Can I help you?"

"No," she said. "Good-by!"

With my hand on the door handle I thought for a moment.

"Do you trust me?" I said in the end.

"Of course."

"Would you like me to bring your money to Nancy?"

"Can you?"

"I am sure I can. Under German guard. That would be some small satisfaction. You would be doing me a personal favor in letting me help you."

She gave me a sealed envelope.

"This afternoon in the Restaurant Stanislas. If we don't meet, ask Jeannine, the waitress, for your envelope."

"My, what connections you have!" she said, laughing and holding out her soft white hand. On the back of her hand there were small round dimples. It was hard to think that outside, by the little black hand-cart, Corporal Josef Berger was waiting for me.

That morning a paralysis had stricken the town. The baker's wife was not sitting outside the bakery rocking her child. I heard that the old cobbler across the street had been deported with his three-months-old baby. The old maid at the Red Cross was not there to give me milk and vegetables; she was helping someone to pack his twenty-five pounds. The little old woman who used to give me marmalade was sitting on her trunk outside her door. She wore a black veil over her head and held a framed picture in her hand—perhaps the photograph of her fallen son which she hoped to smuggle through. The women had not yet received the order to set out, but the little old woman had been sitting on her trunk for hours; she was excited at the idea of her first trip. She looked at me and seemed not to recognize me; she only pressed her picture closer. With pounding heart I went to the Café des Voyageurs. The two women—the diminutive mother and her daughter Stella—were not among the deportees. But Stella, by order of the local commandant, had been drafted for labor service. She would be an agricultural laborer somewhere in Germany. Corporal Kessler had come the day before and brought her the news. Germany needed only girls who worked, he said. Mother and daughter had said nothing. Both would sooner have died than utter a complaint.

In the afternoon I began looking for a German to escort me to Nancy. I chose the stupidest: Corporal Wagner from Magdeburg. Deeply impressed by the fact that we were commissioned to get an accordion for his commander, he carefully secreted one of my two passes in his wallet and went to get his gun. For a patient, we took Alfred, who felt in need of distraction. I did not take any particular measures for concealing the accordion; I felt sure that the officers would not have their party unless they could get along without my accordion.

As we passed through Dieuze, I looked out of my little window and saw that the Elite Guards had entered the hostile town. Like a black rash on a diseased body, the black uniforms suddenly covered the streets of Dieuze.

The Elite Guards—"Do you know what that means?" Captain Brühl had asked me. Now as my ambulance passed through the lofty old city gate, I began to see what it meant. We had scarcely reached the highway when the endless column of women began—and it extended beyond Arracourt. I didn't count them but there were thousands of them, hunted from their homes, separated from their families, thrown into the darkest slavery. Each carried a package or a small suitcase —twenty-five pounds, that was all. In every village we passed, women guarded by Elite Guards stood waiting by the roadside; they were driven into the procession as cows are driven into a herd. When our car approached, the men chased the women out of the way. Old grandmothers came hobbling along with young girls; young women marched along with loose hair and eyes fixed straight ahead. Two women held up a third who kept falling down. One carried her baby in a bundle of rags on her back. Some carried a bit of china in addition to their twenty-five pounds—a bit of their homes following them into exile. A little girl with a running nose and a face full of tears pushed along a light blue doll carriage containing, not a doll, but the family's miserable belongings.

I could not help asking my corporal: "What did these women do?"

He answered promptly: "They showed resistance."

He was not a particularly bad fellow, this Corporal Karl Wagner from Magdeburg. But between him and sentiment the distance was as infinite as between a Nazi and a human being.

At the demarcation line, near the World War cemeteries, we were held up for only a few minutes. This time no one paid any attention to us. The border guards were too busy.

Long lines of women stood outside the wooden barracks, and German soldiers were rummaging in their meager baggage. Suitcases, bundles, knapsacks, cloth lay scattered all over the road. Elite Guards and green-clad border officials passed in and out, pawing over the pathetic articles of clothing. They kicked aside a hat with their boots; they picked up a pair of shoes and threw them down again. Their faces expressed disgust and contempt, as though these women were purposely causing them unpleasant labor. "Out of the way!" and "Clear out!" and "Go on!" they roared—all in the same tone. They shoved women aside when they stood in their way, they trampled dresses and lingerie, they stuck their fingers in bread. When an exhausted woman tried to sit down, they seized her by the shoulders and made her stand up. The whole highway was like the steerage of an emigrant ship, or a Polish village after a Cossack raid. Now and then an Elite Guard would pick up a delicate piece of lingerie, a chemise or a slip, and hold it up to the sun between two fingers. This always gave rise to an outburst of coarse laughter that rolled along the highway like a ball on a bowling alley. Then the shirt would be thrown back into the pile with an obscene joke.

We reached Nancy and made our purchases. I told my corporal that I had to go to the Restaurant Stanislas about the captain's accordion. The music stores, I explained, were all out of accordions; and at the restaurant there was a chance of getting an inexpensive second-hand instrument. Wagner at once accepted my explanation. Alfred, our "gravely wounded" patient, was removed from his blankets and allowed to come with us. Our chauffeur, Jeannot, came along too.

The restaurant was empty, as usual, in the afternoon. Jeannine was standing behind the cash desk. I recognized her at once. She came over to us but we took good care to give no sign of recognition. The corporal put his gun beside him and looked around. I asked him whether he could stand a second lunch. He said yes. Jeannine brought the menu and stood behind me. I studied it.

"Is the roast beef good and rare?" I asked Jeannine.

"Yes. It's very nice."

I took a side glance at Wagner. He was busy picking his teeth and obviously couldn't understand a word of our conversation.

"Very good," I said. "If the roast beef is nice, can you tell me if everything is all right? Can I come tomorrow?"

I went on studying the menu.

"Yes," said Jeannine. "Tomorrow or any time."

She wiped the table with a napkin.

"The landlady is waiting for you," Jeannine smiled.

"What is there for dessert?" I asked. I knew the menu by heart. "A good dessert . . . I'll leave two letters for you on the table in the wash room. One is for you. Would you like a chocolate cake, corporal? The other is for a lady who will call for it today or tomorrow. She will inquire for me."

"Three chocolate cakes, then," said Jeannine, smiling graciously at the corporal. "It will all be attended to. But I don't know your name."

"It's in my letter."

Jeannine went out. When she came back with the food, I excused myself. I had to talk to the restaurant owner, I said; he was the man with the accordion.

"*Ja, ja,*" said Wagner, whose good sense had been completely destroyed by the captain's accordion and two glasses of wine—one red, one white. "Yes, go ahead. But don't be long!" And he went to work on his roast.

353

I was not long. I had nothing to do but deposit my two letters.

"Tomorrow we'll get our accordion," I announced. "The captain will be pleased."

"Sure," said Wagner. "Do you think you can take me tomorrow too?"

He was in a heaven of roast beef and chocolate cake.

I was in a hurry to leave. I still had many things to do in Dieuze.

I asked for permission to open the rear door of the ambulance. Corporal Wagner was magnanimous and had no objections. I sat near the door, deeply breathing the evening air. It had a different smell than usual. The smell of freedom. I waved to an old peasant; he lifted his large straw hat and waved it in reply. The pink sunset was full of the past and full of the future. I was glad that it contained nothing of the present. Everything was still ahead of me—all the dangers and struggles. But a great tranquillity had settled upon me. A few fleecy clouds sailed across the sky. I tried to read my future in their shapes. But they dissolved in the blue infinity.

In Arracourt I had to withstand a final test. The Elite Guards, tired after their work with the women, took no interest in us. They sat in front of their blockhouse drinking beer. Wagner knew one of them. They had a little talk. The guard complained of his day's labors.

I heard him say: "And on top of all that, this lousy deserter. Yesterday a prisoner ran away from Saarebourg. We caught him less than an hour ago. He's on his way back. He'll be shot at once. We make short shrift of those guys."

As he spoke, I looked into my heart. But all was peace in me, like the summer evening on the fields. I leaned back against my car and looked far away—past the Elite Guards, the sentry boxes, and the ambulance. Across the road I saw the crosses on the fallen soldiers' graves. Each of them was like a hand raised up in solemn oath.

That evening in Dieuze, I was feverishly active. Above all, I had to share my chance to escape with another prisoner. It could only be a doctor—for I could not ask for anyone else to accompany me on the trip I planned for the next day. I carefully went over all the physicians. Finally I resolved to take the youngest among them, the courageous Dr. Petit. I admired him especially for his fine work in taking care of the Negroes when an epidemic of scabies broke out among them. The young surgeon from Lyon had the freckled face of a cheerful high school student. He did not hesitate for a moment. I told him of the conversation I had overheard in the blockhouse.

"If you're not afraid of being shot, you mustn't think that I am," he said somewhat rudely. And he added: "Tomorrow morning at eight. I'll stick my toothbrush in my pocket."

We shook hands. That was all.

Then I had to report to Captain Brühl that the matter of his accordion "was as good as settled." Passing by Captain Kohlrusch's office I could not resist the temptation to go in. I reported that I had taken all the necessary measures to locate the persons on his "blacklist."

"If any of them is still in camp tomorrow," I concluded, "he won't escape us."

The captain paced the room with his riding crop. He failed to notice that I spoke like the Delphic Oracle.

At last I had to say farewell to my friends. I gave Alfred a chance to join me in my flight, but at the last moment he declined to risk it. He wanted to explain what deterred him, and I asked him and Count Korzakoff to come to my room, where I had stored all sorts of food and other treasures. These stores had always been a source of inner strife for me, because

355

each time I put something aside, I suspected myself of not taking my plans of escape seriously. I gave Alfred and René my chocolate, my razor blades, shaving cream, two cakes of soap, fifteen packs of *Eckstein* cigarettes, a sausage, five bouillon cubes, and half a bottle of cognac. I bequeathed my pajamas to Alfred and my blanket to René. We packed all this in a large carton and hid it in the attic of the infirmary. I distributed my *Troupe* cigarettes among Poulaine—restaurateur on the Boulevard Diderot in Paris who cooked for the physicians—Jeannot the chauffeur, and a few patients, without, of course, explaining the reasons for my magnanimity. The patients in the "wounded ward" got my three bottles of stewed fruit. Then I set about clearing my desk. I quickly put the names of two dozen comrades on the list of "railroad men," though they belonged to the most varied professions, because I knew that railroad men would be released first. And though Captain Kohlrusch had assured me that he had a copy of the blacklist he gave me, I destroyed it. Finally I threw into the latrine the special list of prisoners drawn up according to "racial" principles. The list had taken ten days' work to compile, and I thought that its loss would necessitate more work. Having thus done everything ordained by the Prussian love of order, I wrote a few letters of thanks to various people in Dieuze. I bade farewell to Madame Jaeger, the pastry shop owner, to the butcher's wife, to the pretty grocery store keeper, to the splendid Madame Klein, and to Stella's mother. "Lorraine," I wrote, "is France at its best. It will not perish."

Meanwhile night had fallen. But I was unable to swallow a bite of food. My heart had withstood the strain, but my stomach weakened. I stayed away from the officers' mess, excusing myself on the ground of stomach trouble. I drained a glass of pernod—all that remained in my bottle—in one gulp, buckled my belt, and went out for a last look at the camp.

I proceeded methodically, as though going about my work, and began with the infirmary wards. The sick and wounded jumped up as soon as the door opened, fearing one of Daxer's sudden inspections. You had to be on the brink of death to rate the privilege of staying in bed when Daxer stormed through the ward with his creaking boots and his leather gloves in hand. The wounded had to stand at attention by their beds. I told them they had nothing to fear for the rest of the day. The *Herr Unteroffizier* was still tired after having satisfied his human needs. I sat down by the bedside of this one and that one and tried to tell them that some day all this would be over. They were always more optimistic than I, and my words cheered them up. As usual, I collected their secret letters to Nancy. I promised Bartolomey, a middle-aged resident of Nancy, to tell his wife of his whereabouts. I promised a boy of fifteen, captured by the Germans and held without any reason and contrary to all law, that I would find someone to look for his parents. This handsome and alert lad was named André Gerald and came from Saint Nicolas-de-Port, a place where the Germans had been particularly brutal. In the confusion he had lost his parents and his elder brother and sister; he had fallen in with a passing Polish battalion and been captured with the Poles. I had assigned him to the hospital shortly before—he was so undernourished that he was unable to walk. Captain Kohlrusch regarded him as particularly "dangerous."

That night I was eager to do everyone favors. The success of my plan was far from sure. Possibly the worst was still to come. But somewhere outside freedom was waiting for me, like spring waiting at the gates of a city in March or April.

I crossed the large dusty drill-ground. The clock on the

commissary building showed a quarter past eight. I stopped to look around. There was Workshop No. 3. Jean, Denis, and Paul had been sent away to the Maginot Line—eight hundred thousand Frenchmen in German bondage were employed to raze France's once famous fortified wall. Prisoners were sitting in the black dust outside the shop. I went over and sat down with them.

They spoke of their coming release. Nothing had changed since I left the repair shop. Time had stood still. The prisoners were sitting on the same spot discussing the same things. *"A quand la classe?"* they were asking—when do we go home? Disappointment had not worn them down: each night they hoped that the following day would bring something new. They looked up to the sky and were glad because there was something of autumn in the air. In the autumn they would be home. They all had hungry eyes and they all played with the dust. Many drew hearts in the sand and smiled. A man came out with some false news. All pretended to believe him so as to have their own lies believed the next day.

"Well, Napier," one of them asked jeeringly, "do you still think we'll be here for a year or two?"

He was an old man with the face of a dwarf.

"No," I said. "I don't think so any more, Monsieur Bayot."

"You see," said Père Bayot. "Even Napier admits that I'm right."

A few looked up. Then they looked down again and went on playing with the sand.

I went to the other yard where the proprietors of the gambling casino were gathering up their roulette wheels and their dirty cards. Here, too, everything seemed to me like a dream. It was as though the gamblers would never cease gambling, the croupiers calling, and the balls rolling. A great weary eternity hung over the noisy yard. The men moved about like tin soldiers with a wound-up spring, ready to run out with a whirring noise. I was reminded of Thomas Mann's *Magic Mountain*. Reality was somewhere far off in the mist, and here, too, you could feel the hard, heavy tread of the times. Time seemed to be walking across the yard, an old, tired man, dragging his feet along step by step. The prisoners, men cut off from life, clung like dead flies to the barrack walls, profiting by the narrow strip of ground that the sun had not heated during the day. They spoke of gains, losses, and freedom. They knew they could not buy anything with the money they had won, and that the losses meant nothing. In them freedom lived as in a vacuum. They wouldn't have known what to do with it if they had won it. The loss of it no longer held any meaning for them.

There was the usual throng around the latrines; half an hour later the latrines meant certain death. The Germans were changing the guard on the roof. Two prisoners were quarreling over a piece of paper. Men were sitting side by side beneath the trees, and one told about a Frenchman who had hissed in the darkness during a propaganda film—the Germans had shot him. No one bothered to pass the story on. The same prisoners as usual stood on the sand-hills looking out into the green. The guards met one another halfway.

I returned to the infirmary. A curious sadness overwhelmed me. Habit seems to be so strong that a man misses even his prison.

I said good-by to the houses, the dust, the people. I was almost sad when I sat down with Alfred and René on the stairs outside the door.

"You mustn't think that I'm a coward," said Alfred suddenly. "Or that I want to leave you in the lurch. But I have

359

to look after my mother. She would never survive my death."

We sat in silence. On the road behind the infirmary, the home-going German soldiers were singing their eternal songs. *"Jetzt geht's ins Heimatland, ins schöne Schwabenland."* I clenched my fist. We too had a native land, we too wanted to go home. But I said nothing. I looked straight ahead of me, at the sinking sun.

Taps was sounded.

My two comrades, to the right and left of me, seized my hands.

"Much luck to you!" said Alfred.

"It will be a fine day tomorrow," said René.

"Yes," I said. "Tomorrow is another day."

It was ten o'clock, and I was alone in my room. There was still a bright strip on the horizon. I knelt by my bed and prayed.

This was my prayer:

"Lord, my God.

"Tomorrow, my Lord, I am going to risk my life and I commend my soul to Thee. O my Father, if it be possible, let this cup pass from me; nevertheless, not as I will, but as Thou wilt.

"But whether I live or die, fulfill, O my Lord, this prayer.

"Suffer not, O my Lord, that injustice triumph on earth. Permit not the unleashed hordes of the Antichrist to corrupt nations, lay waste countries, dishonor women, seduce children. Suffer not violence to conquer so that men will be forced to put their faith in violence instead of love.

"Suffer not, O Lord, that the lie be stronger than truth. Let not the bloody carnival go on, in which criminals, thieves, and murderers disguise themselves as soldiers and judges, to give laws to the world and enforce them. Suffer not the masked denizens of the underworld to hold our world and Thy laws in contempt . . . for hast Thou not sent Him, 'a light unto the world, that those who believe in Him may not remain in darkness.'

"Suffer not, my Lord, the rule of him who divides the world into strong and weak, the sick and the sound. Suffer not the rule of him who would expose the newborn babes on Mt. Taigethos to die before they have lived; who preaches the power of the strong over the weak, the sound over the sick. Suffer not, O Lord, that a man shall choose amongst Thy children with his yardstick and his fist . . . for it is written: 'Blessed are the merciful and blessed are they who hunger and thirst after righteousness.'

"Suffer not, O Lord, that delusions of grandeur should spread abroad, and that pride, self-conceit and self-deification, the heathen cult of a heathen god shall contaminate the earth that Thou hast created. Suffer not delusions of grandeur to confuse men's minds, peopling the earth with false gods instead of good men; suffer not superstition to grow stronger than faith, for Thou lovest those 'that labor and are heavy laden' . . . 'Thy yoke is easy, and Thy burden is light.'

"And so, O Lord, suffer not those who serve Thee to be destroyed. The reward of the just is heaven, and the punishment of the evil is hell. Devils and angels were not wont to pass across our earthly fields. But hell has opened its gates and sent forth its devils over our earth. Send, O Lord, Thine angels down, with flaming sword, as was promised us. Though earth is no heaven . . . it cannot be Thy will that it be a hell. It cannot be Thy will that all those who bear Thy name shall be destroyed. For Thou art not only the kingdom and the glory but also the power, forever. Amen."

CHAPTER ELEVEN: ESCAPE

AUGUST 7TH WAS A GLORIOUS SUMMER'S DAY.

I awoke at six in the morning, refreshed and fully rested. The night had been calm and dreamless. For a moment I lay motionless in my bed. Through the open window, as from afar, came the sound of the camp. In the old cherry tree outside my window the birds were singing heavenward. For them there was no occupied and no unoccupied heaven. In the house across the yard, the German soldiers sang as they polished their shoes.

On the dot of seven I reported to Dr. Frank, the chief physician. He received me in his long nightgown with the red border.

"We have a serious case in the infirmary," I announced. "Lieutenant Dr. Petit has examined the man and requests his immediate transfer to Nancy."

"What's the matter with him?"

"Gastric hemorrhage."

"Gastric hemorrhage? I'll have a look."

Things were taking an unpleasant turn. For some days Count Korzakoff had actually been suffering from a bad stomach (he played sick so long that he finally became really sick), and would have been glad to spend a few days in the hospital at Nancy, where the food was much better than in camp. His wishes had fitted in neatly with my plans. But if

Dr. Frank were to examine him—there was no sign of bleeding, and far more serious cases had not been transferred to Nancy.

"I have to go to Nancy in any case," I said resolutely.

"How so?"

"On account of the officers' party. I am getting a cheap accordion for Captain Brühl."

"Splendid!" said Dr. Frank. The evacuation, the gastric hemorrhage, the examination had suddenly lost their importance. "In that case, you can take the man with you as far as I care."

I clicked my heels.

As I was leaving, I heard the chief physician mutter, "I wonder who is going to play the accordion."

I told Sergeant Daxer that we were going to Nancy with a prisoner suffering from gastric hemorrhage, and that the French doctor was coming with us.

"Very good," said Daxer. "I need new gloves anyway. Do you think you can get me a pair of pigskin gloves?"

I promised I would.

René Korzakoff was carried out of the infirmary on a stretcher. In passing, I pressed Alfred's hand. I had letters to his sister in my pocket. Now I am losing you too, Alfred Sienkiewitz, I thought. As I had lost Pierre Saint-Brice. And little red-headed Dési, and Garai, the brave little Hungarian, my comrades in the observation post. And the lanky Breton, and Mayer-Mayerescu from Bucharest. War kills even those who remain alive. Farewell, Alfred Sienkiewitz, friend of my imprisonment—Alfred Polonais!

Daxer, who took a childish pleasure in driving a car, had told Jeannot, the chauffeur, to stay behind; he drove the ambulance himself. I sat beside him; Dr. Petit tended our patient.

The car moved off slowly. A group of one thousand men was leaving Dieuze that morning, on the march to Germany. In the narrow roadway leading down to Dieuze, I looked back toward the camp and saw the long column of marchers. In the dewy morning mist, there was something unreal about these men, bowed beneath their meager belongings: they were like Volga boatmen on a distant stage. But these thousand men were not actors in a Russian review. They were real Volga boatmen, bearing a real burden. I could almost hear the monotonous *Ei uchnem* rising from their ranks. But behind them the camp vanished in a violet mist: the red administration building, the infirmary, the garages, the riding academy on the main courtyard.

My great calm did not leave me. I no longer remember exactly what I thought about on my way to Nancy; but I do know that I was not concerned with the dangers ahead. I thought that my humiliations—the desperate comedy which I had played—would now be at an end. I took pleasure in the open road and the open fields. I wasted no thought on the countless things that might go wrong.

Once I glanced back at Petit. "How is the patient, *mon lieutenant?*"

As we had previously arranged, the answer came back: "Bad. Try to hurry."

I bent closer to Daxer. "We've got to hurry, sergeant, if the man is to reach the hospital alive."

"Dead or alive," Daxer grumbled. "More than one man has died in this war."

But he drove straight to the hospital all the same. We stopped in the main courtyard. The hospital was a large gray building with broad white windows looking out over the Rhine-Marne Canal. Daxer, the lieutenant and I jumped out of the ambulance. We were alone in the yard.

"Well," said Daxer, looking into the car.

René Korzakoff didn't stir, he just moaned softly.

"Well," I said.

"Well, lift him out," ordered Daxer, suddenly in a hurry. He was probably thinking of his new pigskin gloves.

The lieutenant took me by the arm and said something in French.

"What is he saying?" asked Daxer with impatience.

"We can't take him out," I translated. "We need trained stretcher-bearers. He'd die on our hands."

Korzakoff was gasping.

"You die easy, you Frenchmen," said Daxer and looked around. It was exactly nine by the hospital clock.

Dr. Petit leaned into the ambulance and took the patient's pulse.

I ventured a suggestion: "Perhaps you can call someone to help us, *Herr Unteroffizier*. Then we'll be done here in a minute. I think the captain needs his accordion by noon."

The mention of the instrument and the superior authority did the trick. Daxer lighted his cigarette, played with his gloves, which as usual he held in his fist, and took a few steps across the courtyard.

"You watch the car," he called to us. "I'll get two stretcher-bearers."

He stormed away, bent forward on his toes, as always; a robot wielding a hand grenade.

As soon as he had vanished through the door behind the electric clock, we jumped out of the ambulance and shook Korzakoff's hands.

"Good luck, René."

"Good luck, Count Korzakoff!"

"Best of luck, *mon lieutenant!* Hope you break your neck, Hans!"

365

We left the car, threw a last glance at the hospital, and walked quickly, though without hurrying, to the gate; the ambulance hid us from the hospital windows. The gate was unguarded. We stepped out into the street.

Across the street was the bridge. Some women with shopping bags and a few German soldiers were crossing it. Two children were playing on the bank. We stood, for a second perhaps, breathing deeply the fresh air that blew across from the Marne and the Rhine.

We were prisoners no longer.

Neither the lieutenant nor I knew where the Rue des Quatre Eglises was, much less the Hôtel St. Martin.

It would be five minutes at most before Daxer missed us. We reckoned that five more minutes would be spent looking for us in the courtyard and the hospital. And for another five, Daxer would be engaged in an inner struggle with his motorized self-conceit, before he was prepared to admit that he had fallen into a trap. Only then would he notify the police, the S.A., the Elite Guards, and the nearest barracks. All in all, we had fifteen minutes ahead of us. By that time we should have to reach safety.

Unless we aroused suspicion by some unfortunate move, we had hopes of reaching the Hôtel St. Martin without incident. For the last three weeks they had been discharging Alsatian prisoners, and numerous Alsatians were moving about Nancy in French uniform. These Alsatians of course had a certificate of discharge in their pockets, while we had not. But there was nothing too unusual about a French officer and a French sergeant passing through the town without escort.

We moved away from the hospital. Right behind it lay the narrow streets with the tumbledown old houses, where dismal *filles de joie* plied their trade. These streets and houses and girls had apparently caused some disorganization in the life of the German army, for large signs were suspended from wires across the street, saying: "Members of the German defense forces are permitted to enter this street only between six and ten o'clock at night." Since we were not conscious of being members of the German defense forces, this did not apply to us. Slovenly women in bright dressing gowns and loose hair peered out of the ground-floor windows. We took good care to ask no questions. In half an hour motorcycle details would be looking for two French soldiers. We had to obscure our tracks, and above all avoid mentioning the name of the hotel.

We stopped at the end of the forbidden street. You will see four church towers, the oracular Jeannine had said. The Rue des Quatres Eglises is between Nancy's four churches.

We stopped and looked around.

"Over there!" said the lieutenant, pointing to the right. Not far from one another, four church steeples rose into the sky.

Without a word, we redoubled our pace. Soldiers passed us; S.A. men in brown, Elite Guards in black, members of the labor battalions in brown blouses. We saluted the officers according to regulation, and did our best to look indifferent without losing sight of the four church towers. Two or three times we glanced toward the clock. By this time Daxer must have noticed our absence. Now he was running around the courtyard looking for us. We still had seven minutes.

We reached the bustling Rue St. Nicolas and suddenly faced the cathedral. The three other towers now lay to the left of us. We walked rapidly in that direction. We pricked up our ears, prepared at any moment to hear the police sirens. But everything was calm. In the Rue St. Dizier a boy was

selling a map of the "new France" for five francs. I bought
one and put it away with the one the chocolate manufacturer
had given me. An enormous crowd was standing in front of
a stationery store studying a list of war prisoners pasted up
in the window.

Now, following only our instinct, we crossed the market
place. In the market shed we felt strangely secure. It was
strange that only those things comforted us which reminded
us of an earlier life. The only certainty of survival and a
future life lay in reminiscence. A yesterday's smell, a familiar
word or gesture sufficed to give us confidence. Thus the
market calmed us, with all its childhood smells, its sound of
past carefree days. We would have liked to kiss the stout
fishwives and the two old witches we saw fighting over a
head of lettuce. The clock on the glass wall of the market
shed said nine-thirty. By all human reckoning, we still had
four minutes.

"Should we ask our way?" I said to Dr. Petit between my
teeth.

"No."

"All right. Here goes."

We stepped out of the pleasant dusk of the market shed
into the daylight. We found ourselves in a narrow but clean
street with three- and four-story houses. On the house across
the street a sign in bold letters said: HOTEL ST. MARTIN.

Our hearts hammered in our throats. Dr. Petit wanted to
cross the street. I seized him by the arm. Two S.A. men were
talking in front of the house. They were stout fellows with
red cheeks. They looked like two beer barrels. Two beer
barrels barred the way to paradise.

We waited near a flower stand. If we could only bring
someone flowers, I thought. There were yellow, red, and

violet dahlias. Daxer must have overcome his doubts by this time. We had at most two or three minutes before us.

The two beer barrels shook hands and parted. We looked to right and left. Behind the flower stand a woman was sleeping. Otherwise the street was deserted. We crossed and entered the hotel.

The house was silent. Cautiously we mounted a few stairs. The wooden steps creaked. Suddenly a woman's voice rang out from above us: "*Qui est là?*"

"It's us," I answered, none too brilliantly.

But the answer had sufficed. A woman bent over the railing on the second floor. A deep, warm, masculine woman's voice said in French: "Come right up, children—we've been expecting you."

We dashed up the stairs.

In the door of an apartment on the second floor stood a woman.

Never shall I forget her face. Blessed art thou, Madame Louis Bellonville, née Amalie Roquebrune, of Nancy. I shall include you in my prayers today, tomorrow, and forever. Never shall I forget you, in life and death, as you stood there, in the door of your apartment, big and fat as you were; with a blue apron, your slightly graying hair in great noble waves, and in your bright eyes a heavenly light such as is given only to those on whom God has bestowed the most precious of gifts: a pure heart. As you stood there in the door of your apartment, Mother Amalie, to take in two strangers, smilingly staking your own life for two strangers who were nothing more to you than two men in need of help, you were a mother to Dr. Petit and myself, sent by his mother and my mother, by all the mothers in the world. . . . You were motherhood itself, Mother Amalie. I kiss your hands, your good, soft yet firm hands, your hands without hardness and yet full of strength, which snatched us away from death and harm. Across oceans and worlds I kiss your hands, dear, good, brothel mother, Amalie Roquebrune of Nancy. . . .

"Come right in, children," said Mother Amalie, half laughing and half whispering, trying to be cautious without frightening us.

She led us through a large bright kitchen, through a broad, round salon, through a spacious living room, and at length into a modern bedroom. The curtains were drawn, the window behind them was open. The sun sifted into the room through a narrow cleft in the curtain. Little grains of dust danced peacefully in the sunlight. They too were reassuring.

For some minutes we couldn't utter a word. We were like two children in fairyland. Madame Roquebrune-Bellonville must have noticed it, for she asked no questions. She spoke unceasingly, shoved us into the room with great sweeping gestures, struck us on the shoulders, told us to be seated and make ourselves at home. There was not a word of flight, danger, sacrifice.

"Oh, yes," she said. "Of course I got your letter." And she drew my pink envelope out of her tightly laced bosom. She said it as though the letter had come through the mail and were the most natural thing in the world—a picture post card with greetings from someone on a vacation trip. "It's all arranged," she went on quickly, as though afraid we might thank her. "I only hope everything is all right and the new suits fit you properly."

She scarcely let me open my mouth. She led us to a double bed. It all seemed like a page from *The Thousand and One Nights*. On the bed, as though conjured up by some djinn, lay a gray suit and a green suit, a colored shirt and a white shirt, two dark ties, two handkerchiefs, two pairs of socks;

and at the foot of the bed a pair of black and a pair of brown shoes.

"You can have two hats too," she said quickly, as though that were the most important item, "Louis has plenty of them. Unfortunately he doesn't need them; he's a prisoner of war himself somewhere!"

The word "prisoner" stood hard and cold in the middle of the room. Mother Amalie saw it. She waved her firm arms through the air as though to banish all evil.

"Well, you're not prisoners any more," she said with a laugh. "We'll burn your uniforms. Just take everything out that you want to keep. Make yourselves at home, children; I've got to get back to the kitchen, or you won't get any proper roast for luncheon."

With that she started to leave the room. I began to recover from my paralysis and held her back by the arm.

"One moment, madame."

She stopped and looked at me, as though she knew exactly what I was going to say, and knew her own answer, but let me speak to relieve myself.

"We don't know how we can thank you, madame," I said. Now we were sitting on two chairs facing one another. Dr. Petit stood behind me.

She took my two hands. "No need of all that, *mon petit*," she said. "Have you something sensible you want to say?"

"Yes," I replied. "I just want to repeat to you what I wrote. Dr. Petit was a camp physician and one of twenty-eight officers. I myself, as camp commandant, will be particularly missed. It will be a terrible disgrace for the Germans if the commandant comes to assembly tomorrow without me and has to admit to fifteen thousand men that their chief trusty and official interpreter has slipped through their fingers. We are not like any old prisoners who might escape.

The Germans will move heaven and earth to get us before tomorrow's assembly. I want you to know that, madame."

There was an enduring smile in her clear, sparkling eyes. "Let the Boches look," said Mother Amalie. That was all she said. But it sounded as though Mother Amalie was stronger than the whole German army.

"And one more thing," I persisted. "Have you read the posters?"

"I never read anything printed by the Boches."

"The posters say that anyone giving shelter to an escaping prisoner will be condemned to death."

"Oh," said the woman, and stood up. "Is that all you wanted to say? I know that. Let that be my worry!" And as she was leaving: "Now hurry and dress, so you'll be ready for lunch. We eat early today."

With a wave of her hand she swept out of the room.

I looked at the lieutenant and he looked at me. His freckled, boyish face with the great protruding ears and the sly little eyes was grave and solemn.

"And I—" said Dr. Petit—"I never believed in human nature . . ."

The two of us began to undress. We slipped out of our uniforms as quickly as possible, yet we were performing a solemn rite. A year in uniform lay behind us. A year of war. The camp at Barcarès with the tramontana, the Catalan wind, blowing down from the Pyrenees; the Maginot Line, the Alsatian village, the first air-raid, the dead child on the meadow, Captain Mirambeau, our baptism of fire in the deserted village, the blue Christ of Noirval, the forest of the Ardennes, the dead cows, the woman in the burning house, the barker on the machine gun, the murderer in the barn, Saint-Brice's heroism, the witches' sabbath in the railroad station, the beer in Charmes, Yvette, the real Maurice Napier, the border post near the soldiers' graveyard, the waiter from the hotel in Vienna, the Gestapo list with my name on it, the Germans rebuffed by Stella, the banished women of Lorraine, the plundered factory. And all of Petit's experiences— death in a thousand forms, a thousand faces. In slipping out of our uniforms, we seemed to be leaving all this behind us. Each of us put aside the objects which he particularly treasured. Smiling, I folded up my arm-band—with the Red Cross and the swastika.

We washed at the tap before venturing to don our new civilian clothes. Then we argued a little over the suits, the shirts, and the socks. Finally it was the size which decided. I was a bit larger than Petit, and so I got the green suit and the brown shoes. We stood before the mirror. Both of us had jauntily folded the white handkerchiefs in our breast pockets. The suits were a little too full for us in our emaciated state, but we found them very lovely none the less. We wished one another luck, embraced, shook hands. As we stood there arm in arm, in civilian clothes, before Mother Amalie's mirror, it seemed to us that all the past was extinguished.

"You'll have your *apéritif* in a minute," came Mother Amalie's voice.

We looked at the clock. It was nearly eleven. The Germans had been searching for us for at least an hour.

"Come into the living room," cried Madame Roquebrune.

We went in. There was a little table with a pink table-cloth of pure silk. Tiny pink silk napkins lay beside the plates. In the center stood a lamp with a pink silk shade. The curtains—blue cretonne with pink flowers—were drawn. The lamp on the table was burning. The sun sifted in through cracks and rents, and the whole room with its smooth shining furniture lay in a strange, enchanted twilight.

Mother Amalie brought in two crystal glasses on a tray.

"What would you like?" she asked. "Pernod, Cinzano, or port?"

We decided in favor of the pernod.

"If you'll join us," said the lieutenant.

"Of course, of course," said Mother Amalie, blushing. She blushed down to her soft, wide décolleté.

She brought a bottle of pernod and a third glass. We drank to her health, to our escape, and to France. We wanted her to stay with us, but she was still busy in the kitchen.

When she had gone, we exchanged glances. From time to time we took a squint at the clock. From the street below we could hear German soldiers marching—how well we knew it, that tread of German boots! Through the open window we heard two men speaking German. From time to time a motorcycle rattled through the street. Would it stop? A motorcycle did stop, a door slammed. We held our breath, though we didn't know why. Two market women cursed. We sighed with relief, without knowing why. The lieutenant was pale—I wondered if I was too. Great red dahlias stood on the table. We were calm only when Mother Amalie was in the room.

At length she came back.

"Everything all right?" asked Dr. Petit.

"And why shouldn't it be? Here you are safe. And we have a fine lunch. I only hope you like it."

She began to dish up real miracles. There was goose liver, fish, tender roast beef, a poetic pudding. My stomach was tied up in knots, but I ate everything. The woman sat beside us, her hands folded in her lap. She looked on with a smile and asked us what we would like to have for supper. It was terrible not to be able to pour forth a constant flood of thanks.

"And you, madame? Why don't you eat?" we asked.

"I, children, you know—"

She broke off and blushed again. And only then did we begin to wonder where we actually were. In the Hôtel St. Martin? But this hotel, whose whole first story was a private apartment, had no porter, no *valet-de-chambre*, no maid. It also seemed to have no guests. To be sure, I had seen a board with about twenty numbers on the kitchen wall, but there was a key hanging on every hook. The Hôtel St. Martin seemed to attach no importance to guests. Now I remembered the round salon, the big round table, and the old plush sofa with its lace antimacassar. And the pink-and-blue coquetry of the living room was also rather strange. It seemed hardly suited to the virile domesticity of Madame Louis Bellonville, née Amalie Roquebrune.

"I guess I'll have to tell you," said Madame Roquebrune, grown suddenly grave. "The fact is that this used to be a perfectly respectable hotel. Before the Germans came. If Louis knew what it has turned into! When the Boches took over, there weren't enough brothels for them. So they simply turned respectable hotels into whorehouses. And my hotel was one of them. Of course I could have closed it. But I won't let them drive me out of my house. I'd rather die. I'd rather be a brothel mother. I know what I'm doing—don't worry. Everyone has to fight the plague as best he can. I have my own methods." She took a sip from her wine glass. "And so," she said after a brief pause, "I have to eat lunch with my girls."

A motorcycle stopped below. She stepped to the window, drew the curtain a little aside and looked out.

"No, it's nothing," she said. And with her old smile: "Did it taste good?"

We sang the praises of her royal cuisine. It sounded so strange to hear yourself say something pleasant.

She sat down with us and explained the situation. What she said was simple and intelligent, and what was more, she said it as though everything she projected would succeed beyond a shadow of doubt. She had prepared two attic rooms for us on the fifth floor, where we could spend the whole day. At noon and in the evening, she would arrange to have us come down to her apartment. We would need a breath of air, because it was unbearably hot in the attic rooms. The only danger would be from nine to ten at night, when a police patrol descended on the house. The police examined the young ladies' "working papers," and sometimes looked through the rooms. At this hour, it seemed advisable for us to stay in Madame's private apartment, which no one dared enter. In the afternoon and evening, the house was full of Germans, but that in itself would avert suspicion. Who would conceive of two escaped prisoners hiding in a house frequented during the day by a hundred pleasure-seeking German soldiers and raided every night by the German police?

"There's nothing to be afraid of," said Mother Amalie in her deep, firm voice. "And at night you can rest easy. All German soldiers have to be out of the house at ten o'clock sharp. I have orders from the *Kommandantur* to lock the gate at ten. After that I'm not allowed to let anyone in. Then we can all have a glass of wine together."

She removed the plates.

"For a few days you'll have to be my guests—until they give up looking for you. By that time I'll have found you some false papers. With the false papers you'll get through, to Free France." She sighed. "Free France . . ." she repeated. "If I had my way, I'd go with you." She put down the dishes. "You're not the first, my boys. I disguised the last ones as fishermen and sent them on. They arrived safe and sound too. A captain and his son. Imagine—they were in the same regiment!"

Outside in the kitchen we heard her talking with someone. She spoke French and he spoke German. We looked around. Both of us silently gauged the size of the clothes cupboard.

"If I only had my revolver," I said softly.

"Why not a pocket machine gun?" Dr. Petit whispered.

We heard Mother Amalie at the door and pressed ourselves flat against the wall.

She came in laughing.

"But, children, children . . . Didn't I say you were under my protection?" She stood in the doorway with folded arms. You felt that the only way into the room was over her dead body. She wagged her head toward the kitchen. "That's going too far," she said. "Now they think they can come at noon. I just threw him out." But there was a slight tremor in her voice.

We crept cautiously up to our attic. We had two adjoining rooms, intended originally for the servants. The air was stale and stifling hot. Mother Amalie opened the windows but forbade us to go near them. Our apartments were equipped with the latest comfort, and we overflowed with enthusiasm. At last Mother Amalie showed us a door leading from the hallway to the roof. It was a flat glass roof, ending in a shingled gable. "If the worst comes to the worst," she said with a smile, as though speaking of something impossible. Then she left us alone.

We sat in the lieutenant's room, which was somewhat larger than mine, and waited. The hours crept by, infinitely slow. Every five minutes we looked at the clock and tried to imagine what had happened in our absence. Had Daxer driven back to Dieuze in the empty ambulance, or had he remained in the city to take part in the search? What was Lieutenant Dr. Schmidt saying? And Captain Brühl? Was Captain Kohlrusch mobilizing the Gestapo? The more we thought of it, the less prospect of success there seemed to be. Two men, and against them a whole organized world. From the four churches near by, in the Rue des Quatre Eglises, we heard the hours striking. They were polite clocks and didn't try to interrupt one another by striking simultaneously. At Mother Amalie's order, we had closed the door. From time to time we opened it and listened into the corridor. If a motorcycle or auto stopped in the street, we exchanged a glance and thought the same thoughts. We could hear the hours passing even without the clocks. When we had had our fill of silence, we studied our two maps. A thick red line marked the boundary between occupied and unoccupied France. The map offered comfort and hope. It was very small and the distances seemed short. Only a few centimeters away lay Geneva and Lake Léman, blue as it really was. There was the Jura where I knew every stone. And there was Lyon in the unoccupied zone, only a handsbreadth from Nancy. If it looked so near on the map, it couldn't be terribly far away. We listened. Heavy steps passed on the stairs.

The house began gradually to take on life. Mother Amalie came in with two bottles of ice-cold beer and assured us that everything was going all right. She told us not to be afraid if we heard German voices, and to open only if we heard three knocks on the door.

"We'll take good care of you, *mes pauvres enfants*," she said. "Tonight after business hours, Irène and Jeannine are coming. They asked for you and are glad that you're here." She brought fresh air with her when she came, and when she went she left behind her the cool freshness of her robust optimism.

It was good that she had warned us. For as afternoon descended on the city, the Hôtel St. Martin grew more and more lively. The stairs creaked incessantly; heavy soldiers' boots tramped down the corridor. In the next room a pair of shoes fell to the ground with a thud. A man spoke German, a woman cursed in French.

"Will you do what I tell you?" cried a coarse German voice.

"*Merde!*" said a fragile French voice.

Dr. Petit and I lay on the sofa and put our hands over our ears. The whole house seemed to be one groaning bed. But from time to time, suddenly and without warning, there was an uncanny silence. And then, through the open window, you could hear the women bargaining in the market.

Once or twice every hour we heard the three knocks on the door. Visitors. First came Pauline. She was a big blonde who would have been beautiful if her teeth hadn't been so neglected. Pauline was no longer young and she told us at once that she was Madame Amalie's assistant. She no longer "worked"; at most she helped out on Saturday and Sunday when there was too much of a rush. It was funny, she said, but the Germans bothered *her* the most—probably because of her prominent position. And really she did everything to discourage any attempts at intimacy: she wore a black silk dress, buttoned up high, and a severe hair-do; in fact, she tried her best to look like the directress of a girls' boarding school. She brought us cake, which she had bought in a small but exclusive pastry shop. Next came Mignonette, a little round girl from Algiers. Her skin was the color of ivory. Most likely one of her forebears had loved a native. Everything about her was small and round—her head, her hands, her bosom. She didn't seem very clean, but that may have been a prejudice on our part, for she had a real mania for order. When she came into the room, she "straightened up," put the chairs in place, beat the pillows, and wiped M. Louis Bellonville's razor, which Madame had put at our disposal. The next three knocks were from Nanette, a slender Bretonne in a green wrapper. She was very young, and had only come here since the war; and she was Madame's favorite, as she herself said. I was quite familiar with the little fishing village near Quimperlé that she came from, and we all had a pleasant time talking about it: we spoke about the old house and the grouchy postmaster and the mysterious Englishman who had rented the best villa in town. Nanette was for education; she, too, brought us presents, books from her library: *The Hound of the Baskervilles* for me, and *Lady Hamilton* for Dr. Petit. From time to time Mother Amalie would come up and gently admonish the girls to go down. They would get up with a sigh and pin up their hair. "I can understand that you'd rather stay here," Mother Amalie would say with a smile.

At about eight in the evening, things quieted down. Madame came to get us for supper. The girls watched the door while we quickly descended the stairs, crossed the salon and the kitchen, and sat down in Madame Roquebrune's apartment at the table with its pink cloth. Mother Amalie did not remain with us. She was only at ease when she herself was running things in the salon. In the salon, the German soldiers drank and spoke of warlike deeds in their native tongue, which none of the girls understood. But that didn't seem to trouble the warriors; they worked themselves up into ever-increasing excitement as they told how the *Stukas* would drop tons of bombs on London; how each man of them had swept a whole street bare with his machine gun;

how the shells whistled and burst and thundered. They spoke lovingly, passionately of death, and didn't bargain about the price before they tramped up the stairs with one of the girls. Intoxicated with blood and heat, they had lost all guile. Madame Roquebrune bore our food straight past their noses; they sniffed the air, but asked no questions.

Whenever our hostess came in—we sighed with relief every time the door closed behind her—she sat down with us for a minute.

"Oh, those Germans!" she said. "If only I didn't have to look at them, the barbarians. If I had been different, I would not have complained. We never made so much money—but what good is it? I can't stand the sight of them. What people! Just listen to this. The first day they came here, they asked for champagne. Champagne! They think you drink champagne like water, and that drinking champagne makes you a *monsieur*. So I brought up a bottle of my Mumm's *Cordon Rouge*. I don't know what came over me, casting my pearls before the swine. Well, do you know what they said? Do you think they liked my old *Cordon Rouge?* They looked at the bottle from all sides, then they talked it over, and then they pointed to the red paper around the bottle-neck and said: '*Non gut! Red nicht gut! Gold gut!*' And when I pretended not to understand them, they scratched off a strip of red paper and said: '*Nix gut! Nix rot! Gold gut. Or gut!*' Then I knew what they wanted. I went all over town buying up the worst sparkling wine I could find. Five francs a bottle. And I charge them two or three hundred francs. Now they have all the gold paper they want. I hope they choke on it . . ."

Half angry at the thought of the Boches, half gloating over her success, she arose.

"My only joy is that with their money I can help French

soldiers. The whole house is working for the prisoners. And for their release. I don't want to keep any German money."

"It is nine," said Dr. Petit. "Twelve hours. They've been looking for us for nearly twelve hours."

"Let them look," said Mother Amalie. But her voice sounded a little hoarse.

At the same moment the unmistakable march step rang out from the street. Someone commanded: "Halt!" And immediately afterward: "At ease!" The gun butts struck the pavement.

"Be still," whispered Mother Amalie. "That's the evening raid!"

And she went out with the dirty plates, leaving the door ajar. The voices grew louder. A mist of blue cigar smoke streamed into the room. Through the crack in the door we saw the backs of two field-gray uniforms. We heard laughter. And even in the laughter there was something menacing.

We held our breath.

Now we could clearly make out the voice of the non-com—most likely a drill sergeant—in command of the patrol.

"How many rooms are occupied?"

Mother Amalie's answers were incomprehensible. She must have been standing with her back to the door guarding our hiding place with her body.

"When was the doctor here last?" The drill sergeant had an unpleasant hoarse voice.

A few scraps of the interview escaped us. We sat in the darkness and didn't stir. We heard the ticking of a clock that we hadn't heard before. In the darkness everything was strangely clear and distinct.

"And here next door?" the drill sergeant suddenly asked.

I stood up. Dr. Petit followed me. We went to the clothes cupboard, climbed in, and pressed close to the wall. The clothes hid us and suffocated us. Silk and wool hung around our faces. Automatically we had seized each other's hands. The doctor's nails pressed into my skin, but I didn't feel them.

Outside it was still. I remembered that there were still a few plates from our dinner on the table. The table had been set for two, beyond any disguise. The silk smelled heavy and sweet. I felt blood on my hand.

And then suddenly the cupboard door was thrown open. In the brightly lighted room stood Mother Amalie.

"So there you are, you heroes!" she laughed. She laughed as my mother had laughed to dispel my childhood fear of darkness. "It's all over," she said calmly, as we peeled the dresses off us. "The gentlemen were very curious today. But before a German gets into this room, he'll have to shoot me."

It sounded clear and simple. As she spoke, she removed the rest of the dishes.

"We're going to close the gate in a minute," she said. "And then we'll have a glass of champagne. Without gold paper."

We sat down exhausted. In St. Martin's Hotel, in the Street of the Four Churches, the beds were still creaking.

From morning to noon Mother Amalie worked for us. When we awoke she was out. At noon she came back laden with papers and a large black handbag. But her activities were shrouded in mystery. All she told us was that we would be leaving in one or two days. When we asked for details, her only answer was: "Do you trust me?"

There was a little roguish twinkle in her eyes. I do not know how old Mother Amalie could have been. But when she smiled she had no age. She was as young as only goodness can make a woman. I told her that, and she blushed.

383

"How lovely that you can blush, Madame!"

As I spoke, I was glad to be able to say something that gave pleasure. It was as though I had said nothing at all in the past year.

"How shall we thank you?" Dr. Petit would ask again and again.

"No need to thank me at all," she would answer. "Believe me, children, what I am doing gives me plenty of fun!"

"What are you doing?"

She grew grave. She held her bag in hand, having just returned from one of her investigations.

"I am trying to find some good people."

"And—?" we asked faint-heartedly.

She smiled again. "Of course I find them. Good people can always be found." And right after: "Children! Children! You won't get anything to eat." And she was off, conjuring up a magnificent lunch.

So the days passed. Every morning Mother Amalie rose full of life, energy, and confidence. The girls took care of us. Mignonette was never too tired to make up our rooms early in the morning; Pauline brought us cigarettes and pastry and sat sadly down on our bed with a long cigarette holder in her mouth; Nanette washed and ironed our shirts, she took back *The Hound of the Baskervilles* and *Lady Hamilton* and gave us *Spring*, by Sigrid Undset, and an Agatha Christie novel. Tormented by the unbearable heat, we forged our plans as we lay on the lieutenant's bed. We gazed at the map and took delight in the blue of the sea and the green of the mountains beyond the occupied zone. We pricked up our ears at the sound of motorcycles and tried not to hear the tramp of boots on the staircase. We heard the Germans roar with pleasure, and we could distinguish the soft whisper of the girls' *"Sale étranger."* We hated the sound of the water pipes and the creaking of the beds. All day long we trembled at the thought of the night raid, and we were exhausted when it was over.

After ten, when the door was locked, we sat with Mother Amalie and the girls in the parlor. Jeannine and Irène, our oldest friends, came at about eight o'clock and stayed overnight, because no one was allowed to be out after ten without a special permit. There were usually ten of us in the parlor: Mother Amalie, Pauline, Mignonette, Nanette, Jeannine, Irène, Petit, myself, and two other girls. The lieutenant and I sat in semi-darkness, deep in two large leather armchairs; the girls around the table under the large silk-shaded lamp; Mother Amalie as a rule on the plush sofa, near the wall. The heavy, wine-red curtains were drawn.

The girls worked on their sewing. They worked for the twenty thousand prisoners in the Nancy camp, sewing shirts or knitting socks. Once a week Pauline went to throw the packages over the camp walls. Recently a German soldier had seized her by the shoulders. But she gave him such a look that he let her go.

One night I felt that Mother Amalie had something to say to us, but she was silent as always when the girls were around. She was kind to them, but she knew how to keep her distance. She sat on the plush sofa patching a khaki shirt. Irène, the red-cheeked girl from the Stanislas, was telling how the Germans always annoyed her.

"Haven't they any women of their own?" asked Nanette with disgust.

One of the girls said: "They say there are many German officers' wives in the forbidden zone."

"They're gone now," said Jeannine, who always brought the latest news from her restaurant. She laughed softly to herself. "The Boches had lots of trouble with that. They were allowed to bring their wives, so the women could propagandize us. You can imagine what happened. The Frenchwomen in the forbidden zone received the German bitches with the greatest kindness. They gave tea parties and showered them with gifts: dresses, silks, and stockings. The German women were overwhelmed."

A few of the girls put their sewing aside and listened eagerly.

"Well, and then what?"

"The German women were speechless. Just imagine: coffee and tea and butter and eggs and all sorts of things they hadn't seen for years. And dresses and shoes and silk lingerie. . . . I hear that in Bocheland the women wear woolen underwear. In the end they were so enthusiastic that the Nazis couldn't stand it. Last week all the German women were called back, all in one day. An order from Berlin—and one-two-three, they were all packed off in busses. Well, I won't miss them! *Bon voyage, Mesdames!*"

Everybody laughed. The girls resumed their needlework. Little round Creole-skinned Mignonette wore a pair of glasses on her tiny round nose when she sewed.

"Have you any news of Oscar?" one of the girls asked suddenly.

"No," said Nanette. "No one hears anything from prisoners."

"No," said Irène, "no one."

They were silent again. Each of the girls had her prisoner somewhere. And each of the girls was faithful to him in her own way.

"For the first time in my life I'd like to catch something," said one girl whose name I do not know, but who wore the most make-up of all.

"Why?" said Pauline, somewhat surprised.

"So I could give it to the Germans," said the girl.

"You mustn't have such sinful thoughts," said Mother Amalie in the background.

"Your fiancé wasn't killed by the Germans," said the girl angrily. But no one looked up. She went on knitting. Large thick tears rolled down on her sewing. Her make-up dissolved into round blue rings under her eyes. She made no attempt to hold back her multi-colored tears. From time to time she licked a tear from her lips.

"This shirt is beyond patching," said Nanette. "I'd rather buy a new one tomorrow."

"I saw some cheap ones," said Jeannine. "At Ducloz's near the market place."

Silence. All you could hear was the rustling of shirts and the clicking of scissors. The electric light seemed to buzz. From the kitchen came the sporadic ticking of the gas meter.

"You're so dull today," said Nanette, the tall, slender one, with a yawn.

"Oh, I forgot," said Irène. "Have you heard the big news?"

"No, what is it?" they all asked together.

Before she had time to answer, the long-drawn-out sound of a police siren came from the street.

"Aha!" said Irène.

Pauline approached the curtain.

"Stay where you are," ordered Madame.

There was a sudden nervousness in the air.

"Well?" asked Mignonette, peering from behind her unframed glasses like the grandmother in "Little Red Riding Hood."

"Today thirty French officers escaped from the Nancy camp," reported Irène. "Just think of it! Thirty all at once!"

"Maybe mine is one of them," said Nanette.

"What do you mean, yours?" Pauline asked sternly. There was something of the foreman about her, and she was the only one of the girls who wore a dress instead of a wrapper.

"I mean the one I was trying to get out," replied the Bretonne, almost apologetically.

"Whenever a prisoner escapes," Mother Amalie said, "I know at least why I am here. If it weren't for that I would have blown up the whole place."

They were silent again. I moved my chair so as to get a view of the street through the rent in the curtain. The shadows of two German soldiers were projected on the wall across the way.

I said nothing. I arose, tiptoed around the room, and sat down beside Mother Amalie, on the old plush sofa. The back was decorated with old painted sea shells like those our fathers used to bring home from their wedding trips. As children we liked to put them to our ears and listen to the sea sound captured in the shells.

Suddenly Madame Roquebrune said amid the silence: "Well, children, will you take a letter to the unoccupied zone?"

We stood up, electrified. The girls put their sewing aside. "You don't mean—"

Madame smiled contentedly. She went on sewing.

"Did you think old Mère Amalie would leave you in the lurch? I promised to get you papers, didn't I? I have them."

We all stood around her. Her words sounded like a fairy tale.

She finally decided to tell her story. "I had to find two men. Two men willing to give their own documents to our two prisoners. But that alone wouldn't have been enough. To reach the free zone, you have to pass through Dijon. The border is less than forty kilometers from Dijon. From there

388

it's easy to get through. But Dijon is two hundred kilometers from here. True, it can be done on foot. But two hundred kilometers means at least ten days of marching, and in ten days you can run into lots of danger. You must take the train. There's one at eight every morning. But the passengers must show a pass from the *Kommandantur*. I had to find two good men who would go to the *Kommandantur* and ask for passes to Dijon. I found them. Now each of you has a real pass with a beautiful round swastika seal. But the passes are valid only with other identification papers. As to that—"

She broke off. I was sitting beside her and Dr. Petit at her feet. The girls had pushed their chairs closer to Madame. It was sultry in the room. Some of the girls had half dropped their wrappers and sat there, with naked shoulders, in pink or blue slips. Their flesh breathed forth the heat.

"As to that—" Mother Amalie began once more. But again she broke off, pricking up her ears.

She had heard the sirens first. But now they were clearly audible.

Everything happened with cinematic rapidity. Motorcycles began to rattle through the silent street. A few stopped. Commands rang out. An automobile halted before the house.

The salon was like a frightened beehive. The girls drew their wrappers tighter about them. Jeannine fled into a corner. Mignonette, for some unknown reason, tried nervously to hide her glasses. Pauline, with her long cigarette holder in her mouth, planted herself in the kitchen doorway. Dr. Petit remained seated on the floor as though paralyzed. Nanette began to fold a shirt. I stood motionless and doubtless quite pale, thinking of the shadows on the wall across the street.

In this general confusion only our leader remained cool-headed.

Mother Amalie rose and said in a tranquil, deep, masculine voice: "You two go up on the roof! Until I call you. You others stay where you are. Pauline! You go upstairs with them and then go to your room. Jeannine and Irène, you go to my room. Get into my bed. Quick. If they ask you any questions, say you're my guests. Pauline! You hide our prisoners' belongings under your bed. Understand?"

All her orders were carried out with magnificent precision. Madame Louis Bellonville, née Amalie Roquebrune, stood in the middle of the parlor, erect, cool, every inch a general.

We ran up the stairs. When we reached the fourth floor, the house-bell rang, shrill and imperious.

We opened the door leading to the roof. Pauline hurriedly took our meager belongings and brought them to her room.

"Don't forget our toothbrushes!" I said rather foolishly.

"Don't worry," she said, running along the corridor.

You could literally feel that every movement in the house was governed by one will. The bell rang, a second time, wilder, more impatient.

A narrow staircase led upwards to the roof. The roof was of thick, unbreakable glass. We breathed deeply. From the top step of the staircase, the whole roof was visible. To discover us the Germans didn't even have to come upon the roof. They could look up from the stairs.

I stopped cautiously and took stock of the situation. The air was cool and refreshing. I became aware that I had not left my room in days. A soft wind played around my temples. Beyond the church towers the sky was pink with the few lights of Nancy. This was no night for dying.

"I'm only sorry for Mère Amalie," said the lieutenant.

We heard her voice. We saw nothing, but we knew that

she was calling from the illumined window of her apartment. "What's the matter? We're closed for the night! No Germans allowed!"

"Open!" roared the German patrol commander. The whole street seemed to be full of soldiers. "Open! Police!"

Mother Amalie had apparently gained enough time.

"Police?" we heard her call out in the street. "Why didn't you say so? I thought you were just visitors!"

Then there was silence. We stood on the flat roof waiting. There was a sudden intoxicating smell of life and summer. Beyond the four church towers, the whole city seemed to be aflame.

I peered down the stairs. Suddenly and inexplicably an idea seized me. Above me was the vaulted summer sky with thousands of stars. Was it not wide enough, I wondered, to give aid to one man?

"Come on," I whispered. "Quick!"

Cautiously we groped forward.

"Hold on to the chimney!" I said to Dr. Petit. "Hold fast! And hold my legs. Don't let me go. If you do, I'm done for."

With his left hand, the lieutenant clung to the chimney. He understood my plan at once. Thank God I can count on you, Dr. Petit, I thought. I lay flat on my stomach. The lieutenant's right hand seized my leg. I slid forward slowly to the edge of the roof.

I looked down.

"I'm all right now," I whispered to Dr. Petit. "You can let me go. Crawl close to me. Do you get dizzy?"

"No!"

There was no precipice beneath. No more than two meters below us the tiled roof of the adjoining house bordered on the back wall of the Hôtel St. Martin. Standing on this tiled roof, you could not be seen from the staircase leading to the glass roof.

"Let's go!" I said.

We let ourselves drop from the edge of the glass roof to the solid roof of the adjoining house.

"Hurt yourself?"

"No. And you?"

"No."

I don't know how long we remained there.

"If they come out on the hotel roof," said the lieutenant, "we'll hang by our hands. Then they won't be able to see us."

I nodded.

We said no more. We pressed close to the back wall. My heart was pounding so loudly that I was afraid it could be heard through the walls. From time to time we were startled by the sudden roar of a motorcycle in the street. Aside from that it was still.

Suddenly we both looked up. There were voices clearly audible above us, and very close to us. Our fears were redoubled because we couldn't see the men who spoke. It was like destiny bending over us.

"Two men to the roof!" someone ordered.

Dr. Petit did not understand German. He gave me a dispirited look. I motioned to him. We groped about and managed to crawl to the edge of the roof. We stopped for a while, thinking we had loosened a tile, but it was only our imagination. We lay flat on our bellies. We couldn't look up and we didn't want to. Slowly, slowly we crept to the edge. Our fingers clutched every tile of the almost flat roof. Then we felt our legs hanging down into the void. We clung desperately to the tiles. We could no longer be seen from the hotel roof. At most, our desperate hands, our white fingers might have been seen: but they were covered by the night.

Impossible to say how long this lasted. Each fraction of a second was like an eternity. But what are ten or a hundred eternities to the million eternities of the heavens? If they see us, I thought, I'll let go. Drop into the unknown. They won't get me alive, I thought. Why did I run away? Oh, yes—my mother's birthday is on August 12th. For twenty-eight years I have never failed to bring her flowers on the morning of her birthday. Even when I was far away, I flew home; I rushed into her room on the sunny morning of August 12th. I always wanted to be the first to embrace her. The sun was always shining on August 12th. What is today? August 10th. Will I be able to see her on the twelfth? My fingers hurt. The edge of a tile cut into me, drew blood. How many more eternities?

A voice called softly from above. I do not know whether it came from Heaven or from the Hôtel St. Martin which the Germans had transformed into a house of joy. But what does it matter? The voice called: "Where are you, children?"

It was the voice of Mother Amalie.

The following day passed in feverish preparations. The raid had not been on our account; the police were looking for the thirty escaped officers from the camp in Nancy. However, we would have to get away as fast as possible. In Nancy the air was too thick.

Mother Amalie's interrupted story was no fairy tale. She had actually discovered two men—Charles Boissière, a Swiss wine salesman employed by Bonard Frères, and André Morteau, a radio mechanic. They had agreed to apply for passes at the *Kommandantur*, and, in addition, to let us have their regular French *cartes d'identité*. Both said she could do what she pleased with the documents. Once we were on our way, they would simply announce that they had lost them—and that would cover them. Next day, Charles Boissière, a bald little man with a long beard, who looked less like a salesman than a clay dwarf in an old-fashioned garden, came to the hotel to help us make necessary changes in his identification papers.

We went about this unaccustomed task with the greatest energy. We turned Mother Amalie's dining table into a regular drawing board. We spread out our papers, and posted girls on the staircase as look-outs before getting to work. If anyone suspicious appeared, they were supposed to whistle. One of the girls gave us a bottle of ink eradicator. Another brought pens, paper, pencils, and blotting paper. Nanette, the "intellectual," provided us with a compass, which came in very handy. Fortunately, each of us had a small photo. The lieutenant's was exactly what was needed, but mine had originally been intended for a book jacket and it showed me smoking a cigarette, which was rather contrary to official regulations. But who would bother about such details? Luckily Dr. Petit's surgical training fitted him for the delicate task ahead of us. With admirable care he loosened the radio mechanic's picture from his *carte d'identité,* replacing it by his own. Only a quarter of the original seal happened to show on the original picture: this quarter he reproduced on the photograph of the new André Morteau with India ink. My case was more complicated. We skillfully completed the seal and pasted on the photo, but the bearded salesman, to his and my regret, had been born in 1884: I could not possibly pretend to be that old. Dr. Petit carefully removed the original birth-date and replaced it with 1911. The operation was not entirely successful, for it left a white spot on the green paper specially prepared to make forgeries difficult; and the new date was written in fresh ink, contrasting sharply with the faded ink on the rest of the eight-year-old document. But we could not afford to be too difficult. The main thing was that each possessed a regular pass from the German commandant of Nancy, without photographs or fingerprints, expressly permitting André Morteau and Charles Boissière to go to Dijon. The pass was valid for four days, including the return trip—a privilege of which we had no desire to avail ourselves. These flawless documents were reinforced by the *cartes d'identité* with changed photographs, a seal partly forged and a corrected birth-date: papers of doubtful value, but not to be sneezed at.

The night before our departure—after ten o'clock of course—Mother Amalie gave us a champagne dinner in the salon of the Hôtel St. Martin. The real André Morteau and Charles Boissière attended as guests of honor. On account of the curfew our guests stayed overnight, sharing the attic rooms with their new namesakes. André Morteau took the letters entrusted to me by my comrades and promised to do something for our fifteen-year-old prisoner. Both the banquet and the night passed without incident.

Despite violent protests, Mother Amalie forbade the girls to accompany us to the railway station. We bade them good-by after supper. But the next morning at seven, when we came into the salon for our coffee, the ladies of the house—by previous agreement or spontaneously—were all gathered around the table. Each of them had prepared a gift. The little suitcases which Mother Amalie had bought us could scarcely hold all the splendors they bestowed on us. Nanette, as might have been expected, gave us two books by Pierre Bénoit; Jeannine and Irène gave us some *Gauloises Bleues* as on the day of our first meeting. Mignonette presented each of us with a fresh shirt, and Pauline with sublime neckties; one of the two girls without a name pressed her dead fiancé's cuff links into my hand. Madame herself naturally took care of our earthly needs: each of the two suitcases contained a can of sardines, a bag of pralines, and a roast chicken. Dr. Petit received a dark gray, and I a light gray, hat from Monsieur Louis Bellonville's wardrobe.

It was half-past seven when Madame called me to her room. She took my head in her hands and said: "I would like to give you one more thing. Now listen carefully! I had a boy once, from a man—I don't know what became of the man. He left me. I brought up my boy, honorably, openly. At the age of nineteen he left me like his father. I never heard of him again. He is about your age. You remind me of him. I was happy all the time you were here. Our Lord God will help you. Take this handkerchief. It contains something I once gave him, something that belongs to him. You must promise me that you won't open it until you are safe. Its contents will protect you. *Au revoir!*"

She kissed my forehead. Her words sounded simple and not the least solemn. She turned away quickly to conceal her tears.

"Have you a knife to cut your chicken with?" she asked.

I kissed her hands. I put the lace handkerchief in a small side pocket.

It had been decided that the lieutenant and I should go to the station separately. I went first, with Mother Amalie. He was to follow a few minutes later, with Charles Boissière. The girls stood in the kitchen doorway. Each gave me a kiss. Bad girls have never given more virtuous kisses than those seven in the doorway of the Hôtel St. Martin.

My knees were like rubber as we cautiously went out into the Rue des Quatre Eglises. Mother Amalie had previously gone out to have a look at the street. Of course, I saw ghosts everywhere; it seemed to me that every German soldier stared at me, that every policeman's eyes followed me; and I was certain that Sergeant Daxer in person would be awaiting me at the station. But nothing of the kind occurred. It was pouring rain and the passers-by were all in a hurry. No one looked up. The oppressive heat of the last few days had given place to a pleasant coolness. Women and girls were hurrying to their offices and shops; the iron shutters of the *Magasins Réunis*—a department store across from the station—were being opened. I felt curiously light. German soldiers with steel helmets and shouldered guns were patrolling the station and the platform, but they showed no interest in me; they were too busy trying to keep out of the rain.

Dr. Petit arrived shortly after me. We took seats in two different compartments of the same car. Mother Amalie vanished and came back with newspapers. When I opened one I found a red dahlia in between the pages.

A few minutes after eight the train began to move. I leaned out of the window and waved to Mother Amalie. She stood on the platform in a light violet raincoat, with a thin cape over her hair. My heart overflowed and I thought: Surely you have not said everything you meant to. I thought of the little garret where by now Mignonette must be busy cleaning. With a heavy heart, I thought of Mother Amalie going back to her hotel, feeling that she had lost her son for a second time. But my mother, too, was awaiting her son somewhere. My beloved hostess vanished in the smoke and steam of the Nancy station.

A woman and two men sat in my compartment. The woman had come to Nancy to look for her husband, who was a prisoner. But the day before her arrival he had been transported to Germany. The two men, both in their fifties, were government officials. One was a railroad employee, the other a postal clerk. Both lived in Dijon and had been in Nancy on business. They discussed the difficulties of the trip; they said that the stretch between Nancy and Dijon was particularly unpleasant and that the German control at Langres was unusually strict. Permission to go northward from Dijon could be obtained only as a special favor. The control was equally strict for southbound travel, but the local authorities granted passes from Nancy to Dijon much more readily than from Dijon to Nancy.

I immersed myself in Pierre Bénoit's novel. I had a superstitious fear of cutting all the pages—I thought that I might be arrested before I could finish the book. I cut no more than four or eight pages at a time. I often had to reread a page three or four times before grasping its simple meaning; everything was confused in my mind—the Indian princesses, the girls in the Hôtel St. Martin, the control at Langres, the oriental adventurers, the droning of the wheels, the conversations between the railroad employee and the postal clerk, the panting of the engine. Again and again I looked out of the window. The rain had ceased. The sun was slowly breaking through the clouds. Prisoners under German guard were working on the tracks. They followed the train with a longing gaze. I looked into their emaciated, tired faces and promised myself never to forget them. Here and there a horse and carriage stood at a grade crossing. In some bright summery houses the white shutters were open and children played in the gardens. So undemanding had I become that I said to myself: Even if they arrest you at Langres, you will have breathed some life. Then once more I became absorbed in the adventures of a troupe of European players in the land of the maharajahs.

I felt someone looking at me. I looked up. Dr. Petit had passed through the corridor for the second or third time.

398

I rose and went out. He leaned out of the window beside me.

"Well," he said. "Did you hear?"

"What?"

"The control at Langres is very strict. They examine your liver and kidneys."

"What can I do about it?"

"How about getting off before Langres?" he proposed.

"Are you losing your nerve?" I asked.

"No," he said. "But it might be wiser to go on foot. I was told they examine every single document."

I shrugged my shoulders.

"Too late."

I went back to my seat. We were approaching the control station. For the first time I spoke to my fellow passengers: "The control is at Langres, isn't it, Monsieur?"

"Yes, Monsieur," said the railroad employee.

"And is it very hard to get back to Nancy?"

"Very!"

"Thanks."

The train stopped with a jerk. Four soldiers jumped into each car. Hundreds of persons, among them many women and children, were sitting on the platform.

"They are all being sent back," explained the railroad employee.

A German sergeant followed by three soldiers tore open the door. He walked exactly like Daxer, like a grenade thrower, and he had a pair of leather gloves in his hand.

"Passes! Identification papers!"

The postal clerk's papers were the first to be examined. The examination was painfully minute. I knew that if he spent even half as much care on my own documents . . .

The woman's identification card was examined with much less care.

"What was your business in Nancy?" the sergeant asked her.

She failed to understand him.

"Some day they'll have to learn German," said the sergeant with annoyance and became absorbed in the railroad employee's documents.

Then my turn came.

I presented the pass from the *Kommandantur*, but held the false *carte d'identité* in my hand. The sergeant stretched out his hand for it. Then I said in my best Swiss-German accent: "Please, *Herr Offizier*, would you mind giving me some proof that I've come from Nancy, so I will be able to go back tomorrow. I was told—" I mentioned the difficulties of the return trip. Talk, keep on talking no matter what you say, I thought: that was the main thing.

"You can return within four days without difficulty," said the sergeant, handing me back my documents. He did not examine the *carte d'identité*.

I thanked him as I returned my papers to my pocket. Once again the tested recipe had worked, the gamble on human stupidity had worked out. I had commissioned the non-commissioned officer and had asked him a favor that proved his importance to him. I returned to my seat and cut all the pages of my Pierre Bénoit. But my chest felt as though my heart had hammered a hollow space all around itself.

"Yes, they sure have order," said the railroad employee.

"And organization!" echoed the postal clerk.

"After all, they're human beings like us," said the railroad employee.

"They're all right," echoed the postal clerk.

The woman in the corner sighed.

"They're very polite," began the railroad employee.

"There can be no doubt about it," echoed the postal clerk. "And very *correct*. Did they pay you your salary punctually?"

"On the dot," confirmed the railroad employee.

"In marks?"

"In marks."

"Marks or francs—it doesn't make any difference," declaimed the postal clerk. "After all we're no worse off than before. And you must bear in mind that they saved us from anarchy."

The woman in the corner sighed again. Her husband had been dragged away to Germany—to a Silesian coal mine or a bombed munitions plant or a slave camp—before she had been able to see him. She could scarcely have agreed that the Germans had saved France from anarchy. But she said nothing.

"What do you want?" said the railroad employee. "They'll always need us."

"Germans or Frenchmen," confirmed the postal clerk, "we're indispensable."

"Yes," agreed the railroad employee, "indispensable . . ."

"Did you see how friendly he was when he saw I was a postal clerk?"

"And how polite he was when he saw my railroad card?"

"Yes, you've got to hand it to them. They're *correct* and polite."

"Yes, *correct* and polite."

I rose and went out, not to vomit, though I felt like it, but to see how my companion had fared with the control officials. Dr. Petit was cheerfully leaning out of the window, smoking a *Gauloise Bleue*.

In Dijon we easily slipped through a second, superficial

control. Then we were outside the station of the occupied city—barely forty kilometers from freedom.

Bearing our suitcases we walked down the Avenue du Maréchal Foch. The sun was shining and I was in high spirits.

"What's the next step?" asked Dr. Petit.

"Now . . ." I said gravely, "now I am going to the German *Kommandantur* to ask for a pass to unoccupied France."

CHAPTER TWELVE: THE LAST GAMBLE

I MUST SAY HERE THAT MY MADNESS WAS NOT WITHOUT method. The plan that took hold of me was founded on a deep contempt for the judgment of the German police. In the preceding two months I had seen clearly enough that the world-famous Gestapo was rather inefficient in its work and that its success was chiefly due to the fear it inspired. A police force boosted by advertising—that was the Gestapo; and the advertisements promised much more than the firm could deliver. My books had been burned by the Germans, yet I became camp commander by their grace; they condemned me to death and I became the confidant of my executioners; my name was put on a blacklist which was handed to me; I fled from the Nazis and was provided with a Nazi pass—how, after all this, could I respect the all-seeing, all-knowing, all-powerful Gestapo?

Dr. Petit refused to follow my line of thought. We decided to take a room together, but to act separately.

For hours we tried in vain to get a room. Almost all the hotels of this city with its eighty-six thousand inhabitants were occupied by the Germans. The largest in town, the Hôtel de la Cloche, was reserved for official visitors. A police cordon of steel-helmeted and armed soldiers was drawn around the Place Darcy. In the Hôtel Central German officers were sprawled in leather armchairs all over the lobby, and a uniformed Gestapo official stood on watch beside the porter. Here, outside the "forbidden zone"—that is, the military zone proper—you could see to what an extent the Germans had made themselves at home in France. The officers had their open cars, and in nearly every one sat an officer's wife or mistress; in every store German women were asking for French merchandise; German girls wearing picturesque uniforms instead of rouge and lipstick, and German Red Cross nurses with their severe long gray coats buttoned up to the neck, with their little white bonnets or gray Boy Scout caps, thronged all the cafés, bars, and restaurants. In Dijon, on the way out of bleeding occupied France, the relations between the conqueror and the conquered were palpably friendlier. The stores were open and selling goods to the Germans. German films were playing in the cinemas; waiters cringingly served German generals; and here and there you could see a Frenchwoman sitting with a German officer on a café terrace. We were no longer in proud Lorraine.

Countless times our requests for lodging met with a regretful shrug of the shoulders, but we finally found shelter in the Hôtel Terminus. The old woman in the porter's lodge eyed us somewhat suspiciously and asked to be paid in advance. Then she gave us a small room on an airshaft, though it was blessed with a private bath.

I set out at once to execute my plan. Hundreds of people were lined up outside the prefecture. The whole length of the Rue de la Préfecture up to the church of Notre Dame was besieged by waiting applicants. German soldiers aided by French *Gardes Mobiles* maintained order. Significantly, the *Gardes Mobiles* were the first—even before the railroad employees—to be released from the prison camps. Faithful servants of whatever masters, these *Gardes Mobiles*, but recently released and already restored to the dignity of uniforms, showed themselves more zealous than their jailers. They tried—too late—to maintain an iron discipline on the Prussian model. Whenever a German officer passed, they sprang to attention with ludicrous haste.

A map was posted on the gate of the prefecture; on it the various zones were marked by letters. All those in line were awaiting their turn to apply for passes. The unoccupied zone was marked on the map as the "blocked zone"—that is, it was futile to ask for passes to this part of France. I was told that it took no less than two weeks to obtain a pass even to other zones. But a German soldier informed me that "special permits" could be obtained at the *Kommandantur* in the Rue Devosge.

In view of the superabundance of *Kommandanturen*, it was no simple task to find this particular one. At every street crossing a black and white sign indicated some *Kommandantur:* there were field, local, and district *Kommandanturen.* Finally I found the one I was looking for, the City-*Kommandantur.* In the vestibule forty or fifty persons were waiting, mainly women, under the friendly protection of Germans and *Gardes Mobiles.*

In a small adjoining room a German secretary was drumming away on a typewriter. She was blonde and wore her hair like a German Gretchen, with braids twisted around her head. A sprinkling of rouge showed that she had not entirely resisted the temptations of France. I, too, approached her as a tempter.

"*Mein schönes Fräulein, darf ich's wagen . . .*" I began, like Faust. She was less severe than Margarethe and did not reject my advances. I told her that I was a Swiss and that I had to go to Lyon on importing business. Today, I said, is Saturday; my return pass to Nancy, where I reside, will expire on Tuesday. Would she be good enough to introduce me to the competent officer?

Gretchen rose, glad perhaps to have met an applicant whose language she could understand, and disappeared into another room. A few minutes later she returned and bade me go in.

An immense captain was sitting at an immense desk in an immense hall. Everything here was theatrical; every inch was a piece of Hollywood. Behind the immense captain's immense desk hung an immense picture of the immense Führer, and above the immense Führer's immense picture an immense swastika glittered in its immense frame. I couldn't help thinking of Kaiser Wilhelm who had said that everything about him was big: when he had a cold it was a big cold.

I sneezed. The captain looked up.

"What do you wish?"

"*Herr Offizier*," I said in my Swiss accent, pretending not to know his military rank, "I have come to ask you a favor."

The introduction pleased him. He began to wipe his eyeglasses.

"I am a Swiss," I went on, stepping closer. (I recalled the little bearded man whose name I had assumed and I could not help smiling.) "I am a wine salesman. So far I never had to use a passport, though I have lived in this country for ten years. Five years ago my passport expired, but my *carte d'identité* was sufficient. But today—it goes without saying—you can't do without a passport . . ."

This remark, too, found favor with the important man. He nodded sympathetically. The Führer on the wall seemed to nod, too.

"Unfortunately the Swiss consulate in Nancy is closed." I kept harping on the same string. "But the German *Kom-*

mandantur was good enough to grant me a pass for a round trip to Dijon."

I approached the desk and laid my pass on it. I thrust it under his nose; why be shy when you have *one* "authentic" document? The captain put on his glasses and examined my pass. Over his shoulder, the Führer on the wall likewise examined Hans Habe's pass.

"To my great disappointment," I went on, "our consulate in this town refused to give me a passport. I can get one only in Lyon, because Lyon is in unoccupied France. But my pass expires in three days. Tuesday I must be back in Nancy, or I'll lose my job. I have worked for six years with the firm of Bonard Frères, wine and champagne dealers."

I presented the whole matter as though I had no doubt that I would get a pass, and that the favor I was asking consisted merely in having the pass made out as quickly as possible.

"Wine and champagne?" the captain asked amiably.

"Yes, wine and champagne," I answered with proud firmness.

The captain cleared his throat.

"Have you any left in stock—I mean wine, champagne?" he asked, trying to sound unconcerned.

"Not much," I said with a scarcely perceptible smile of understanding.

The captain balanced my pass in his hands, as though trying to gauge its weight. The Führer looked down at his follower and shook his head. But being only a picture, he could say nothing.

"Hm," grunted the captain. "Could you get me a few bottles of champagne? I'll pay, of course."

"Let me see," I said graciously. I hoped that the captain

would drink my champagne at the same gathering where Captain Brühl would play the accordion.

"How much would it be?"

"I would be able," I said, every inch a wine salesman, "to deliver twelve bottles of Veuve Cliquot at twenty-five francs per bottle."

The captain's large protruding eyes popped so far out of their sockets that I was afraid they would drop on the smooth, polished desk top.

"Yes, this is confidential of course," I said softly, probably to conceal it from the Führer. "Wholesale prices . . ."

"Perfect," said the captain. He laid my pass on the table. Apparently he had found it heavy enough.

A few minutes later my pass to unoccupied France was made out. The German authorities were requested by the City-*Kommandantur* in Dijon to permit Charles Boissière, Swiss wine salesman, to cross the demarcation line in both directions. My false *carte d'identité* now lay on the desk beside the two passes. I leaned over the desk as though trying to help the captain to spell my name. I pressed my thumb on the forged part of the seal. The large white spot around my birth-date—1911 instead of 1884—failed to attract the captain's attention. He was thinking of the champagne—a dozen bottles at twenty-five francs apiece . . .

The pass was made out and sealed.

"Now all we need is the major's signature," said the captain, rising. He looked like an equestrian statue.

I remained alone with the Führer. My heart pounded loudly. I had a ten-ton load on my stomach.

The minutes went by. An alabaster clock was ticking away on the white marble mantelpiece.

The door opened.

"I am sorry," said the captain, entering, "but the major has left. Bad luck! Today is Saturday. He won't be back till Monday."

My temples throbbed. The Führer seemed to smile.

"But you needn't worry," said the officer, sitting down again. "I'll simply extend your return pass to Nancy. Call for your papers Monday morning. At eight. At nine there is a train for Lyon. You'll be back in Nancy by Tuesday evening."

"That's true," I said. There was nothing else I could say.

I took my old papers and thanked the captain. As I was in the doorway, the captain called after me: "Don't you want to take my address?"

"Of course."

I noted his name and address.

"As soon as I am back from Lyon," I reiterated my promise.

The captain accompanied me to the vestibule. The *Gardes Mobiles* sprang to attention. Some of their zeal was on my behalf, so reverently did the captain treat me.

"Admit this gentleman at once on Monday morning," said the captain to Gretchen.

I went out into the occupied city.

My Sunday passed between hope and fear. Dr. Petit reproached me bitterly for my rashness. He advised me against going back to the *Kommandantur* on Monday. He, for his part, had sought out the parents of a school friend who himself was a prisoner of war. They had promised to furnish him with a bicycle and an exact description of the route that night. All day long we didn't stir from our room. Two young men, at large and not demobilized (the demobilized soldiers all wore uniforms and an arm-band saying "demobilized"), would have attracted too much attention in Dijon. At every step, we had felt ourselves watched and suspected.

Besides, I was haunted by the fear that one of the numerous Austrians in the army of occupation might recognize me. To be sure, I wore my glasses, which I normally didn't use on the street, but they were a scanty disguise. We devoured the last of Mother Amalie's provisions. From time to time I cautiously touched the lace handkerchief she had given me, but resisted the temptation to open it.

Toward evening, we took leave of one another. The few days had brought us close together. Everything would be doubly hard, I thought, without the lieutenant's good boyish face. Garai, Saint-Brice, René—I had lost them all. Silently we shook hands and embraced. Dr. Petit ran down the stairs. I never heard of him again.

I was alone. The heat in the room became more and more oppressive. I dressed and finally ventured into the street. I bought cigarettes, fruit, a newspaper. Then I went to the movies. I don't remember what the picture was. But there was a big sign in two languages over the door: JEWS AND DOGS NOT ALLOWED. And beneath it, the stamp of the *Kommandantur*. An order of the *Kommandantur* also prohibited Jews from entering the hotels and restaurants. "In case of doubt," said the notice, "the landlord has the right to turn any person of Jewish appearance out of his premises." On the sign over the window of the Chapeau Rouge Restaurant, the owner had added: *"Et je le ferai!"*—"And I'll do it!"

As I say, I don't know what the picture was. I sat squeezed in between two German soldiers. At one moment in the picture, a man was clapped into handcuffs. I felt the handcuffs around my own wrists. And around my neck as well. The German newsreel showed the victorious German army. The Führer was shown feeding a horse, somewhere on the front. Führer and horse exchange tender looks. A few generals—on the screen—looked on at the solemn meeting between battle-leader and battle-horse. The soldiers beside me applauded. I felt that they were staring at me in the darkness because I didn't clap my hands. I fled from the movie before the lights went up.

The night was restless. In the next room two French women were entertaining two German officers. I had no sooner fallen asleep than I was awakened by the familiar step of German boots. There was a violent knocking at the door. Someone cried: "Open up!" A woman screamed—half in terror, half laughing. I lay propped up on my elbows, bathed in sweat. I heard the word "police" and a few disjointed words of explanation on the part of the officers. I reached in the darkness for Mother Amalie's lace handkerchief. It crossed my mind that tomorrow was the twelfth, my mother's birthday. Someone said: "Hand over the revolver!" Then there was a tinkling of glasses. A few minutes later it was still.

At the stroke of eight next morning I presented myself at the *Kommandantur*. Though thirty or forty people were waiting, Gretchen recognized me at once. She went out to announce me.

It was quite some time before she came back. I felt a chill spreading around my heart. Icy rivers were flowing through my veins.

Suddenly the captain stood before me.

"*Herr* Charles Boissière!" he said.

He emphasized each single word. Herr was the indictment; Charles, the verdict; Boissière, the sentence.

In his hand the captain held my pass to Lyon. It was canceled in red pencil.

"Come with me!" said the captain.

We went into his office. The August sun shone through the high windows. But it was icy cold in the room. The marble fireplace was like a giant block of ice.

"Your papers!" said the captain.

More than ever in the field, more than in the rain of bombs at Noirval, I felt that my life hung by a hair. I fumbled for my papers. Gain time, I said to myself. Gain time at any price!

"The major spoke to the Swiss consul this morning," said the captain. He stood menacing and immense, bent forward beneath the picture. "The consul says that he can issue a passport to a Swiss subject at any time."

I was still rummaging in my pocket.

"*Why* do you want to go to Lyon?"

The question hung menacingly in mid-air. The oversized swastika on the wall began to turn. It revolved with maddening speed. It was no longer a swastika, it was a number of whirling circles.

I found my papers. And at the same moment, a great calm seemed to descend on me.

I heard myself speaking: "What? Is the consul out of his mind? Giving me false information? Is he trying to make a fool out of me? He's positively insane. I'm wasting my time here. I'll lose my job."

I do not know where my words came from. I screamed. I cursed. I was red with fury. The German was still bending forward, like a gorilla ready to pounce. He stretched out his hand. His hand, too, was oversized. Your papers! said the hand.

And then I was calm. The swastika stood still. The Führer's picture paled. The Iron Cross shone on the Führer's left lapel. And suddenly it was the Cross, not the Iron Cross.

"Unspeakable!" I shouted. "Only in Switzerland can a thing like that happen. I'm going right back and—" And with a sudden inspiration: "Can I mention your name, *Herr Hauptmann?*"

The gorilla's outstretched paw sank down.

"You not only can," cried the captain, "you must. Who do they think they are, these little Swiss? Always giving wrong information. We'll have to march in and clean up your impudent little Switzerland."

It was still. The sun sent its warming beams through the window.

"Yes indeed," the captain continued. I had struck his weak point. Little Switzerland—disorder—German authority. "Yes," he said. "I *demand* that you go and straighten the matter out. You can mention me all right. I'll expect you this afternoon. You will report on what they tell you."

There was no further mention of my papers. Two minutes later I stood outside in the street. It was an August morning and all was not yet lost.

The hardest hours of my flight were the next hours in Dijon. I couldn't go back to my hotel. If I didn't report to the *Kommandantur* that afternoon, I could be sure that they would come looking for me. Monsieur Charles Boissière, wine salesman from Nancy, had been regularly registered in the Hotel Terminus; it would be child's play for the *Kommandantur* to find him. What was more, the captain might easily get the idea of calling up the Swiss consulate again. The first time they had said only that the Dijon consulate was empowered to issue passports; this time they would doubtless report that they had never seen or heard of Monsieur Charles Boissière.

For these reasons I could not return to my hotel, and I knew that I would have to get out of Dijon by that night at the latest. But I had no map of the region; all the maps had been bought up by the Germans. I hadn't the slightest idea

413

exactly where the demarcation line ran, or where a crossing could be attempted with any hope of success.

Until noon I wandered aimlessly about the city. I knew all the shop windows in the business street which—ironically perhaps—was still called the Rue de la Liberté, and I had read all the signs at least twenty times. I had made friends with the newspaper vendors, who advised me against buying their wares: "Nothing but German lies, monsieur!"

For hours I sat in the great park behind the Place Darcy, where the flowers were in full bloom. A little girl ran up to me and asked me to explain the pictures in her picture book. We made friends. I told her about the flying carpet and Aladdin's miraculous lamp. And then I had to tell about the flying carpet all over again. Nothing could have done me so much good as talking to this child. I myself sank into a world of fairy tales.

In the noon hours I looked across toward the hotel. I walked up and down on the opposite side of the street. Whenever a police car stopped, my stomach contracted. Whenever a carful of prisoners drove by, my heart shriveled up.

I went into the Café Central, which is on the Place Grangier, opposite the Hotel Central. I sat down in a quiet corner, asked for paper and pen and wrote a few lines to my wife. I decided to mail the letter, though there was little hope of its reaching Switzerland in the next few weeks. But on my trips to Nancy I had smuggled so many letters for my comrades that I began to speculate like my fellow-prisoners: either I would be home soon, or the letters would mean something even after months. And so I wrote: "Tonight I am making the decisive attempt. If it succeeds I will be with you before this letter. If it fails, it was the last, the great adventure."

414

I was about to seal the letter when a merry group attracted my attention. As I was writing, four or five young fellows had sat down beside me. Then three or four girls appeared, and the whole gathering breathed so much freshness, so much lightheartedness, that it really soothed my spirit to watch them. They were all between seventeen and twenty years of age. They must have been students, for they obviously belonged to different social classes; only their wonderful great youth united them. A privilege of their youth was courage; for while German officers drank beer all about them, German women read old French fashion magazines, German soldiers tramped in and out, and civilians with enormous swastikas in their buttonholes spread themselves out on the red leather sofas, these young people calmly discussed the reasons for the defeat, making ample use of the designation "Boche" in referring to the Germans. From the moment of their arrival we exchanged looks, and a strange contact was established. I saw two or three of them put their heads together, apparently talking about me.

I sealed my letter and approached them.

"May I sit down with you?" I asked softly, trying not to attract the attention of the Germans.

The permission was granted.

I sat down between a big blond lad with a pimply but courageous face, giving promise of true manhood, and a blonde girl who looked like an American.

"I don't know why I trust you," I began. "But I have a feeling that you can help me . . ."

Filled with a solemn curiosity, the young people moved closer.

I briefly told them my story. From time to time they interrupted me with an intelligent question; otherwise they listened with silent interest.

When I had finished, the young people exchanged looks. There was a moment's silence. Then the girl beside me said: "Of course we'll help you!"

All agreed. There were eight of them, five men and three girls. And how alone I had been half an hour before! Suddenly I felt that I had eight friends. Eight friends whom I could trust.

"Let's go over to Manon's and hold a council of war!" suggested a little fellow with glasses, who looked like a fifteen-year-old professor.

His suggestion was adopted. We paid and left the café. Manon was a lovely brunette with dazzling white teeth. She was the daughter of a manufacturer with a villa on the Boulevard Carnot. We installed ourselves in the ample salon. I said hardly a word, for the council of war deprived me of all independent decision. Each of the eight had his own strategy, and each vehemently defended his own ideas. Names flew through the air—names of places and people I had never heard. Now and then one of the young people came over to me and slapped me on the back with a laugh, saying, "We'll fix it, *mon vieux*." Countless cigarettes were smoked and the ashes strewn on the carpet. At length Henri—a big, fat boy with sluggish movements—was sent out to speak with someone whose name of course meant nothing to me.

The blond man with the courageous face came close to me. "This much is definite," he said. "You'll have to pass through the village of Seurre. The train leaves at six in the evening, doesn't it, Gabrielle?"

"Right, *mon colonel*," said Gabrielle, a little student with pink-framed glasses.

"Seurre is about six kilometers from the border and is the one place where you can slip through in comparative safety. But we'll know in a moment. Henri has gone to see his uncle,

Monsieur Lion, who has a sausage factory and delivers sausages in unoccupied France. Probably he can hide you in among his crates."

A slender lad with the face of a girl sat down beside me. "Can I go with you?"

A girl of the same age, but grave and dignified, said: "We need you here, baby-face."

"If it doesn't work with Henri's uncle," said a young man with his hair cut *en brosse*, "we'll get a truck and drive you across ourselves."

"Papa will give us the money," Manon agreed.

A few minutes later Henri came back. He still had clips around his trousers; he had gone on his bicycle and was all out of breath. All gathered around him. "Well, Henri?"

"Unfortunately my uncle can't do anything himself."

"Damn!"

"What can he do?" Henri tried to excuse him. "It's just hard luck. Since yesterday the border has been hermetically closed. All traffic between the two zones has been cut off."

Monsieur Lion was roundly cursed just the same.

"No," said Henri. "Everything will be all right. Lion has given us two addresses. A big one and a little one. The big one is Monsieur Roy, the biggest peasant in Seurre." And turning to me: "In Seurre you just go to see Monsieur Roy and tell him Monsieur Lion sent you. The two are close friends. Roy makes sausage too. And Roy has helped several escaped prisoners across the border. He'll get you across just like that. But use the little address too. It's a sausage-maker by the name of Nollet. They say he's an old fool, but his wife is the most famous cook in the whole Côte d'Or." The report was received with enthusiasm. Henri gradually caught his breath.

"Yes, before I forget," he added. "My uncle said to be

careful in Seurre. It's the last station in occupied territory. All the trains stop there. And then they go on across the border. Consequently, the control is very strict in Seurre. But you'll get through all right, my uncle says."

Glasses were brought in and we drank to my success. We exchanged addresses, with a view to writing . . . some day when things were different.

"And they will be different," said Manon, her glass in hand.

The big blond lad sat down at the piano.

"What should I play?" he asked.

Everyone except me stood round the piano, and I sat wearily in a big easy chair. I felt old in the presence of so much youth.

No one answered. Vigorously the young man began to play. I arose. We all stood silent. And softly we began to sing the *"Marseillaise."*

All eight of them brought me to my train. For reasons of caution, we reached the station only a minute before train-time. I entrusted my letter to Manon. When I looked out of the window, my eight musketeers stood there lined up like organ-pipes—waving.

Eight handkerchiefs flew into the air like white doves.

The local train puffed through the countryside. The August evening was warm and clear. The fields lay yellow in the evening light; trod by no peasants, they breathed a holiday peace. From time to time I saw a solitary girl with a water jar on her head. At the stops, an old station-master would stand yawning in the door of his office. I thought of summer evenings on the Balaton, the "Hungarian ocean" where I grew up. On Saturday evenings, the young women, dressed in white, stood on the station platforms, waiting for their men to come back from the city. Young girls had tennis rackets in their hands. Horses were hitched to the hotel wagons behind the one-story station, and the flies buzzed around the horses' ears. Something of the mood of those past summers lay over the conquered countryside.

I went up and down the corridor. So the control would be strict in Seurre. Seurre—the last station before the border. Perhaps I could get out before the last stop and go into Seurre on foot. But my traveling companions, whom I felt out as cautiously as possible, told me the road led across a bridge, where the control was even more severe than in the station. It seemed best to stay in the train.

I had no baggage and no pass for the trip from Dijon to Seurre. The guards would be bound to notice me. I don't know exactly what I was looking for as I passed up and down the corridor; but involuntarily I must have been searching for something that would help me through the inspection.

An old lady sat in a compartment alone.

I sat down beside her and struck up a conversation. She was a distinguished old lady who lived in Seurre. She had on a black dress and a long chain of beads, and she had soft yellow hair, just beginning to turn white. She told me that her son and grandson—army officers released from a prison camp a few days before—were expecting her. She told me how all the men in Seurre had left town when the Germans approached. But the women had stayed behind. She herself hadn't so much as left her house. She asked me what I was going to Seurre for. I told her I was a salesman for a Swiss sausage factory. I don't know whether she believed me.

As we spoke, I kept squinting at the lady's suitcase, which lay in the baggage net. It fascinated me as much as if I had been a railroad thief. From time to time we looked out over the landscape and sighed. The old lady probably sighed because she felt that her country was dying. I sighed because on that beaming August day I had less desire than ever to die.

The German guards became more and more frequent at the way stations. In my shirt sleeves as I was, I leaned out of the window at every stop. The little stations smelled of flowers and beer. Beside the station-master stood two or three German soldiers with shouldered guns. Every French railroad official was accompanied by a German official in the solemnly ludicrous dark-blue railroad official's uniform with the gold or wine-red trimmings—each man a general of the local railway.

"This isn't Seurre," said the old lady, every time I looked out.

"But we'll be in Seurre soon?"

"Yes," she said. "Are you nervous?"

"Nervous?" I asked. "Perhaps . . ."

After that we scarcely spoke.

Then the little locomotive steamed into Seurre. The train stopped. At the same moment I seized the old lady's bag.

"No, don't bother."

"Yes, yes," I said. "Let me carry it."

I carried the bag—but actually it carried me. I helped the old lady out of the car, I walked beside her, I didn't budge from her side. I kept talking to her—talk, talk, I said to myself, it doesn't matter what you say, but go on talking—no pauses, no breaks—and keep smiling, smiling. At the end of the long village station, at the exit, stood two German soldiers.

The station seemed interminable. Flowers—red pelargonium —grew between white stones. Two officials were unloading a chest. I spoke and smiled, smiled and spoke; I was the devoted grandson, carrying grandma's bag. And the station never ended.

Finally we stood at the gate. Grandma held out her papers and was let through at once. Still bearing the suitcase, I wanted to follow her.

"Hey, you there!" cried the German, and seized me by the arm. He was a young fellow with eyeglasses, one of the thousands of uniformed gymnastics teachers.

I brought out my pass for Nancy. He returned it at once.

"Passport or *carte d'identité!*" he said.

I gave him my false *carte d'identité.*

The man looked at me from all sides. The old lady stood outside the gate, waiting for me and her bag.

The *carte d'identité* was slowly unfolded.

Outside was a village. Summer. Life. Six kilometers distant lay freedom.

The sergeant looked at the card. Now he was examining the photo. He raised the card closer to his eyes. He looked at me. A quarter of the stamp over the picture was my own amateurish drawing. I tried to stand firm under his glance. Again he examined the *carte d'identité.*

"Charles Boissière . . ." he said.

He sounded dubious.

"Yes," I said, "Charles Boissière."

Again he was concentrating on the picture.

"That's not you," said the man.

It sounded sharp and definite.

But I was relieved. The picture actually was my picture. As long as he was finding fault with the picture and not the stamp, nothing was lost. I had a sudden inspiration. I took the unaccustomed spectacles off my nose.

The German examined me again. Then he said with a smile: "Oh . . . the glasses change you completely."

"Yes," I said amiably. "This kind of glasses."

He folded the paper and gave it back to me. We exchanged smiles.

"Good day," I said with a politeness that was the expression of my gratitude. Toward God, to be sure, not toward the nearsighted German soldier.

"*Heil Hitler!*" said the German soldier.

Outside the gate stood the old woman with her son and grandson, waiting for me and her suitcase.

I carried the bag to their house, which was near by, and then went out to look for Roy, the sausage manufacturer. The village reminded me pleasantly of the Hungarian villages of my childhood. The dust lay thick on the street. A few peasant girls were walking along in their Sunday best, and a few consumptive little acacias stood before the houses. Only consumptive little acacias that have to be tied or propped up can smell so wonderful. The entire dusty street, with its one-story houses and little gardens, was full of the fragrance of the acacias. The evening air was still filled with all the heat of the day. Here and there the roll shutters in front of the windows were drawn up with a clatter. And again I felt the security arising from contact with the past.

The house of Roy, the sausage manufacturer, was the biggest in the village. I went in, followed by a gigantic shepherd dog.

Monsieur Roy was a stout man in his fifties. With a glance at the maid, I asked to speak to him alone, and he led me into a drawing room. His wife sat by the open window.

She may not have been much younger than he, but she seemed young and delicate, with her wavy, graying hair. She nodded to me and went on reading.

We sat down.

"I was—" I began—"I was a war prisoner. I escaped from the Germans."

The man laid a heavy index finger on his lips. He pointed to the door of the next room. Before it lay the big sheep dog.

"The major's dog," said my host.

I couldn't tell whether he was afraid that the major's dog might hear us or merely wanted to indicate the officer's presence.

I explained my business. The woman with the pale delicate cheeks and high cheekbones still sat by the window. Now and then she looked out, dreaming into the summer evening.

The sausage-maker—strange contrast between him and his wife, I thought—listened to me in silence.

"And so," I concluded, "I've come to ask your help."

The man leaned his heavy head in his hairy hands.

"I don't know if I can help you," he said.

There was silence. The dog wagged his tail to drive away the flies. In the next room someone began to speak with a Prussian intonation. Two German cyclists drove down the dusty street.

"I'll try to help you," the man said finally.

He stood up and moved silently around the room, his hands folded behind his back. A clock ticked. The furniture was old and in fine taste. What was it doing in this house?

I too arose. I waited. Outside the dusk was falling.

"Occupied and unoccupied France," said the man, stopping before me, "are separated by the River Doubs. But this bank is guarded by hundreds of German soldiers. . . ."

Again he began to wander. The man in the next room shouted for his orderly. I felt that Roy was waiting for something, and that he wouldn't make up his mind before that something happened.

"So Monsieur Lion sent you?" he asked suddenly.

"Yes."

He resumed his walk. The woman turned the pages. It was far too dark for her to read anything.

Then suddenly the man stopped in front of her.

"What do you think? Can I help him?"

"No!" said the woman.

Suddenly the man seemed changed. His fat face was hard and, at the same time, tired.

"I'm sorry," he said. "The risks are too great. I can't help you."

I tried to say something.

"No," he said. "Come!"

He led me to the door. The dog stood up slowly, majestically, and followed us. I began to look on the whole thing as a fairy tale about a wicked sausage-maker; the sheep dog was the enchanted princess. The woman by the window nodded her head once more.

We passed through the little front garden. At the gate we bumped into a German officer who shoved his way in, paying no attention to the master of the house.

The sausage-maker suddenly bent over me.

"Spend the night at the Hôtel de la Gare. You will hear from me."

I hurried through the town and found a room at the hotel. Then I went down to the dining room. Two of the tables were occupied—by Germans. Two officers at one; at the other, two railroad employees who somehow made the officers seem like railroad employees too.

I ordered what was available on the restricted menu. The two officers had been drinking a good deal of wine, and were discussing military questions in a loud, swashbuckling tone. I listened with interest, forcing myself to gaze out of the window with an air of indifference.

The two officers were discussing the two million French prisoners.

"I ask you," said the lieutenant, setting the wine glass to his mouth. "I ask you. . . . Why should we release the prisoners? France pays us eleven francs a day per man. At most we need two francs for their food. That makes eighteen million straight profit a day. Then the French pay the German guards twenty to forty francs a day per man. On top of all that, they have to pay the imprisoned men and officers, who have to spend their wages in camp. So we get that too. Not to mention the unpaid labor. I tell you our good prisoners net us about twenty-five million francs a day. I ask you. . . . A baby can figure it out."

They went on arguing about their calculations for a while; finally they clinked glasses. The railwaymen looked at the clock. The waitress removed the paper flowers from the tables.

I went up to my room. I sat by the open window and looked out at the fields. It was too dark to see much. Suddenly I was aware that somebody was standing in the room.

"Bonsoir," said Monsieur Roy.

He sat on the bed and spoke rapidly, breathlessly, without interruption, like a man intent on unburdening his heart.

"You must forgive me," he said. "I couldn't speak before. You can't imagine what we've been through in the last ten days. We smuggled a dozen released prisoners across, and it leaked out somehow. There was no proof, but the village was fined fifty thousand francs. We're not allowed out in the street after ten. There are Germans living in every house. The commandant is quartered in mine. He was eating in the next room when you came in. He sleeps in my bed, and his dog in my wife's bed. Since they penalized us, we have to put on fresh sheets every day—for the major's dog."

He broke off. He looked nervously at the clock, listened at the door, suddenly opened it and quickly closed it again. There was an uneasy flicker in his eyes. It was curious to see this huge strong man trembling.

"Two people in our village," he said, "have disappeared. No girl is safe. They behaved correctly enough before. But now they have a pretext."

He stopped.

"Now you'll understand," he said quickly, "that my wife— yes, she's been strange lately. Very, very strange. But"—he hesitated for a minute—"I'll help you just the same. We can't do anything here. But fifteen kilometers away, beyond Montagny-lès-Seurre, my friend Bray has his farm. Give him our greetings. Bray will take you across the border."

He rose quickly and went to the door. I wanted to thank him.

"You must excuse me," he repeated, bowing his head. "My wife—so strange—so strange . . ."

There was nothing more I could say.

It was nearly ten o'clock. Somewhere a stream was murmuring. Somewhere a train whistled. Somewhere freedom was awaiting me.

I awoke on a beaming summer's day. It was August 13th.

I dressed, paid my bill, and set out for Montagny-lès-Seurre. After a march of seven or eight kilometers, an old peasant and an ancient peasant woman picked me up in their cart and took me nearly as far as Montagny. It was no more than eleven in the morning when I reached Monsieur Bray's farm.

The farmer—obviously very well-to-do, more gentleman than farmer, dressed in city clothes and busy over his ledgers —was very friendly when I told him that I came from Monsieur Roy. We sat on a sunny, glassed-in porch. There was fruit on the table, and toys; wooden horses and dolls were scattered over the stone floor. Now and then a child came in, took a toy, and reached up for a fruit. Everything breathed comfort and peace.

Once again I gave a brief account of my adventures and plans.

The man let me speak to the end.

"Have you finished?" he asked.

I said yes. He stroked his little black mustache like a man preparing a complete and final answer.

"I have two things to tell you," he said. He expressed himself with the fastidiousness of the half-educated. "The first is this: I have never yet taken a prisoner across the border. I don't even know where the border runs. Intentionally or not, Monsieur Roy has misinformed you."

My heart stood still.

"And in the second place," the man went on, "you Germans always seem to take us for bigger fools than we are!"

I jumped up.

"We Germans?"

He, too, stood up. I was two heads taller than he, but he faced me like a small turkey-cock ready to fight.

"Yes," he said. "You Germans. If the Germans must send an *agent provocateur* to tell me fairy tales, why can't they find someone who speaks French like a Frenchman."

I was white as a corpse. But I understood.

"Monsieur Bray," I said, "I assure you—"

"Don't assure me of anything! Leave my house!"

I did not budge. A child came in, a small blond boy. He took a tin soldier and an apple.

"Look here, Monsieur Bray," I began once more. I had to make a last desperate attempt. "I do understand you. But

427

please understand me, too. I am lost if you don't help me. I swear by everything I love that I am no German."

"You can swear as much as you want," he answered. "I don't believe a single word you say. You are no French soldier."

"Listen to me, Monsieur Bray," I went on, clenching my fists. "I won't ask you to help me if you don't want to. If you're afraid. But give me a map at least. I'll go to the border alone. If I fall into German hands, I'll have tried at least. Do you understand? I'll take a chance. I'll cross the Doubs somewhere. God will help me. But I don't even know where the river is."

A road map lay on the table. The farmer put his hand on it. He laughed raucously.

"We know all those tricks from the last war. There are hundreds of my fingerprints on this map. If I give it to you, I'll be shot tomorrow."

A little girl of about the same age as the boy ran in from the garden and asked for her doll.

"I have four children," said the farmer. "I don't want to die."

I saw there was no hope.

"All right," I said. "But may I ask you one favor?" I was full of bitterness and hatred. How could I hurt this man? "May I hope at least that you won't denounce me to the Germans after I leave your house? You might want to just so as not to be compromised."

We were still facing one another. The man stood behind a chair. Both his hands—curiously small feminine hands, surprising in a farmer—lay on the back of the wicker chair. He pressed the wicker so hard that his wrists grew white. Two tears glistened in his dark southern eyes.

"I am a Frenchman, Monsieur," he said.

428

He swallowed his tears.

"Thank you," I said, somewhat ashamed.

I left the house. The summer noon was full of bees, butter-flies, warm fragrance. I couldn't believe that everything was lost.

I walked slowly down the road to Seurre. Suddenly I heard a name spoken in my mind. A voice. A phrase. Someone said: "Go and see Monsieur Nollet. They say he's an old fool, but his wife is the most famous cook in the whole Côte d'Or." Monsieur Nollet, Monsieur Nollet, I repeated to myself. Was that really his name?

The shoes of Monsieur Bellonville of Nancy were a bit too small for me and my feet ached. A short distance beyond Montagny-lès-Seurre I sat down on the grass to rest. I sat by the roadside, at the edge of a forest. I watched carefully for German patrols. But only old peasant women passed by on their bicycles. When I rose, I noticed something that had escaped me before: a little chapel at the edge of the woods.

I went closer, and as I approached it, I felt as though a purifying storm had fallen from the skies after an unbearably sultry day. It was like the warm raindrops in June. Like the first kiss after a great longing.

On the small altar of the stone chapel stood the blue Christ of Noirval.

Like the other, he held his arms outspread: full of kind-ness, acceptance, forgiveness.

Then I knew that I was saved.

What followed happened so quickly that it must be told quickly. After some search, I found old Nollet's house. It was an old one-story house in the middle of the village. You went through a kitchen to an old-fashioned sitting room. The old peasant woman was busy in the kitchen. Old Nollet sat in an armchair making cigarettes. He was a white-haired man of about seventy, but he must have been in the World War, for on his lapel he wore the ribbons of the *Légion d'Honneur,* the *Médaille Militaire,* and the *Croix de Guerre.*

The old man looked at me with good, understanding eyes while I spoke. Then he tapped on the floor with his stick. His wife came in and stood respectfully in the doorway. Standing like this, ready to serve, she was the symbol of peasant marriage and of good marriage in general: an upright, noble servant.

"Bring us a drink," said the old man.

The woman brought a bottle of spirits and two glasses. As the warming drink flowed down my throat, I realized that my strength was at an end.

The old man stroked his silky white hair.

"Are your sons here?" he asked.

He called his children "hers," in the manner of peasants.

The old woman went out into the garden and returned with her two sons. They, too, stood respectfully in a corner.

"Go and get all the fishermen you can find," said the father. And as both sons approached the door: "Richard, Jérôme, and Matthieu. Especially Richard!"

"Yes, father," said the sons. They were mature men, but they obeyed like little boys.

The old man sipped at his glass.

"Well," he said reflectively. "It wasn't you who lost this war."

Then his wife spoke: "But you," she said with glowing eyes, turning to her husband, "you would have won it."

The old couple exchanged a look of understanding.

"Perhaps . . ." said the old man. "Perhaps . . . We were not betrayed."

In the meantime the room filled with people. Both sons

came back. Each brought a fisherman. We waited a short time for Richard, but he too came finally, wearing a torn cap and smelling of brandy. He bowed respectfully and remained standing, although the host asked him to sit down.

"Well," said Monsieur Nollet. "Which one of you is going to take this escaped prisoner across the Doubs?"

His tone suffered no contradiction. He bent forward on his cane and looked at the three fishermen.

"Did you hear my question?"

No one spoke. The woman played with her apron. The veins began to show on the old man's forehead.

"Do you want to disgrace me?" he asked, tapping the floor with his stick. "I'll take him myself if you refuse. We aren't scared . . . we of the old guard."

The fishermen began to speak. The day before a Negro trying to cross the river had been shot dead by the Germans. The guard in the frontier zone had been steadily increased in the last ten days. There were German soldiers in nearly every fisherman's house. Jérôme and Matthieu had had their boats confiscated, having been accused of smuggling men across the border.

The old man tapped on the floor with his cane.

"You're not going to tell me that the Germans are lined up arm in arm all along the river? For that they would need two million men. There must be a gap somewhere. You've got to take this soldier across!"

A voice said: "I'll take him!"

It was Richard who spoke. He was no more than five feet three inches tall, and he had the leathery face of a seaman. His eyes were bright blue like the waters of a mountain spring.

"Well said!" said the old man. He leaned back in his chair and drew the blanket over his knees.

"But we'll have to go through Longepierre," said the fisherman. "There's no other way to the spot where my boat is hidden. And in Longepierre alone there are two hundred German border guards."

A silence followed. We all awaited old Nollet's decision. I felt sick with hunger and nervousness. Madame Nollet saw me turn pale and brought a second big glass of herb spirits.

"Alphonse!" said the old man to one of his two sons. "How much gas have we left?"

"The last gallon," said Alphonse.

"Good. You take the car and a load of thirty sausages to Madame Dabèze in Longepierre. Deliver the sausages to her store. And while you are busy with the sausages, Richard and our soldier will get away. Won't you, Richard?"

"Yes, *mon capitaine*," said Richard. He laughed a kindly, silent laugh without opening his mouth. The wrinkles ran merrily up and down his face like the little cars of a scenic railway.

Ten minutes later the old Citroën rolled out with a rattle that sounded like a protest against the last gallon. Alphonse sat at the wheel, I beside him. Richard sat with his arms lovingly embracing the thirty sausages. I ran quickly back to the house: I wanted to kiss the old man's hands. But he took my head and kissed me on both cheeks.

"The *anciens combattants*," he said, "have done their duty in this war, too. God bless you, my boy!"

The kiss of a marshal decorating me for bravery could not have been sweeter than the kiss of the old sausage-maker of Seurre.

We reached the frontier village of Longepierre in a few minutes. Alphonse immediately drove to the *épicerie* of Madame Debèze—it was across the street from the headquarters of the frontier guards. Ten or twelve German soldiers were patrolling outside their headquarters; an equal number, dressed in trunks, were taking a sun bath.

Alphonse got out first and went into the grocery. Then Richard and I began unloading the sausages and taking them into the tiny shop. We were deliberately slow and cautious. The proprietress, a woman of at least eighty, stood behind the counter, speechless with amazement at the unexpected delivery. Then she cast a glance at me, and I saw at once that she understood.

A few seconds later, we were no longer alone. Like all great military leaders, old Nollet needed no knowledge of the terrain to sketch a plan of battle: psychology sufficed. And no one is more susceptible to sausage psychology than the Germans. Within a few minutes not a single German remained outside the store. They crowded into the tiny shop with its cardboard bouillon cubes, its rolls of fly-paper, and its smell of spices and paint. There was a welter of naked flesh, bayonets, guns, swimming trunks, boots and bare feet; suddenly the whole shop was enveloped in a smell of human bodies and sweat. There was a scuffle, half-serious and half-joking, over the thirty sausages; but the jokes were no more than a pretense. The little old woman soon gave up all resistance and withdrew into her room behind the counter—I had a last view of her gray head in the doorway of a room full of lithographed saints. Then a mass of field-gray, fat, bayonets, sausages and heads passed before my eyes. That was the last I saw of the Germans.

Behind the "barracks," there was an open field. Richard made a sign to me, and we began to run. The field soon turned into a sort of dune. We ran across the sandy ground, stumbling over the rushes; we crossed a small woods, crept through a thicket, and suddenly found ourselves before a small white house.

We caught our breath.

"Hello, mother!" called Richard.

A woman came out of the house, followed by six or seven children.

"They're all mine," said Richard proudly but with mock annoyance.

The woman wiped her hand on her apron and held it out to me. She must have spent many years with the fisherman, because only old couples can resemble one another as closely as they did.

"We'll have a chicken for dinner," said Richard somewhat breathlessly. "The gentleman will eat here today. I'll take him over tonight."

I stood there looking about me. There were bushes all about us, all green and fresh. But a little farther down, something gleamed amid the bushes.

"What's that?" I asked Richard.

I was hypnotized by the silvery gleam amid the green shrubbery.

"That is the Doubs," said Richard.

I went down to the bushes. I parted them and moved forward. Before me lay the river, silvery, gleaming and clear, rushing impetuously downwards. A few yards from the opposite bank was a clump of woods.

I stretched out my hand: "What's that over there, Richard?"

"The right bank of the river."

"Is that free France?"

"Yes. *C'est la France libre.*"

My chest expanded.

We went back to the house. The fisherman's wife was chasing a chicken—our dinner.

I took her by the arm.

"Please don't go to any trouble, Madame Richard," I said. "I can't accept your invitation. I'm going to swim for it right away."

Richard protested violently.

"You're out of your mind! At night I'll take you across without the slightest danger. Now the German guards can turn up at any moment."

"No," I said, smiling. "Thank you, Richard. I have lost two months already. I have no more time to lose. Have you got some swimming trunks?"

I went into the house. Still violently protesting, Richard brought me a pair of trunks. I made my will quickly and gaily. I bequeathed my suit, shoes, and hat to Richard. I bade him share with Alphonse what remained of my money. After much hesitation, he accepted. Then I fished into my pocket a last time.

"Can you get me a piece of oil-cloth and some string?"

I hurriedly removed my suit and shirt. I felt that every minute was precious.

Richard brought some black oil-cloth and string. He looked at me, shaking his head.

"At night it will be nothing at all," he said. "Why don't you wait? Can't you see how strong the current is?"

"Current or no current . . ." I said.

I packed three things in the oil-cloth: the little notebook in which I had kept a record of all my experiences; my wrist watch, which had never left me—I loved it because it had been a gift from my father; and, finally, Mother Amalie's lace handkerchief.

"What's in there?" asked Richard when he saw how carefully I packed the handkerchief. And he was quite at a loss when I answered: "I don't know . . ."

I tied the oil-cloth package around my neck.

"Well, if you insist," said Richard resignedly, "I'll go and see if the coast is clear."

He went down to the bank.

I heard him shout through the bushes: "Come ahead!"

I ran down to the river.

We quickly shook hands.

"*Merci*, Richard!"

"*Merde, mon vieux!*"

The little man gave me a tap on my naked shoulder.

I jumped into the water. The current was strong, and I had to fight against it. The waves broke over my head. I took a deep breath each time my head emerged from the water. I was aware that my friends were anxiously watching me from the bank. Freedom, I thought . . . on the other side is freedom. Does anyone who has not lost freedom know what freedom means? . . .

The rushing current seized me like a pair of brutal hands trying to tear me apart. I swallowed a good deal of water. I thought of my torments in the camp. How had I survived them? I thought of my swimming instructor at the Lido and of my plump, comical gymnastics teacher who never dared to go into the water but walked around the edge of the swimming pool in thick overalls. I recalled the moment when Bray told me I was a German. The water was like a wrestler pressing me down with his knees.

And then—I touched land. The bank was brown, wet, loamy. A tangled thicket. Twice I pulled myself up and slid down again. Branches broke. The ground slid from beneath my feet. Finally I found a root to hold on to and pulled myself up. There was a crashing of branches, but I was on firm ground.

Suddenly I became aware that I was not on the opposite bank. I was on a narrow neck of land, a sort of peninsula between the two shores. Beyond the brushwood something glimmered. I had another, wider arm of the Doubs before me. Was I on French or German soil? I wondered. . . . But even before I had time to consider this question, it was answered. A few yards to my right I heard approaching steps— the steps of a German soldier.

I had no more than the fraction of a second to make a decision. Should I hide until he had passed me? Or jump into the water on the other side of the thicket? And save myself by swimming? But wouldn't he shoot if I tried that?

I made my decision. Rather dead than a prisoner. I rushed through the brushwood, unconcerned with the noise I was making. I jumped into the river. I tried to swim as fast as I could against the current, keeping my head under water except to breathe.

I was about thirty yards from the bank when the first shot rang out, immediately followed by another. The bullets splashed in the water with a curious little bubbling sound. The first shot landed no less than ten yards to the right of me. The second about five. The third was three or four yards to my left. Now I was considerably further away from the bank. Would the German improve his aim? Right, left, center. No—the fourth shot landed six or seven yards to my left. Each time I heard the splash. Now I had only five yards to go at the most. A big arm stroke. What did I think about? Once again I recalled my swimming instructor at the Lido when I was a little boy. Bend your knees as far as they go! he used to cry. He was a fat man with a rubber belly. Then I had a vision of the camp in Dieuze. Could it all have been a nightmare? I pulled my knees up to my stomach. One more stroke, and my arms touched the bank and salvation.

I climbed out cautiously. Looking back, I saw the German

soldier leaning his gun against a tree. And the thought passed through my mind that he had not meant to hit me.

I ran across the meadow that sloped gently down to the Doubs. A young man was peacefully fishing at the bank. I called out to him. He stopped fishing and came over to me.

Still fearful, I asked: "Is this free France?"

"Yes," he said.

"No Germans?"

He laughed. His teeth were white and he had a kind mouth.

"No. No Germans."

I took him in my arms and kissed him on both cheeks. . . .

We sat for a few minutes on the meadow, and I tried to dry myself. Finally he took me to his mother. She was a poor fisherwoman. She had given clothes to twelve escaped prisoners. I was the thirteenth. But for me too she found a shirt, trousers, a coat, something resembling shoes. For me too she had cheese, wine, a baked fish.

The young fisherman's name was Robert. We sat outside his hut while his mother was preparing the fish. I removed the oil-cloth from my neck and opened Mother Amalie's handkerchief. It contained a rosary of pure crystal.

"You see," I said to Robert, "this thing saved me."

He took the rosary in his hand and let the beads slip through his fingers.

I thought of the boy to whom it had belonged. Never be unfaithful as he was, I thought. Remember what another has done for you. Have faith and do not despair.

I put the watch to my ear. It was still going. The time was twenty minutes to seven.

I partook of the fish and cheese.

"This is the happiest meal of my life," I said to Robert's mother.

438

"We must share what we have," she said.

She gave me a comb and brush and I combed my hair at a little mirror hanging on the wall. I did everything according to a wonderful ritual. I blinked a few times at the late sun. It was as though I had not seen the sun all that sultry summer in the camp of Dieuze.

The fisherman's mother showed me the picture post card sent to her by some sergeant she had welcomed into unoccupied territory. He had come like me: without clothes, without money, without shoes. He, too, had gone away clothed. He wrote full of gratitude.

I inquired about conditions in the unoccupied region, about possibilities of communication. I wanted to know everything at once.

"This can't go on forever," said the woman. "France will live again. Evil cannot triumph forever."

"No," I said. "Evil cannot triumph."

I learned that there was a train from St. Bonnet-en-Bresse to Bourg, and from Bourg to the Swiss frontier. I made up my mind to walk to St. Bonnet the same evening, so as to make the train the next morning. The town was nine kilometers away, and I set out. I said good-by to the old fisherwoman. But before I left, I wanted to give my name and address to my hostess. She brought paper and ink.

With the pen in my hand I hesitated. Everything became suddenly and fearfully alive. The retreat. Ste. Menehould in flames. Vienne-la-Ville. Lieutenant Saint-Brice and his canal. The forgotten scouts. The names. Maurice Napier the interpreter. Charles Boissière, wine salesman. The sausage-maker.

I wrote quickly: "Hans Habe. *21-ème Régiment de Marche des Volontaires Etrangers.*" And my address in Geneva.

439

I was myself again only after I had written down my true name.

Robert walked with me across flowering gardens to the main road. He showed me the way. Straight ahead to St. Bonnet. We waved to one another and I marched off.

I breathed deeply the fresh air of the silvery summer evening. The sky gleamed like a frozen lake. But in some places a deep blue broke through the silver. The ice on the heavenly lake was broken. And where the silver ceased you could look deep into the sky.

I greeted the passers-by. I called to them that I had escaped a thousand hells, eluded a thousand devils, fled a thousand demons. I greeted the houses on the road, the cows in the pastures, the butterflies in the air; the earth that was fragrant and the heavens that were close to me.

I tried to find someone whom I could help. Never was anyone in rags so rich.

Three girls in white dresses rode by on bicycles. A hay wagon passed with a sleeping driver. The river behind me was as wide as the ocean.

And so I walked singing into the falling dusk.

I had the best things that a man can have on earth. I felt that a fight had not been in vain.

Night came—without fear of the morrow. There was a great silence around me. I inwardly folded my hands and was silent lest I disturb the divine calm. In a distant village the bells rang.

But before me lay the road—beautiful, wide, and free as life itself. . . .

EPILOGUE

Next day at annecy on the swiss border, i met my wife, who had been without news of me for two months.

Twice I illegally crossed the Swiss border to see my parents.

On August 31st, 1940, I was demobilized in the barracks of the *Chasseurs Alpins* in Annecy, as No. 9124.

A few days later I received a certificate from Colonel de Buissy, the commander of my regiment. It included these consoling words: *"Sa conduite au feu a toujours été parfaite."*

There was the comfort of having performed my duty. But it did not sweeten the realization which soon came to me— that "free" France was not free. On September 26th, I crossed the Spanish border. There were other adventures, but of a kind that are the common lot of all those who have fled from Europe.

I shall always remember those who died for the cause of freedom. My comrades of the glorious Twenty-first Foreign Volunteers which went down in defeat but did not give up. . . . The heroic Pierre Saint-Brice, who is languishing in a German prison camp. . . . My comrades who escaped, and whom the new France, to thank them for what they had done, sent to concentration camps or delivered into the hands of the German executioners.

I shall never forget them.

But I put my hopes in:

The British fighters for human ideals.

The pilots of freedom in the Royal Air Force.

The sailors of democracy in the Royal Navy.

The front line soldiers of mankind in the Territorials of His Britannic Majesty, George VI.

They carry forward the banner that had fallen from our hands.

I arrived in the harbor of New York on December 3rd, 1940. Prominent Americans had helped me obtain admission to this country. I feel the need to thank them—Dr. Frank Kingdon of the Emergency Rescue Committee, Mr. George Warren of the Presidential Advisory Committee, Mr. Morris Troper of the American Joint Distribution Committee.

But above all I must thank the country where a man is permitted to be a man. And where a book like this can be written. No escape would have been complete without the haven of the United States.

I conclude this book with three words which today must stand at the beginning and the end of all free writing:

"Thank you, America!"

HANS HABE

Spring 1941, New York

442